ANTARCTIC ECOLOGY
VOLUME 2

ANTARCTIC ECOLOGY

Edited by

M. W. HOLDGATE

The Nature Conservancy

London, England

VOLUME 2

Published for

1970

THE SCIENTIFIC COMMITTEE ON ANTARCTIC RESEARCH *by*
ACADEMIC PRESS
LONDON AND NEW YORK

ACADEMIC PRESS INC. (LONDON) LTD
BERKELEY SQUARE HOUSE
BERKELEY SQUARE
LONDON, W1X 6BA

U.S. Edition published by
ACADEMIC PRESS INC.
111 FIFTH AVENUE
NEW YORK, NEW YORK 10003

Library of Congress Catalog Card Number: 70-92399
SBN 12-352102-5

PRINTED IN GREAT BRITAIN BY
W & J MACKAY & CO LTD, CHATHAM, KENT

Contents

Contents of Volume 1

Part IX. Ecology of Antarctic Birds

Part X

FRESHWATER ECOSYSTEMS

Freshwater Ecosystems*

The numerous freshwater bodies scattered about the coastal zones of Antarctica and in the interior dry-valley systems have attracted scientific study since the pioneer expeditions in the Ross Sea area at the beginning of the century. Most limnological research, however, has been (and still is) restricted by lack of resources and by logistic problems, and in many areas has scarcely advanced beyond the collection of samples and the publication of often incomplete lists of flora and fauna, occasionally supplemented by brief descriptions of the environment.

In the area around McMurdo Sound and the Victoria Land dry valleys, where the highly unusual saline lakes with deep warm layers have attracted especial attention, much work has been done by United States and New Zealand scientists, and this is reviewed by C. R. Goldman in the present section. Detailed information about summer conditions in these lakes has been obtained, but seasonal changes in habitat and biota are only slightly documented. Elsewhere in continental Antarctica lakes along the Prince Olav Coast have been examined by Japanese workers and described in recent papers by Sugawara and Torii (1959), Meguro (1962) and Fukushima (1962). Extensive diatom material collected from a range of localities is described by H. Fukushima in this section. Soviet scientists have likewise surveyed lakes in the Vestfold, Bunger and Obrushev Hills, Wilkes Land, and at Shirmacher Ponds, Queen Maud Land (Korotkevich, 1958; Simonov, 1963; Simonov and Fedotov, 1964; Bardin and Leflat, 1965; Lavrenko, 1966). These papers supplement and extend the McMurdo and Victoria Land work, but provide considerably less comprehensive limnological information.

In the maritime Antarctic region Corte (1962) has described work by Argentine scientists at Hope Bay, on the Antarctic Peninsula, and a detailed study has been made of the lakes on Signy Island, South Orkney Islands, by R. B. Heywood (1967a, 1967b, 1968). The paper by G. E. Fogg and A. J. Horne in this section discusses the physiology of aquatic algae in this area, while R. B. Heywood considers the ecology of two of the species of Crustacea which are abundant there. The work at Signy Island has been continued over several annual cycles and appears to be the most complete ecological study of Antarctic freshwater bodies so far.

Even the relatively species-rich freshwater ecosystems of the Maritime Antarctic are impoverished compared with those of corresponding Arctic latitudes, reviewed by J. Kalff in this section. Aquatic insects and fish are absent, and food chains short. This simplification, evident in the predator-prey interaction described by R. B. Heywood, provides opportunities for detailed analysis that are likely to be pursued increasingly in the future.

* This introduction was compiled by R. B. Heywood and the Editor.

References

Bardin, V. I. and Leflat, O. N. (1965). Khimizm vod oazisa Shirmakhera (Chemistry of waters in the Shirmacher Ponds). *Inf. Byull. sov. antarkt. Eksped.* **52**, 51–55.

Corte, A. (1962). Algas de aqua dulce en lagos semicongelados de Bahía Esperanza, Península Antárctica. *Contr. Inst. antart. argent.* **69**, 38 pp.

Fukushima, H. (1962). Diatoms from Shin-nan rock ice free area, Prince Olav Coast, Antarctic Continent. *Antarctic Rec.* **14**, 80–91.

Heywood, R. B. (1967a). The freshwater lakes of Signy Island and their fauna. *In* Smith, J. E., organizer, "A discussion on the terrestrial Antarctic ecosystem". *Phil. Trans. R. Soc.*, Ser. B 252 (777), 347–62.

Heywood, R. B. (1967b). Ecology of the fresh-water lakes of Signy Island, South Orkney Islands: I. Catchment areas, drainage systems and lake morphology. *Br. Antarct. Surv. Bull.* **14**, 25–43.

Heywood, R. B. (1968). Ecology of the fresh-water lakes of Signy Island, South Orkney Islands: II. Physical and Chemical properties of the lakes. *Br. Antarct. Surv. Bull.* **18**, 11–44.

Korotkevich, V. S. (1958). Naselenie vodoemov oazisov v. Vostochnoi Antarktide (Concerning the population of water bodies in the oases of East Antarctica). *Inf. Byull. sov. antarkt. Eksped.* **3**, 91–98.

Lavrenko, G. Ye (1966). O vodoroslyakh odnogo iz ozer v. rayone standsii Novolazarevskoy (Algae of a lake near Novolazarevskaya station). *Inf. Byull. sov. antarkt. Eksped.* **56**, 57–61.

Meguro, H. (1962). Report on the pools and some products of weathering around the ponds on the coast of Antarctica. *Antarctic Rec.* **14**, 44–47.

Simonov, I. M. (1963). Prilivnyye yavleniya v. morskikh zalivakh oazisa Shirmakhera (Tidal phenomenon of the sea inlets of the Shirmacher Ponds). *Inf. Byull. sov. antarkt. Eksped.* **41**, 25–26.

Simonov, I. M. and Fedotov, V. I. (1964). Ozera oazisa Shirmakhera (Lakes in the Shirmacher Ponds). *Inf. Byull. sov. antarkt. Eksped.* **47**, 19–23.

Sugawara, K. and Torii, T. (1959). Chemical composition of the waters of some ponds in the East Ongul Island, Antarctica. *Antarctic Rec.* **7**, 53–55.

Antarctic Freshwater Ecosystems

CHARLES R. GOLDMAN
Institute of Ecology, University of California, Davis, California, U.S.A.

I. Introduction

The Antarctic continent, considering its great land mass, is characterized by a paucity of water in the liquid state. Glaciers and precipitation in the form of snow provide melt water for a variety of shallow, often highly productive, lakes along the coast and on some of the islands. Most of the studies of Antarctic freshwater ecosystems are concentrated near Antarctic research stations. The early work was, for the most part, limited to observations and collections made during pioneering expeditions. Some of the earliest investigations were carried out by German workers in Queen Maud Land and Kaiser Wilhelm Land (Wille, 1902). Features of the Cape Evans area, which will be considered in some detail here, appear in the published results of the 1910 British Antarctic (*Terra Nova*) Expedition (Scott, 1913; Taylor, 1916; Debenham, 1921; Cherry-Garrard, 1930). Murray (1909), of Shackleton's 1907–9 *Nimrod* expedition, provided some particularly careful observations on freshwater life.

More recently the lakes of Ross Island and Victoria Land have been surveyed during the summer of 1960–61 by Armitage and House (1962) and have been the subject of considerable investigative effort since. The dry valleys hold some unique permanently frozen lakes of greater size than most of the coastal environments. They are of particular interest because of their unusual chemical and thermal relationships featuring the storage of solar energy (Angino and Armitage, 1963; Bell, 1967; Hoare *et al.*, 1964, 1965; Nichols, 1963; Ragotzki and Likens, 1964; Shirtcliffe and Benseman, 1964; Wilson, 1964; Wilson and Wellman, 1962).

Similar collections and observations have been accumulated in the Peninsular sector of the Antarctic by the Scottish National Antarctic Expedition (1902–4), the *Discovery* investigations (1925–37), the British Graham Land Expedition (1934–7), and the Falkland Island Dependencies Survey (1945–62), and the British Antarctic Survey has done recent work in the South Orkney Islands (Heywood, 1967a, 1967b).

The "oases" of east Antarctica have a number of lakes which were first observed by M. E. Vingradov in 1956 and lakes in the Bunger, Obruchev and Vestfold Hills between Ingrid Christensen Coast (74°E) and Budd Coast (111°E) have now been surveyed by the Soviet Antarctic Expedition (Korotkevich, 1964; Fukushima, 1968). The Japanese have worked around Showa Station and the Ongul Islands (Meguro, 1962; Watanuki, 1963; Fukushima, 1966).

Until the last decade biological work on the Antarctic freshwaters was almost entirely restricted to a few collections. In recent years increasing attention has been given to the ecology of the flora and fauna of this unique environment.

II. Lake Types

The majority of the inland water bodies which have been investigated to date in the Antarctic region are shallow lakes near the coast. These could be classified as ponds, following the suggestions of Røen (1962), since they usually freeze to the bottom. In my own studies I have considered these as lakes because they lack any higher plants. In general, for the sake of simplicity, I favour considering all Antarctic freshwater bodies as lakes. Knowledge of whether or not a given example actually freezes to the bottom in winter is often lacking. When they do freeze to the bottom the salts are concentrated in a brine in the deepest part. When temperatures are low enough to freeze this brine, a portion of the centre of the lake may explode, forming a small crater, termed a hydrolacolith. These features were in evidence on several lakes in the immediate vicinity of the McMurdo Station.

Antarctic lake basins are usually associated with ice action. Small lakes often develop on the surface of glaciers or along their margins, while others are formed in ice or moraine-dammed valleys such as those in the dry valleys of Victoria Land (Péwé, 1960). Péwé has found evidence of at least four major quaternary glaciations in the ice-free valleys and associated mountains to the west of McMurdo Sound. Lake Vanda has been the most intensively studied lake. It occupies an undrained bedrock basin in the Wright Valley and at one time its surface was about 185 ft higher (Nichols, 1962). A small saline lake in the south fork of the Wright Valley is described by Tedrow *et al.* (1963). It is a shallow depression in an ice-free U-shaped valley of obvious glacial origin. The Taylor Valley contains Lakes Bonney and Fryxell. These are shallower than Lake Vanda and have not yet been studied as intensively. The most southern of the dry-valley lakes is Lake Miers (78°07′S, 163°54′E), which has been studied by Baker (1967).

In Queen Maud Land (70°45′S, 11°20′E) the German expedition of 1938–9 discovered a series of lakes named the Schirmacher Ponds (Die

Deutsche Antarktische Expedition, 1942). These lakes are formed in depressions between hills which have been deepened by ice erosion. They are supplied with melt water from adjacent glaciers and snowfields during summer. Lakes in the smaller depressions dry up in winter and the larger ones grow smaller.

The lakes of Signy Island in the South Orkney Group have been described by Heywood (1967*b*) and appear to have been formed by glacial activity. Some are in cirque-like basins of the "paternoster" variety, while others occupy drift basins and may be considered as kettle lakes or those associated with the ground moraine.

III. Physical Characteristics

Antarctic lakes provide unique environments for ecological studies. Meromictic conditions may be maintained by a combination of permanent ice cover and chemical stabilization of their bottom waters. Even the shallow lakes along the Ross Sea, that completely melt in summer, may exhibit a *cryogenic meromixis* as the freezing-out phenomenon concentrates the salts at the bottom, where they impart sufficient stability to successfully resist wind mixing with the overlying water (Goldman *et al.*, 1967).

Since Armitage and House (1962) visited Lakes Bonney and Vanda and reported on their unusual thermal and chemical properties, they have attracted a number of investigators. Wilson and Wellman (1962) considered Lake Vanda to be a solar energy trap, while Ragotzkie and Likens (1964), like Nichols (1963), concluded that geothermal heating was largely responsible for the high water temperatures (25°C) of the brine layer near the lake bottom, with solar heating providing some additional heat during summer. This conclusion was based on both thermistor probe measurement in Lake Vanda sediments and flux plate determinations at the sediment water interface. Wilson (*personal communication*), however, remains convinced, from thermal gradient considerations, that solar heating is the single source of heat for the monimolimnion of Lake Vanda. There is general agreement that Lake Bonney derives its heat strictly from solar heating (Hoare *et al.*, 1964; Shirtcliffe and Benseman, 1964; Goldman *et al.*, 1967), and Lake Miers would fit the same category (Baker, 1967; Bell, 1967). The dry-valley lakes characteristically have little snow cover and undergo considerable sublimation in the summer. Their surfaces are irregular and etched with melt-water patterns, and they melt in summer for a few feet around their margins.

The remarkable transparency of the ice and water of these lakes allows considerable light penetration. As much as 20% of the total incident light reaches through the ice cover of Lakes Vanda and Bonney. The water in Lake Vanda has an extinction coefficient of from 0·041 to 0·049 and photosynthesis has been measured to a depth of 60 m where there remained about 0·5% of surface light.

The origin of the brine layer in Vanda has been considered by several investigators. Wilson (1964) has developed a model diffusion system that would explain the salt distribution of the basis of a concentrated volume that was covered by a fresh inflow of glacial water following a climatic change. Low deuterium content relative to sea water has led Ragotzkie and Friedman (1965) to consider a similar source and to eliminate the possibility of a marine origin for the brine. Angino et al. (1965) considered the origin of the lake water to be from volcanic hot springs on the basis of Li/Na and K/Na ratios. Jones and Faure (1967) have found no evidence for either a direct marine or volcanic origin for Vanda water from studies of the isotopic composition of strontium and conclude that the salt is largely derived from weathering of bedrock. Chemical stratification of Lake Fryxell (77°35′S–163°35′E) in the lower part of the Taylor Dry Valley has also been investigated (Angino et al., 1962). They were not able to suggest a single origin for its stratification or salt content. Another explanation for the actual concentrating mechanism of salt may be found in the cryogenic meromixis which was described by Goldman et al. (1967) in relation to some shallow lakes and implied (?) by Antino et al. in reference to Lake Vanda.

IV. Chemical Characteristics

The inland waters of the Antarctic continent are as varied in chemical composition as those encountered on other continents. The most extensive studies are again those of the McMurdo area, especially on Lake Vanda.

There is really no suitable basis on which to frame a general discussion of the chemistry of Antarctic inland waters. Most Antarctic limnology has been carried out in coastal desert areas, and the waters encountered have reflected the rather special hydrologic conditions of coastal desert areas anywhere. The lakes of the Taylor and Wright Dry Valleys are deep, chemically stratified, desert lakes lying in glacial troughs that also contain brine pools and evidence of precipitates from previous lacustrine environments. Many biological specimens have been collected from small pools of melt waters very near the coast and occasionally water samples have been analysed in conjunction with these collections. The analyses usually are not very complete, but generally reveal a preponderance of NaCl among the dissolved salts. Table 1 summarizes some observations of various workers on the chemical composition of waters in the McMurdo region. The high chlorinites of Cape Evans, Cape Royds, and the Dry-valley lakes are characteristic of the region and suggest a marine origin for a major portion of the salts dissolved in these waters. In Lake Bonney sodium and magnesium chloride make up 96% of

TABLE 1

Chemical Composition of some Inland Waters in the McMurdo Region. Lakes Fryxell, Vanda, Bonney and Don Juan are Dry Valley Lakes. The others are on Capes Royds and Evans.

Lake and Depth (m)	Na	K	Ca	Mg	Cl	HCO3	SO4	$(Ca+Mg)^0/(Na+K)$	SO4/Cl
FRYXELL[i]									
4·5	172	23	42	108	640	252	40	·770	·062
6·0	1350	108	77	129	1640	1332	144	·141	·088
12·0	2050	187	33	229	2740	2136	460	·117	·168
VANDA[ii]									
6	28	10	46	9	150	—	—	1·44	—
11	34	11	—	—	200	41·5	7	—	·035
24	26	9	43	11	150	—	—	1·54	—
36	120	40	190	47	600	—	—	1·48	—
48	185	80	1070	293	3350	—	—	5·14	—
60	5120	690	20534	7039	64500	—	—	4·75	—
65	6761	766	24254	7684	75869	126	770	4·24	·010
BONNEY[ii]									
11	1500	180	45	43	750	87·8	127	·052	·169
30	43333	3000	1109	26253	143,333	378	525	·590	·0037
MIERS[vi]									
6·1	5·6	3·2	9	2	6	26		1·3	—
10·7	5·7	3·2	12	1	6	38		1·5	—
19·8	6·9	4·7	54	4·5	8	195		5·0	—
DON JUAN[iii]	11500	160	114,000	1200	212,000	49	11	·099	·00005
SKUA[iv]	274	23·8	22·0	52·6	523	37·8	76·4	·250	·146
ALGA[iv]	466	30·1	28·1	85·1	915	37·8	148	·228	·162
POND #2[v]	—	—	—	—	2270	—	380	—	·167
HOME[v]	—	—	—	—	1675	—	1220	—	·728
COAST[v]	—	—	—	—	275	—	40	—	·145
GREEN[v]	—	—	—	—	2715	—	480	—	·177
CLEAR[v]	—	—	—	—	220	—	44	—	·200
SEAWATER	10556	380	400	1272	18980	140	2649	·153	·140

i, Data from Angino et al., 1962; ii, data from Angino and Armitage, 1963; iii, data from Meyer et al., 1962; iv, data from Goldman et al. (unpubl. ms.); v data from Armitage and House, 1962; vi, data from Bell, 1967.

the dissolved salts (Angino, *et al.*, 1964). Lake Vanda, the largest lake of the area, is the least marine-like of the brackish desert lakes. Divalent cations predominate in Vanda, especially in the deeper layer, where the divalent to monovalent ratio is some thirty times that of sea water. Throughout the water column in Vanda calcium concentrations exceed magnesium concentrations by a factor of 3 or more. There is no calcium carbonate precipitation occurring in Vanda, the pH is around 6·5 and there is relatively little bound CO_2 even in the extremely brackish deep layer which shows strong light absorption at about 350 mμ. In the brine at the bottom of Lake Bonney magnesium is greatly enriched relative to calcium. Chloride is enriched relative to sulphate and gypsum has been precipitated as a thin layer in at least some areas of the basin.

Small ponds in the Antarctic freeze solid during the long winter. The freezing out of salts introduces a severe annual fluctuation in the ionic content of the liquid phase, so that a pond with moderate salinity in the summertime when it is free of ice may give rise to an ice sheet of low ionic content capping a thin layer of brine that may never freeze solid. Such is the environment of the algal felts that line the bottoms of small ponds in the McMurdo region.

Korotkevich (1964) summarizes observations on fourteen lakes and ponds in east Antarctica. Chemical characterization was limited to noting that four of the fourteen were brackish (Table 2).

V. Freshwater Biota of Antarctica

Only the lower groups of plant and animal life have been recorded from the freshwater catchments of Antarctica and of these the algae contain the most diversity. Arctic areas have long been recognized as regions of few species where interactions could be studied more easily (Elton, 1928). The Antarctic also offers the ecologist this advantage.

A. ALGAE

Early collections were made by Hooker of the British Expedition (1839–43) under Ross from Archipel de Kerguelen and Cockburn Island (lat. 64°S, 57°E long.). Additional collections from the British ship *Venus* were made by A. E. Eaton in 1874–5 and were identified by Reinsch (1876). The first records of freshwater algae from the Antarctic continent itself were made by the Belgian Antarctic Expedition of 1897–99, which visited Graham Land on the Antarctic Peninsula, where M. E. Racovitza collected two species. Victoria Land was next reported to have two species of freshwater algae by the Norwegian Expedition in the *Stella Polare*. This material was described by Wille (1902).

TABLE 2

East Coast of Antarctica. Fourteen Lake Samples by the Soviets in 1956 and 1957

Region	Depth	Date	Temp.	Salinity	pH	Oxygen %	Organisms	Reference
BUNGER HILLS								
Lake Figurnoye	130 m	3/1/57	3·2°C	Fresh	6·8	100·2	Cyanophyta, Chlorophyta, Copepoda, Rotatoria. Crusts of blue-green and green algae and moss	Korotkevich, 1964
Small Lake (40 m across)	Bottom visible	1/1/57	2·4°C	Brackish	8·1		Green algae rings banks; Rotatoria, Tardigrada	Korotkevich, 1964
VESTFOLD HILLS								
Lake Krukvatnet (6 km across)	143 m	12/12/56 (under 160 cm ice)	2°C	Fresh			Cladocera, Rotatoria Copepoda	Korotkevich, 1964
Lake Lebed' (1 km across)	27 m	13/12/56	11° to −5°C	210			Copepoda	Korotkevich, 1964

Plankton was sampled in these lakes with mesh #64 and #38; benthos samples with Sigsby trawl and bottom dredge. Bedrock in this area is predominantly crystalline schists and gneisses representing a granulitic metamorphic facies, migmatites and pegmatites in the Bunger Hills region (Ravich, 1964).

Collecting on the continent was intensified at the beginning of the present century. The list of freshwater algae began to grow with the French Antarctic Expedition of 1903–05 collections on the Antarctic Peninsula. Shackleton's *Nimrod* Expedition of 1907–09 made collections from Ross Island in McMurdo Sound and in Victoria Land, and the 1909 Belgian Expedition in *Belgica* collected additional material from Archipel de Kerguelen. The *Scotia* Expedition of 1902–04 described red and yellow snow algae from the South Orkney Islands and the *Discovery* Expedition of 1901–04 sampled Cape Adare in the McMurdo Sound area (West and West, 1911). Fritsch (1910, 1912), in examining these collections, made the generalization, which still holds, that there is a paucity of green algae relative to other groups. Collections from the coast of east Antarctica have been made by Soviet scientists in 1956 and 1957 and the Japanese took samples on the Prince Olav Coast (Fukushima, 1966). Corte (1962) reported on the Argentine collecting at Hope Bay on the Antarctic Peninsula. Holm-Hansen (1964) made collections during 1959 and 1960 from Ross Island and South Victoria Land.

The collections of indigenous algae made in 1960 by Holm-Hansen were for physiological studies in laboratory culture. Habitats from which samples were obtained included Lake Vanda and a number of shallow freshwater lakes as well as dry rocks. The samples were transported to Wisconsin, where they were placed in different inorganic nutrient media in an attempt to obtain growth and eventually isolates. No diatoms were obtained in unialgal culture; many centric and pennate diatoms flourished when growing together with green or blue-green algae. All attempts to grow diatoms in culture without other algae were unsuccessful, and the number of species that grew in culture was far smaller than the number originally present in the samples. This may be explained by considering that the culture of many algae is still difficult, and it is always possible that the nutrient media and laboratory conditions were not right. Only inorganic nutrient media were used, and diatoms may have a requirement for some organic substance which was furnished by other algae. It is also possible that some species simply did not survive transport from the Antarctic.

The number of species of freshwater algae recorded from the Antarctic continent and adjacent islands is now over 200. Hirano (1965) in his excellent review of the freshwater algae of the Antarctic regions summarizes, in a table, all the recorded species made to that date. Fukushima (1966, 1967, 1968) has added to the list of diatoms. Table 3 gives a general picture of the range of algal types. No Chrysophyta nor Xanthophyta are represented and clearly the filamentous forms of the blue-green algae are dominant.

Hirano estimates that only one-third to one-half of all Antarctic diatom forms are found on other continents. This is further substantiation for Greene's (1964) statement that a "high rate of endemism among the cryptogamic flora of the Antarctic continent is one of its most striking features".

Fukushima (1967), in examining the diatom flora, found a higher rate of endemism around McMurdo Station than on the coast of east Antarctica and about Showa Station. He suggests that there is a dividing line between the cosmopolitan types and the Antarctic types between latitudes 68°S and 77°S and notes that a difference of only 10° in latitude will cause a remarkable variation in the flora.

Although Hirano feels that there is not yet sufficient data to form any conclusions about distribution of algae in the Antarctic, several trends can be observed. First, the rapid decrease in the Conjugatae and Desmids toward the high latitudes is a distinctive feature, since these are the most common members of the temperate algal flora. Secondly, blue-greens are the dominant components of the flora, and Hirano suggests a number of reasons for their success in Antarctica. A third characteristic of the Antarctic algal flora pointed out by Hirano is the presence of many coccoid forms of green algae.

Ankistrodesmus was first reported by Goldman *et al.* (manuscript) from Skua Lake and may represent contamination from any one of a number of possible sources. It might have come in with the straw for Scott's ponies, or it may have been carried by a collector's plankton net to the lake. It will be interesting to follow any dispersal of this form if this is, in fact, the only record on the continent.

B. MICROMETAZOA

The freshwater benthos and zooplankton have been less well recorded and studied. James Murray, who wintered over with Shackleton's party in 1909, made collections at Cape Royds on Ross Island. Dougherty and Harris (1963), also collecting in the McMurdo area, reported Rotifera, Tardigrada, Nematoda, and Turbellaria. A Heliozoan protozoan was found in Lake Vanda by Goldman *et al.* (1967), and the Russians sampling the lakes of East Antarctica found crustaceans which included copepods and one *Daphnia* (Korotkevich, 1964) among the net plankton. The micrometazoa were nearly always found in wet algal felt. Dougherty and Harris (1963) reported the red-pigmented rotifer *Philodina gregaria* as extremely abundant on the bottom of many shallow ponds of the Ross Island area, as Bryant (1945) reported from the Antarctic Peninsula. Dougherty and Harris also observed great abundance of tardigrades which are rarely as abundant in warmer climates. In 1958 Kiryanova (1964) recorded six species of freshwater nematodes, two of these endemic, in collections from the Antarctic. At the time, about thirty species were known from Subantarctic regions. Heywood (1967*a*) reported eight species of Crustacea from Signy Island as well as Annelida, Nematoda, Tardigrada, Rotifera and Protozoa. There is certainly a need for more detailed study of the Antarctic Micrometazoa.

TABLE 3

Genera of Freshwater Algae Collected from Antarctica

	Number of species		Number of species
CYANOPHYTA (blue-green)		**CYANOPHYTA (blue-green)**	
Coccoid forms		Filamentous forms	
Aphanocapsa	1	Anabaena	2
Aphanothece	1	Calothrix	4
Chroococcus	11	Lyngbya	16
Eucapsis	1	Microcoleus	2
Gloeocapsa	3	Nodularia	2
Merismopedia	2	Nostoc	13
Microcystis	5	Oscillatoria	19
		Phormidium	15
		Plectonema	1
		Schizothrix	1
		Tolypothrix	1
CHLOROPHYTA (green)		**BACILLARIOPHYCEAE (Diatoms)**	
Flagellated forms		Centric Diatoms	
Chlamydomonas	5	Melosira	3
Chloromonas	1	Coscinodiscus	7
Pteromonas	1	Cyclotella	1
		Triceratium	1

Coccoid forms		Pennate Diatoms	
Chlorella	2	Tabellaria	1
Chlorococcum	1	Diatoma	2
Chlorosarcina	2	Fragilaria	5
Trochiscia	4	Synedra	3
Scotiella	2	Cocconeis	2
Pseudotetraspora	1	Achnanthes	2
Mycacanthococcus	4	Frustulia	2
Ankistrodesmus	1	Stauroneis	3
		Navicula	17
Desmids		Pinnularia	4
Cosmarium	6	Trachyneis	1
Cylindrocystis	1	Cymbella	4
Ancylonema	4	Tropidoneis	1
		Denticula	1
Filamentous forms		Epithemia	1
Binuclearia	1	Rhopalodia	1
Hormidium	1	Hantzschia	3
Schizogonium	1	Nitzschia	7
Stichococcus	3	Surirella	6
Ulothrix	7		
Protococcus	6		
Foliose forms			
Prasiola	?		

VI. Low-temperature Physiology

This approach to the biota has been popular with terrestrial and marine ecologists who have studied the metabolism of fish, seals and penguins. Limnologists and algologists have used the area to collect cryophilic organisms and, as one would expect, some Antarctic forms are more successful at low temperature or are better able to survive freezing than are related species from temperate regions. This has been demonstrated by Holm-Hansen's (1963) viability studies. Further, diatom inhabitants of the brine layer appear to be both healthy and active at zero temperatures in Cape Evans ponds. Bunt (1963) has described a similar situation in the "truly indigenous flora" of epontic diatoms associated with the sea ice. These exist under conditions of both low temperature and low light and may find the salinity in their immediate vicinity reduced rather than increased by freezing out. Thus, a freshwater community may be forced into a much higher salinity range than its marine, cryophilic relatives.

Fog and Stewart (1968), making direct nitrogen fixation measurements on Signy Island, found that although appreciable fixation took place at 0°C, the optimal temperature for fixation is probably 10°C. Boyd and Boyd (1962) found some soil micro-organisms of the Antarctic are able to carry out certain reactions of the nitrogen cycle at a very slow rate. Small clumps of blue-green algae have been observed by the author to move slowly through solid ice by absorbing solar radiation during summer days to provide a liquid microhabitat for the colony. It would be useful to check these for nitrogen fixation, as the ice is extremely low in nutrients except where dust accumulates in the crevices.

VII. Low-light Physiology

Low light is as much a characteristic of the Antarctic environment as is low temperature and, considering the long winter, it is actually more characteristic. Studies of inhibition and injury to the photosynthetic mechanism of algae from high light intensities were conducted *in situ* on Cape Evans, Ross Island (Goldman *et al.*, 1963). A maximum photosynthetic rate was found at about 20% of incident light at noon. The overall efficiency of photosynthesis was inversely proportional to light intensity during the major part of austral summer days (Goldman *et al.*, in press).

Baker (1967) has shown that in Lake Miers in Victoria Land algae tend to form aggregations in the warmer regions of the lake. Lake Miers, a shallow, thermally stratified lake with a permanent ice cover, has been described by Bell (1967) as a solar heat trap. Near the lake bottom at 18 m the water temperature was over 5°C. He found more algae were present here than at the surface directly below the ice layer, even though only 1% of the sunlight penetrated to a depth of 15 m. He suggests that these algae are adapted to grow in low light intensities during the Antarctic summer and that they probably assimilate dissolved organic substances heterotrophically during the Antarctic winter, when they would not receive enough light below the ice to carry on photosynthesis.

Bunt (1963) observed that there was very little real difference in the rates of carbon fixation between planktonic and ice populations at high light intensities. He felt this indicated an adaptation to shade in both groups of plankton.

Bunt's (1965) work on the relationship between respiration and photosynthesis shows that the ^{14}C method of measuring carbon fixation gives a close approximation to net photosynthesis where excretion of organic compounds is insignificant. Thus, if this method is to be used to measure gross photosynthesis, knowledge of the extent to which respiration is inhibited is necessary. Bunt considers that the process of inhibition of respiration is dependent on a number of factors, including the nature of the pigment, the quality and intensity of the light, possibly temperature and the condition of the organism.

VIII. Ecological Studies in Antarctic Lakes

Detailed studies of the aquatic freshwater ecosystem in Antarctica currently span less than a decade. With greatly improved field facilities, experimental work has been increasing rapidly.

The aquatic freshwater flora can be considered as three assemblages occupying three distinct levels. The first are the meteor-like clumps of algae in the solid phase of the lakes that have already been mentioned. A second is the planktonic assemblage which exists when lakes are at least partially thawed, and the third is the rich growth of periphyton (largely *Nostoc* and *Phormidium*) to be found on the bottom of many of the shallow lakes. Komarek and Ruzicka (1966), for example, working on an ice-covered lake in the Schirmacher Oasis (70°45'S, 11°43'E) found the lake to be highly productive of algae even at temperatures of 0–5°C. The main component of the algae was the blue-green *Phormidium*, which, in large fan-shaped colonies, supersaturated the water with oxygen.

Although Heywood (1967*a*, *b*) made no primary productivity measurements, he felt that the phytoplankton play a minor role in the productivity of the lakes which he studied on Signy Island.

Fogg (1967) found carbon fixation was generally low for snow algae in the South Orkney Islands, and the apparent 'bloom" is really just the accumulation at the surface, with ablation of the snow, of cells previously distributed throughout the snow column.

Armitage and House (1962) made a few measurements of primary productivity using the oxygen method in Skua Lake and some other coastal environments and found a range of 326 to 1008 mgC/m³ day. Goldman (1964) made measurements in Lakes Vanda and Bonney in 1961 and in Cape Evans lakes during that and the following season (Goldman et al., 1967). For accurate estimates of productivity, diurnal studies are essential, since minimum rates may be measured at midday and maximum values during periods of lower (less inhibiting) light intensity. Productivity measurements are summarized in Table 4.

The importance of the periphyton production is particularly obvious from the two-season study of Alga and Skua Lakes on Cape Evans. In 1961–62 the periphyton production was about three times the phytoplankton production in the highly turbid Skua Lake, while in the more transparent Alga Lake it was over twenty times as great. During the second season the productivity of the periphyton was much higher in both lakes, nearly doubling in Alga. In Skua Lake the phytoplankton production also increased markedly, so that it nearly equalled periphyton production. In Alga Lake the second year's phytoplankton production was insignificant when compared with the periphyton. When the contribution of the phytoplankton and periphyton in Skua and Alga Lakes are added together, productivity ranges from about 2 to nearly 5 g of carbon/m² of lake surface per day. This is a very high rate and shows the high fertility of these environments when compared with the ultra-oligotrophic dry-valley lakes or, for that matter, with others anywhere on the globe. It should be kept in mind, however, that the summer growing season is very short and its intensity is partly the result of there being continuous light. The periphyton appears to be specially adapted to utilize any slight increase in environmental temperature and to be protected from the injurious light intensity by the carotenoid shielding which gives the algal felt its reddish appearance (Goldman et al., 1963).

The unusual vertical profiles of productivity in the dry-valley lakes have been presented by Goldman (1964, 1968), and Goldman et al. (1967). Despite the low light intensity below 50 m in Lake Vanda (less than 1% of that at the surface), the high temperature (15–25°C) and concentration of nutrients resulted in a photosynthetic maximum at this depth. Q_{10} values from about 5 to 9 had been measured between 4° and 14°C in the Cape Evans lakes by Goldman et al. (1963).

D. K. Koob (personal communication) and the Ohio State workers have found a peak in ¹⁴C uptake in Lake Bonney, 2 m lower than the peak for cell counts and chlorophyll a; however, he suggests this may be due to sampling. They also record a high carbon uptake (dark bottles) at 15 m below the ice which they feel can be correlated with an extremely dense population of bacteria at this level.

TABLE 4

Primary Productivity of Various Aquatic Communities of the Antarctic

LAKE	PRODUCTIVITY		REFERENCE
South Orkney Islands (snow algae)	10 mgC m^{-2}day^{-1} (of snow surface)		Fogg, G. E., 1967
Cape Evans, Ross Isl.	1961–2	1962–3	
Skua Lake	542 mgC m^{-2}day^{-1}	2352 (plankton, 3 mo. ave.)	Goldman et al., MS
	1560 mgC m^{-2}day^{-1}	2560 (periphyton, 3 mo. ave.)	Goldman et al., MS
Alga Lake	91 mgC m^{-2}day^{-1}	66 (plankton, 3 mo. ave.)	Goldman et al., MS
	1910 mgC m^{-2}day^{-1}	3630 (periphyton, 3 mo. ave.)	Goldman et al., MS
Evans Pond #3	47 mgC m^{-3}day^{-1}		Goldman et al., MS
Coast Lake	326–1008 mgC m^{-3}day^{-1} (net)		Armitage and House, 1962
Victoria Land			
Lake Vanda	29 mgC m^{-2}day^{-1}	(to 60 m depth, 14–2–63)	Goldman et al., 1967
Lake Bonney	31 mgC m^{-2}day^{-1}	(to 10 m depth, 29–11–61)	Goldman et al., 1967
Don Juan Pond	No C fixation could be detected by ^{14}C method 8 Jan. 1962		Goldman et al., MS
Antarctic Ocean	10–150 mgC m^{-2}day^{-1}		Saijo and Kawashima, 1964

IX. Studies on Nutrient Limiting Factors

Limiting nutrient studies were conducted by Goldman (1964) in the littoral water of Lake Vanda. Considerable stimulation (mainly double the control value) was obtained *in situ* with the addition of 0·5 mg NO₃-N per litre. Phosphorus was only very slightly stimulating and trace elements inhibited photosynthesis. In the skua-fertilized Cape Evans lakes nutrient response was almost totally lacking. Nitrogen appears also to be the most likely candidate for nutrient limitation on Signy Island. Holdgate *et al.* (1967) "have shown that N is the only major nutrient likely to limit plant growth on Signy Island". Wille (1902) also suggested the poverty of the algal flora of Kaiser Wilhelm II Land was attributable to lack of nitrogen-fixing organisms in the soil and deficiency of N-containing compounds in the water.

X. Conclusions

Future limnologists can look to the Antarctic lakes for nearly closed ecosystems. These are advantageous for study because of their simple trophic structure and rigorous climatic restriction. The organisms must be adapted to withstand high light intensities, but at the same time to endure many months of darkness. There is a need to continue and to improve the taxonomic work, to better define Antarctic endemism. Eventually, most of the organisms should be examined in pure culture.

The role of heterotrophy in summer, and especially in winter darkness, recalls the provocative speculations of Rodhe (1955) which remain as yet unsolved. Also needed are biochemical studies of enzyme systems which continue to operate down to at least zero levels and of nitrogen fixation in the periphyton mats of the shallow lakes. The possibility that the biota is dependent on energy sources other than organics and light should not be neglected.

With a proper combination of ecological research talent, Antarctic aquatic ecosystems can yield a wealth of new knowledge applicable to aquatic systems everywhere.

Acknowledgements

The author expresses thanks to the National Science Foundation for support (GA-1368) and to Mary Major, Richard Armstrong and John Coil for bibliographical and editorial assistance in researching this material.

References

Angino, E. E. and Armitage, K. B. (1963). A geochemical study of lakes Bonney and Vanda, Victoria Land, Antarctica. *J. Geol.* 71, No. 1, 89–95.

Angino, E. E., Armitage, K. B. and Tash, J. C. (1962). Chemical stratification in Lake Fryxell, Victoria Land, Antarctica. *Science, N.Y.* 138, 34–35.

Angino, E. E., Armitage, K. B. and Tash, J. C. (1964). Physicochemical limnology of Lake Bonney, Antarctica. *Limnol. Oceanogr.* 9, No. 2, 207–17.

Angino, E. E., Armitage, K. B. and Tash, J. C. (1965). A chemical and limnological study of Lake Vanda, Victoria Land, Antarctica. *Kans. Univ. Sci. Bull.*, No. 45, 1097–1118.

Armitage, K. B. and House, H. B. (1962). A limnological reconnaissance in the area of McMurdo Sound, Antarctica. *Limnol. Oceanogr.* 7, 36–41.

Baker, A. N. (1967). Algae from Lake Miers, a solar heated Antarctic Lake. *N.Z. Jl Bot.* 5, 453–68.

Bell, R. A. I. (1967). Lake Miers, South Victoria Land, Antarctica. *N.Z. J. Geol. Geophys* 10, 540–56.

Boyd, W. L. and Boyd, J. W. (1962). Soil microorganisms of the McMurdo Sound Area, Antarctica. *Appl. Microbiol.* 11, 116–21.

Bryant, H. M. (1945). Fresh-water flora and fauna of East Base Palmer Peninsula. *In* "Reports on the Scientific Results of the United States Antarctic Service Expedition 1939–41". *Proc. Am. Phil. Soc.* 89, No. 1, 264.

Bunt, J. S. (1963). Diatoms of Antarctic sea ice as agents of primary production. *Nature, Lond.* 199, 1254–57.

Bunt, J. S. (1965). Measurements of photosynthesis and respiration in a marine diatom with the mass spectrometer and with Carbon-14. *Nature, Lond.* 207, 1373–75.

Cherry-Gerrard, A. (1930). "The Worst Journey in the World. Antarctic 1910–1913". Dial Press, New York.

Corte, A. (1962). Fresh-water algae in semifrozen lakes of Hope Bay, Antarctic Peninsula. *Inst. Antart. Argentino, Contrib.* 69, 38 pp.

Debenham, F. (1921). Recent and local deposits of McMurdo Sound Region. *Nat. Hist. Rep. Br. Antarct. Terra Nova Exped.* 1, No. 3, 63–100.

Dougherty, E. C. and Harris, L. G. (1963). Antarctic micrometazoa: Freshwater species in the McMurdo Sound Area. *Science, N.Y.* 140, No. 3566, 497–8.

Elton, C. S. (1928). "Animal Ecology". MacMillan, New York (3rd ed., 1947).

Fogg, G. E. (1967). Observations on the snow algae of the South Orkney Islands. *Phil. Trans. R. Soc.* B, 252, 279–87.

Fogg, G. E. and Stewart, W. D. P. (1968). *In situ* determinations of biological nitrogen fixation in Antarctica. *Br. Antarct. Surv. Bull.* 15, 39–46.

Fritsch, F. E. (1910). Freshwater algae collected in the South Orkneys by R. N. Rudmose Brown, B.Sc., of the Scottish National Antarctic Expedition, 1902–1904. *J. Linn. Soc. Bot.* 11.

Fritsch, F. E. (1912). Freshwater algae. National Antarctic Expedition, *Nat. Hist., N.Y.* 6.

Fukushima, H. (1966). Diatoms from Molodezhnaya Station and Mirny Station, Antarctica. *Antarctic Rec.* 24, 2121–25.

Fukushima, H. (1967). A brief note on Diatom flora of Antarctic Inland waters. *JARE Sci. Rep. (Tokyo)*, Sp. Issue 1, 253–64.

Fukushima, H. (1968). Algal vegetation of the Kasumi rock ice-free area, Prince Olav Coast, Antarctica. *Antarctic Rec.* **31**, 73–86.

Goldman, C. R. (1964). Primary productivity studies in Antarctic lakes. *In* "Biologie Antarctique: Antarctic Biology" (Carrick, R., Holdgate, M. W. and Prevost, J., eds). Hermann, Paris.

Goldman, C. R. (1968). Aquatic primary production. *Am. Zoologist* **8**, 31–42.

Goldman, C. R. (in press). Variations in photosynthesis in two shallow Antarctic lakes. Paper presented at the XVII International Congress of Limnology, Israel, August 1968.

Goldman, C. R., Mason, D. T. and Hobbie, J. E. (1967). Two Antarctic Desert Lakes. *Limnol. Oceanogr.* **12**, No. 2, 295–310.

Goldman, C. R., Mason, D. T. and Wood, B. J. B. (1963). Light injury and inhibition in Antarctic freshwater phytoplankton. *Limnol. Oceanogr.* **8**, No. 3, 313–22.

Goldman, C. R., Mason, D. T. and Wood, B. J. B. (MS). A comparative study of the limnology of two small lakes on Ross Island, Antarctica.

Greene, S. W. (1964). Plants of the Land. *In* "Antarctic Research", (Priestly, R., Adie, R. J. and Robin, G., eds). Butterworths, London.

Heywood, R. B. (1967a). Antarctic ecosystems. The freshwater lakes of Signy Island and their fauna. *Phil. Trans. R. Soc.* B. **261**, 347–62.

Heywood, R. B. (1967b). Ecology of the Freshwater Lakes of Signy Island, South Orkney Islands. Catchment areas, drainage systems, and lake morphology. *Br. Antarct. Surv. Bull.* **14**, 25–43.

Hirano, M. (1965). Freshwater algae in the Antarctic regions. *In* "Biogeography and Ecology in Antarctica". Junk, The Hague.

Hoare, R. A., Popplewell, K. B., House, D. A., Henderson, R. A., Prebble, W. M and Wilson, A. T. (1964). Lake Bonney, Taylor Valley, Antarctica: a natural solar energy trap. *Nature, Lond.* **202**, 4935, 886–8.

Hoare, R. A., Popplewell, K. B., House, D. A., Henderson, R. A., Prebble, W. M. and Wilson, A. T. (1965). Solar heating of Lake Fryxell, a permanently ice-covered Antarctic lake. *J. Geoph. Res.* **70**, 1555–8.

Holdgate, M. W., Allen, S. E. and Chambers, M. J. G. (1967). A preliminary investigation of the soils of Signy Island, South Orkney Islands. *Br. Antarc. Surv. Bull.* **12**, 53–71.

Holm-Hansen, O. (1963). Viability of blue-green and green algae after freezing. *Physiologia Pl.* **16**, No. 3, 530–40.

Holm-Hansen, O. (1964). Isolation and culture of terrestrial and fresh-water algae of Antarctica. *Phycologia* **4**, 43–51.

Jones, L. M. and Faure, G. (1967). Origin of the salts in Lake Vanda, Wright Valley, Southern Victoria Land, Antarctica. *Earth Pl. Sci. Letters*, No. 3, 101–6.

Kiryanova, E. S. (1964). Antarctic specimens of fresh-water nematodes of genus *Plectus bastian* (Nematoda, Plectidae). *Inf. Byull. sov. antarkt. Eksped.* **1**, 163–5.

Komárek, J. and Růžička, J. (1966). Freshwater algae from a lake in proximity of the Novolazerevskaya Station, Antarctic. *Preslia* **38**, 237–44.

Korotkevich, V. S. (1964). Concerning the population of water bodies in the Oases of East Antarctica. *Inf Byull. sov. artarkt. Eksped.* **1**, 154–61.

Meguro, H. (1962). Report on the pools and some products of weathering around the ponds of the coast of Antarctica. *Antarctic Rec.* **14**, 44–47.

Meyer, G. H., Morrow, M. B., Wyss, O., Berg, T. E. and Littlepage, J. L. (1962). Antarctica: the microbiology of an unfrozen saline pond. *Science, N.Y.* **138**, No. 3545, 1103–4.

Murray, J. (1909). On collecting at Cape Royds. *Br. Antarct. Exped.* 1907–09 **1**, Part 1.

Nichols, R. L. (1962). Geology of Lake Vanda, Wright Valley, South Victoria Land, Antarctica. *Am. Geophys. Union, Geophys. Monogr.* **7**, 47–52.

Nichols, R. L. (1963). Origin of chemical stratification in Lake Vanda, South Victoria Land. *Polar Rec.* **11**, No. 75, 751–2.

Péwé, T. L. (1960). Multiple glaciation in the McMurdo Sound region, Antarctica—a progress report. *J. Geol.* **68**, 498–514.

Ragotzkie, R. A. and Friedman, I. (1965). Low deuterium content of Lake Vanda, Anarctica. *Science, N.Y.* **148**, 1226–7.

Ragotzkie, R. A. and Likens, G. E. (1964). The heat balance of two Antarctic lakes. *Limnol. Oceanogr.* **9**, 412–25.

Ravich, M. G. (1964). The absolute age of the Precambrian rocks of the central sector of East Antarctica. *Inf. Byull. sov. antarct. Eksped.* **1**, 18–20.

Reinsch, P. F. (1876). Species or genera nova algarum aquae dulcie quae sunt inventa in speciminibus in expeditions "Venus" transit hieme 1874–1875 in insula Kerguelensis a clar. Eaton Collections. *J. Linn. Soc.* Bot. **15**.

Rodhe, W. (1955). Can plankton production proceed during winter darkness in sub-arctic lakes. *Verh. Int. Verein. theor. angew. Limnol.* **12**, 21–28.

Røen, V. I. (1962). Studies on freshwater Entomostraca in Greenland, II. *Meddr. Gronland,* **170**, Part 2, 1–249.

Saijo, Y. and Kawashima, T. (1964). Primary production in the Antarctic Ocean. *Jap. J. Oceanogr.* **19**, No. 4.

Scott, R. F. (1913). "Scott's Last Expedition". Dodd, Mead, New York.

Shirtcliffe, T. G. L. and Benseman, R. F. (1964). A sun-heated Antarctic lake. *J. Geophys. Res.* **69**, 3355–9.

Taylor, G. (1916). "With Scott: The Silver Lining". Dodd, Mead, New York.

Tedrow, J. C. F., Ugolini, F. C. and Janetschek, H. (1963). An Antarctic saline lake. *N.Z. Jl Sci,* **6**, 150–6.

Watanuki, K. (1963). Geochemical researches in the 6th Japanese Antarctic Research Expedition (1961–1962). *Antarctic Rec.* **18**, 45–49.

Wille, N. (1902). Mitteilungen über einige von C. E. Borchgvevink auf dem antarktischen Festlande gesammelte Pflanzen III. Antarktische Algen. *Nyt. Mag. Naturvid.* **40**.

Wilson, A. T. (1964). Evidence from chemical diffusion of a climatic change in the McMurdo dry valleys 1,200 years ago. *Nature, Lond.* **201**, No. 4915, 175–7.

Wilson, A. T. and Wellman, H. W. (1962). Lake Vanda: an Antarctic lake. *Nature Lond.* **196**, No. 4860, 1171–3.

West, W. and West, G. S. (1911). Freshwater algae. *Rep. Brit. Antarct, Exped.* 1907–09. *Rep. Scient. Invest.* **1**, No. 7, 263–98.

Notes on the Diatom Flora of Antarctic Inland Waters

HIROSHI FUKUSHIMA

Biological Institute, Yokohama City University, Yokohama, Japan

I. Introduction

The writer has been investigating the inland-water diatoms of Antarctica, in the hope of clarifying their distribution and dominant species. The purpose of this report is to summarize the results so far obtained.

II. South Georgia (54°13′S, 36°33′W)

The writer found forty-nine taxa of diatoms. Among these, only *Achnanthese mulleri* is endemic, while *Navicula megacuspidata* is endemic to this island and Tierra del Fuego. The only Antarctic endemic species found was *Navicula muticopsis*, but the writer found that South Georgia is the northern limit of its distribution. The freshwater diatoms of South Georgia thus include only a slight Antarctic element and very few endemic species, and the island is occupied for the most part by cosmopolitan species.

III. Shinnan Rocks (67°57′S, 44°29′E)

The writer found thirty-two species of diatoms here, of which six were Antarctic endemic species. *Hantzschia amphioxys*, *Navicula gibbula* and *Nitzschia palea*, all cosmopolitan species, were dominant in the four lakes. In the diatom flora of Shinnan Rock, cosmopolitan species outnumbered Antarctic endemic species and were also represented by more individuals. It can be assumed, therefore, the freshwater diatom flora of Shinnan Rocks has only a slight Antarctic affinity.

IV. Kasumi Rock (67°57′S, 49°29′E)

The writer found thirty-three species of diatoms in eight lakes here. Among them, fourteen were Antarctic endemic species and the others were cosmopolitan. Among the fourteen Antarctic endemic diatoms, four were inland-water species and the remaining ten were salt-water species. *Navicula muticopsis*, *Tropidoneis laevissima* and *Navicula cryptocephala* were dominant, the first two being Antarctic endemic species and the third cosmopolitan. Of the eight lakes examined, one supported a *Navicula muticopsis* association, six the *Navicula cryptocephala*—*Tropidoneis laevissima* association, and one an association in which dominant species could not be determined.

Judging from the above, it seems that at Kasumi Rock cosmopolitan species and Antarctic endemic species are evenly balanced.

V. Molodezhnaya Station (67°40′S, 45°50′E)

Three of the five species identified were Antarctic endemic species and two were cosmopolitan. In one of the two lakes examined the cosmopolitan *Stauroneis perminuta* was dominant, but in the other no dominant species could be determined. It can therefore be assumed that around Molodezhanya Station the cosmopolitan factor is predominant, although the Antarctic endemic factor also exists.

VI. Mirny Station (63°33′S, 93°01′E)

Among the ten species identified, six were Antarctic endemic species, and four were Antarctic Ocean endemic species. Dominant species were recognized in three samples, the Antarctic endemic *Navicula muticopsis* association predominating in two, and the cosmopolitan *Pinnularia borealis* association in the third. In the locality of Mirny Station, the Antarctic endemic factor seems predominant, but the cosmopolitan factor is also prominent.

VII. McMurdo Station on Ross Island (77°32′S, 166°12′E)

Thirteen taxa were identified, among which eight were Antarctic endemic species and five were cosmopolitan. The Antarctic endemic *Navicula muticopsis* predominated in the only sample to show a clear dominant. Thus, it may be stated that the diatom flora around McMurdo Station has a stronger Antarctic endemic than cosmopolitan element.

VIII. Cape Barne, Ross Island (77°32′S, 166°12′E)

Among the eleven diatoms found, nine were Antarctic endemic species. *Navicula peraustralis* predominated in one of the two collections in which the dominant species could be found, and *Tropidoneis laevissima* in the other, both being Antarctic endemic species. Thus, it can be stated that diatoms of

Cape Barne have a strong Antarctic endemic element and a very small cosmopolitan component.

IX. Cape Evans, Ross Island (77°32'S, 166°12'E)

Among the fifteen diatoms found, nine were Antarctic endemic species. Dominant species were determined in seven lakes. The *Navicula muticopsis-Pinnularia cymatopleura* association was recognized in three of these and the *Tropidoneis laevissima* association was recognized in four more. Thus, it can be said that diatoms of Cape Evans mostly belong to the Antarctic endemic group and very few are cosmopolitan.

X. Cape Royds, Ross Island (77°32'S, 166°12'E)

The writer identified twenty-one species of diatoms in seven lakes. Among them, twelve were Antarctic endemic species and nine were cosmopolitan. Dominant species were determined in three lakes; they were *Navicula muticopsis* + *Pinnularia cymatopleura*, *Nitzschia* sp. and *Tropidoneis laevissima* respectively, all being supposedly Antarctic endemic species. Thus, it can be stated that the diatoms of Cape Royds are mostly Antarctic endemics, but that a few are cosmopolitan.

XI. Distribution of Cosmopolitan Species and Antarctic Species

Table I shows the locations and the number of cosmopolitan species and Antarctic endemic species found at each locality.

At South Georgia, Shinnan Rocks and Kasumi Rock cosmopolitan species were remarkably more numerous than Antarctic endemic species; whereas at Molodezhnaya Station, Mirny Station, McMurdo Station, Cape Evans, Cape Barne and Cape Royds, Antarctic endemic species outnumbered cosmopolitan species. In terms of the number of individuals, however, cosmopolitan species were most abundant at South Georgia, Shinnan Rocks, Kasumi Rock, Molodezhnaya Station and Mirny Station, whereas Antarctic endemic species were most numerous at McMurdo Station, Cape Evans, Cape Barne and Cape Royds. At South Georgia, Shinnan Rocks, Kasumi Rock, Molodezhnaya Station and Mirny Station, cosmopolitan species were often dominant, whereas at McMurdo Station, Cape Evans, Cape Barne and Cape Royds Antarctic endemic species were generally dominant.

Thus, the cosmopolitan element is predominant among the diatoms of Antarctic inland waters at South Georgia, Shinnan Rocks, Kasumi Rock, Molodezhnaya Station and Mirny Station, while at McMurdo Station, Cape Evans, Cape Barne and Cape Royds the Antarctic element is noticeably predominant. The two regions differ in the period for which the lakes are frozen and in temperature, these factors in turn depending on differences in altitude and latitude. Since the material described here was all collected from sites near sea-level, differences in temperature can be represented by differences in latitude.

TABLE 1

The Location and Number of Cosmopolitan Species and Antarctic Endemic Species in Different Localities

			Cosmopolitan species		Endemic species		
	Latitude	Longitude	Freshwater	Marine	Freshwater	Marine	Totals
South Georgia	54°16′S	36°36′W	43 (92%)	0	3 (6%)	1 (2%)	47
Shinnan Rocks	67°57′S	44°29′E	26 (82%)	0	3 (9%)	3 (9%)	32
Kasumi Rock	67°57′S	49°29′E	11 (34%)	9 (27%)	5 (15%)	8 (24%)	33
Molodezhnaya	67°40′S	45°50′E	2 (40%)	0	1 (20%)	2 (40%)	5
Mirny	66°33′S	93°01′E	2 (25%)	0	2 (25%)	4 (50%)	8
McMurdo	77°32′S	166°12′E	5 (40%)	0	8 (60%)	0	13
Cape Barne	77°32′S	166°12′E	2 (18%)	0	8 (73%)	1 (9%)	11
Cape Evans	77°32′S	166°12′E	6 (40%)	0	7 (47%)	2 (13%)	15
Cape Royds	77°32′S	166°12′E	8 (38%)	1 (5%)	7 (33%)	5 (24%)	21

The southern limit of predominance of the cosmopolitan factor lies at 67°57′S, at Shinnan Rocks and Kasumi Rock, whereas the ice-free area of Ross Island where the Antarctic element predominates lies at 77°32′S. Consequently the boundary between the zone where the cosmopolitan element is predominant and that where the Antarctic element is predominant is considered to lie between 68°S and 77°S.

The Physiology of Antarctic Freshwater Algae

G. E. FOGG AND A. J. HORNE
Department of Botany, Westfield College, London, England

Algae are usually present and sometimes abundant in freshwater habitats in the Antarctic. These algae are likely to have special physiological features enabling survival and activity at low temperatures and during prolonged periods of darkness. Limnological investigations carried out by Rodhe (1955), Goldman and his collaborators (1963, 1967) and Baker (1967) indicate that algae in polar and subpolar lakes do indeed possess such features, but physiological studies have scarcely begun. The purpose of this paper is to discuss the available information with special reference to our own studies on the lakes of Signy Island, South Orkney Islands.

The primary photochemical processes which provide the main energy source for algal growth are essentially temperature independent, but since they are complex and depend on ancillary non-photochemical reactions for the supply of reactants, this is only manifest at low light intensities. At high light intensities photosynthesis, and hence growth, is limited by enzyme-catalysed reactions and is consequently temperature dependent with a Q_{10} of 2 to 3. To a limited extent the effect of low temperature might be offset by increase in enzyme concentrations. That this happens in cold-water plankton has been proposed by Steemann Nielsen and Hansen (1959) on the basis of their finding that light-saturated photosynthesis, as expressed in terms of carbon fixed per unit amount of chlorophyll, proceeded at about the same rate in phytoplankton from sea water at 5°C as in that from water at 15°C. Observations by Fogg and Belcher (1961) on the growth of a planktonic strain of *Chlorella pyrenoidosa*, isolated in pure culture from a Subarctic lake, point to a similar conclusion. It was found that the relative growth rate in cell number of this strain at 20°C continued to increase up to the highest light intensity used, 15,000 lux. Since growth of algae is usually light saturated at much lower intensities, about 4000 lux, this suggests a greater than usual capacity for carrying out the non-photochemical reactions of photosynthesis. It should be remarked that these observations were made after the alga had been cultured for over a year at room temperatures and it is somewhat surprising, in view of the rapidity with which algae have been found to adapt to change in factors other than temperature, that such a characteristic should have been retained. Recently, Steemann Nielsen and Jørgensen (1968) and Jørgensen (1968) have shown that although under otherwise similar conditions rates of photosynthesis are nearly the same in cells of the marine diatom *Skeletonema costatum* adapted to grow in culture at 7° and 20°C, the relative growth rate is less than half at the lower temperature of what it is at the higher. In accordance with this it is found that cells grown at 7°C are larger and contain more protein than those adapted to 20°C. For final proof it is obviously desirable that the hypothesis of Steemann Nielsen and Hansen should be tested by direct assay of photosynthetic enzymes such as ribulose 1,5-diphosphate carboxylase, and, of course, it is desirable to check its validity for freshwater algae.

Another possibility that must be considered is that algae may achieve temperatures above that of their surroundings by absorption of radiant energy. Simple calculation shows that the temperature differences that can arise are negligible for the plankton algae but may be significant for the benthic algal felt characteristic of Antarctic lakes. The rate of heat loss, Q, from a sphere in a motionless medium is given by:

(1) $Q = 4\pi k\ r\ \varDelta T$

where k is the thermal conductivity of the medium ($1 \cdot 348 \times 10^{-3}$ cal/cm^2 sec (°C/cm) for pure water at 0°C), r the radius of the sphere and $\varDelta T$ the temperature difference between the cell and a point at an infinite distance from it. The typical plankton cell of an Antarctic lake may be taken as being a sphere 5μ in diameter and may be considered as absorbing energy effectively as a disc normal to the direction of illumination.

(2) $Q = E\pi r^2$

From (1) and (2)

(3) $\varDelta T = \dfrac{Er}{4k}$

Taking E as being, under the most favourable circumstances, $2 \cdot 7 \times 10^{-3}$ cals/cm^2 sec, this gives the temperature difference as $1 \cdot 25 \times 10^{-4}$°C. The heat conduction from a plane surface is given by

(4) $Q = kA\dfrac{\varDelta T}{x}$

which gives for an area A of 1 cm^2, assuming the same intensity of solar radiation and a depth, x, of still water of 1 cm, a temperature difference of $2 \cdot 0$°C. Such temperature differences may be accentuated by convection, as occurs to an extraordinary degree in Lake Vanda, Victoria Land (Wilson and Wellman, 1962).

In the Signy Island lakes we have observed temperature differences between the algal felt and the water surface of 1 to $2\cdot3°C$; such differences would be expected to have effects on rates of metabolism which would be biologically significant. It may be noted that the algal felt, which consists mainly of *Phormidium* spp., shows a distinct structure with a rusty red layer above and a blue-green layer below, which may be one which gives most efficient absorption and utilization of the available radiation. The benthic algal felt is obviously successful; in water up to 1 m in depth its productivity has been found to be of the order of twenty-five times as great as that of the phytoplankton in the overlying water (Horne and Fogg, unpublished).

Growth occurs when photosynthesis exceeds respiration, that is, above the compensation point. It is generally found, both with higher plants and algae, that compensation occurs at lower light intensities at low temperatures (Rabinowitch, 1956), and it is reasonable to surmise that the ability of Antarctic algae to grow at low temperatures and low light intensities is, at least partially, due to this effect. Goldman *et al.* (1963), in their study of photosynthesis by light-inhibited phytoplankton of lakes on Ross Island, determined dark uptake of radiocarbon from ^{14}C-bicarbonate, which, being presumably due to Krebs cycle activity, may be taken as a measure of respiration rate, but their results show scarcely any increase in dark fixation at $14°C$ as compared with $4°C$. On the other hand, in a study by mass-spectrometry of the oxygen exchanges by pure cultures of a diatom, *Fragilaria sublinearis*, which grows in Antarctic sea ice at temperatures as low as $-2°C$, Bunt *et al.* (1966) found complicated effects of light intensity, wavelength and temperature on oxygen uptake in the light. The outcome seems to be that, whereas the optimum for photosynthetic oxygen evolution by this diatom occurs at around $7°C$, oxygen uptake, either in the light or in the dark, is at a maximum between $10°$ and $24°C$, so that in this temperature range net oxygen production cannot occur and the organism is thus obligatorily psychrophilic. Another feature which contributes to its inability to grow at temperatures as high as $24°C$ is that at such temperatures it is unable to compensate for photo-destruction of its pigments. Investigations along similar lines with freshwater species are desirable.

Survival by freshwater algae of long periods of minimal light intensity probably depends to a large extent on low rates of respiration, but there is also the possibility that dissolved organic substances are utilized. Rodhe (1955), who found apparent growth of nannoplankton in Subarctic lakes during winter darkness, put forward the suggestion that this growth depended on heterotrophic assimilation of organic matter produced during the summer period of photosynthesis. Rodhe *et al.* (1966) demonstrated heterotrophic uptake of glucose and acetate by natural populations of phytoplankton from such lakes, this uptake being relatively greater in winter than summer. However, it appears that heterotrophic uptake under these circumstances is more likely to be due to bacteria than algae, a conclusion that is reinforced by the finding that the planktonic strain of *Chlorella pyrenoidosa*, the only plankton alga from this type of lake to have been studied in pure culture, seems incapable of growth in darkness whatever organic substrate is supplied (Fogg and Belcher, 1961).

Preliminary results from studies in freshwater lakes on Signy Island show dark uptake of ^{14}C-labelled glycollate at low concentrations. This uptake is presumably bacterial and prevents glycollate concentration ever reaching levels at which the algae could use it heterotrophically, even though active algal dark uptake of glycollate occurs at higher substrate concentrations (Horne and Eagle, unpublished).

Photoassimilation of organic substrates, a process of general occurrence in the algae, by which the substrate is assimilated directly using photo-chemically generated high-energy phosphate and hydrogen donors, may be of more significance. By starting with an already reduced carbon source algae are thereby enabled to produce more cell material with a limited amount of light energy. Fogg and Belcher (1961) found that the relative growth rate of the *Chlorella* just referred to was more than doubled at light intensities below 5000 lux and temperatures between 10 and 20°C in the presence of 1·8% glucose as compared with that in inorganic medium. Sen and Fogg (1966), working with the same strain of alga, found that the relative growth rate was doubled at 500 lux when 1 mg/l glycollate was added to the medium. The addition of glucose or glycollate at light intensities approaching saturation did not increase the relative growth rate. It is suggested, therefore, that al-though plankton cannot grow at the expense of dissolved organic substances in complete darkness, they can do so at low light intensities and that this may help them to survive the Antarctic winter. To check this theory it would be desirable to compare the relative efficiencies of bacteria and algae in taking up organic matter using the methods of Rodhe *et al.* (1966), but carrying out the experiments at low light intensities instead of in darkness.

Baker (1967), who found algae under anaerobic conditions near the bottom of Lake Miers, South Victoria Land, has suggested that the development of hydrogenase activity under these conditions may be important for their survival. The process of photoreduction, using molecular hydrogen, liberated by anaerobic decomposition, instead of water as hydrogen donor, which can take place in the presence of this enzyme at low light intensities, would not, however, appear to be of biological advantage, since its quantum efficiency is the same as that for normal photosynthesis (Rieke, 1949). Chemotrophic growth, utilizing the energy released by oxidation of molecular hydrogen, which may be possible in adapted algae might, on the other hand, be able to sustain algal growth just above the deoxygenated layer of water.

If growth of freshwater algae does occur during the Antarctic winter, organic matter will be required whether the assimilation process is hetero-trophic, phototrophic or chemotrophic. In many lakes a large part of this organic matter is allochthonous, being derived from marine phytoplankton via penguins, skuas and elephant seals, but in others, e.g. Lakes Miers and Vanda, the main source must be autochthonous. Apart from that made available by death of the algae, it is likely that a substantial amount is liberated by living algae as extracellular products of photosynthesis. It is now well established (Fogg et al., 1965) that plankton algae normally release material in this way and that the release is relatively greater when photo-synthesis is inhibited by high light intensities and in oligotrophic conditions (Watt, 1966). In agreement with expectation, it has been found by ^{14}C experiments (Horne and Fogg, unpublished) that phytoplankton from Signy Island lakes release large proportions of extracellular products, samples incubated at surface light intensity on four different occasions showing between 23 and 40% of the total carbon fixed appearing in extracellular form. The release of extracellular products from the algal felt is relatively much smaller, about 0·4% but it is interesting to note that the concentration of ^{14}C-labelled extracellular products was about the same as in a parallel experiment with phytoplankton.

TABLE 1

Fixation of radiocarbon in 25 ml samples from Lake 5, Signy Island, incubated with ^{14}C-bicarbonate (activity 7×10^6 c.p.m.) for 4 hrs at $0°C$ with surface illumination under overcast conditions. Each value is the mean of two concordant results

	(a) Particulate (c.p.m.)	(b) Organic matter in filtrate (c.p.m.)	(c) b as percentage of a + b
Lake water	3110	2357	43
Lake water + 2·85 cm² of algal felt	668310	2820	0·4

The chemical nature of the extracellular products remains to be determined, but it is possible that glycollate forms a substantial fraction of the total (see Watt, 1966). It is tempting to suppose that during the summer period potential chemical energy is stored in the water in the form of such extracellular pro-ducts of photosynthesis, and that these are used to sustain growth by photo-assimilation during the winter. It may be noted that freezing will result in concentration of such organic solutes—this has, in fact, been used as a means of concentrating them for chemical analysis (Shapiro, 1961)—giving local

THE PHYSIOLOGY OF ANTARCTIC FRESHWATER ALGAE

conditions suitable for bacterial growth or even resulting in precipitation of particulate organic matter which could be used directly as food by zooplankton.

Finally some comment may be made on an apparent contrast between the paucity of phytoplankton in the Signy lakes, which seems to be characteristic of Antarctic lakes in general (excluding those heavily contaminated with organic matter), and its abundance in the near-by inshore sea water. Thus in February 1967 the chlorophyll a content of surface water from Lake 2 was 3·6 mg/m³ as compared with 30–40 mg/m³ in Orwell Bight. It is, of course, unwise to place too much reliance on isolated measurements of this sort, but the impression is that they are typical. If the difference is real, it is unlikely to be due to differences in temperature, illumination or availability of nutrients (unpublished results of Mr R. B. Heywood show the concentration of nitrate to be between 0·03 and 0·08 p.p.m. and that of phosphate up to 0·016 p.p.m. in the Signy Island lakes). Grazing by the freshwater crustacea, loss in the outflow or the production of antibiotics by the benthic algae might be involved, but perhaps the most likely possibility is that it is due to differences in penetration of damaging ultraviolet radiation. According to Rodhe et al. (1966), 10% of incident radiation between 300 and 400 mμ may be transmitted as deep as 28 m in clear mountain lakes. The absorbency of sea water for these wavelengths is about twice that of distilled water (Armstrong and Boalch, 1961). High light intensities have been shown to have a marked inhibitory effect on Antarctic freshwater phytoplankton, which is perhaps largely due to ultraviolet light (Goldman et al., 1963) and it seems plausible to ascribe the better development of Antarctic marine phytoplankton to the decreased penetration of this radiation into sea water. The success of the benthic algal felt may be ascribed to its high content of carotenoid pigments selectively absorbing the damaging wavelengths.

References

Armstrong, F. A. J. and Boalch, G. T. (1961). The ultra-violet absorption of sea water. *J. mar. biol. Ass. U.K.* **41**, 591–7.

Baker, A. N. (1967). Algae from Lake Miers, a solar-heated Antarctic lake. *N.Z. Jl. Bot.* **5**, 453–68.

Bunt, J. S., Owens, Olga van H. and Hoch, G. (1966). Exploratory studies on the physiology and ecology of a psychrophilic marine diatom. *J. Phycol.* **2**, 96–100.

Fogg, G. E. and Belcher, J. H. (1961). Physiological studies on a planktonic "μ-alga". *Verh. int. Verein. theor. angew. Limnol.*, **14**, 893–896.

Fogg, G. E., Nalewajko, C. and Watt, W. D. (1965). Extracellular products of phytoplankton photosynthesis. *Proc. R. Soc.* B **162**, 517–34.

Goldman, C. R., Mason, D. T. and Hobbie, J. E. (1967). Two Antarctic desert lakes. *Limnol. Oceanogr.* 12, 295–310.

Goldman, C. R., Mason, D. T. and Wood, B. J. B. (1963). Light injury and inhibition in Antarctic freshwater phytoplankton. *Limnol. Oceanogr.* 8, 313–22.

Jørgensen, Erik G. (1968). The adaptation of plankton algae; II. Aspects of the Temperature Adaptation of *Skeletonema costatum*. *Physiologia Pl.* 21, 423–7.

Rabinowitch, E. I. (1956). "Photosynthesis and Related Processes", Vol. II (2). Interscience, New York.

Rieke, F. F. (1949). Quantum efficiencies for photosynthesis and photoreduction in green plants. *In* "Photosynthesis in Plants", (Franck, J. and Loomis, W. E. eds), Iowa State College Press, pp. 251–72.

Rodhe, W. (1955). Can plankton production proceed during winter darkness in subarctic lakes? *Verh. int. Verein. theor. angew. Limnol.* 12, 117–22.

Rodhe, W., Hobbie, J. E. and Wright, R. T. (1966). Phototrophy and heterotrophy in high mountain lakes. *Verh. int. Verein. theor. angew. Limnol.* 16, 302–13.

Sen, N. and Fogg, G. E. (1966). Effects of glycollate on the growth of a planktonic *Chlorella*. *J. exp. Bot.* 17, 417–25.

Shapiro, J. (1961). Freezing-out, a safe technique for concentration of dilute solutions. *Science, N.Y.* 133, 2063–4.

Steemann Nielsen, E. and Hansen, V. K. (1959). Light adaptation in marine phytoplankton populations and its interrelation with temperature. *Physiologia Pl.* 12, 353–70.

Steemann Nielsen, E. and Jørgensen, Erik G. (1968). The adaptation of plankton algae; I. General part. *Physiologia Pl.* 21, 401–13.

Watt, W. D. (1966). Release of dissolved organic material from the cells of phytoplankton populations. *Proc. R. Soc.* B 164, 521–51.

Wilson, A. T. and Wellman, H. W. (1962). Lake Vanda: an Antarctic lake. *Nature, Lond.* 196, 1171–3.

The Mouthparts and Feeding Habits of *Parabroteas sarsi* (Daday) and *Pseudoboeckella silvestri*, Daday (Copepoda, Calanoida)

RONALD B. HEYWOOD
British Antarctic Survey Biological Unit, Monks Wood Experimental Station, Abbots Ripton, Huntingdonshire, England

I. Introduction

The small, shallow freshwater lakes of Signy Island, South Orkney Islands, are frozen to depths of 1–2 m for eight to eleven months of each year and are extremely harsh environments for plant and animal life (Fogg and Horne, 1970; Heywood, 1967, 1968). There is, however, a crustacean fauna of eight species:

Branchinecta gaini Daday	Anostraca
Parabroteas sarsi (Daday)	Copepoda
Pseudoboeckella silvestri Daday	Copepoda
Macrothrix hirsuticornis Norman and Brady	Cladocera
Alona rectangula Sars	Cladocera
Ilyocryptus brevidentatus Ekman	Cladocera
Cypridopsis frigogena H. Graf	Ostracoda
Eucypris sp.	Ostracoda

The anostracan overwinters in the egg stage, but the other Crustacea do not appear to be adversely affected by the severe physical and chemical winter conditions. Food supply is a probable limiting factor and this paper presents some results from a continuing study of trophic interrelationships and the degree of competition between the crustacean species.

II. Methods

The mouthparts of preserved animals were removed in lactic acid and mounted for examination in polyvinyl lactophenol containing cotton blue or carmine red. Whole animals were embedded in low viscosity nitrocellulose, sectioned at 70μ and 140μ and stained with Mallory's triple stain to determine the spatial relationships of the various limbs. Guts of preserved animals were dissected out and crushed under a coverslip on a glass slide before being examined. Polarized light aided the examination of the unstained material. Only a few observations were made on living animals and none of these was made with a microscope. This work formed only a small part of a broad-based ecological survey carried out under rather primitive conditions and neither time nor equipment were available for experimental work.

III. Results and Discussion

Although the mouthparts of both species have already been described (*Parabroteas sarsi*, Daday, 1902, Sars, 1909; *Pseudoboeckella silvestri*, Daday, 1902) the drawings given are inaccurate. For this reason, and to facilitate discussion, detailed drawings are presented in this paper.

A. PARABROTEAS SARSI

Some forms of morphological adaptation in copepod mouthparts are already known (Anraku and Omori, 1963; Beklemishev, 1959; Fryer, 1957; Gauld, 1966). The mouthparts of *Parabroteas sarsi* are of a typical carnivore form. The maxillae and maxillipeds are raptorial; their strong curved setae, armed with small blunt setules (Figs 1 and 2), are ideally suitable for grasping and retaining struggling prey. The well-developed maxillulary gnathobases have similarly armed, stout setae and each mandibular blade carries two long sharp incisor-like teeth (Fig. 3).

Examination of gut contents confirms that the animal is carnivorous and shows that it feeds mainly on the copepodid stages of *Pseudoboeckella silvestri*. A little algal material was found in most of the guts examined, but all of it came from the guts of prey.

Several observations were made of *Parabroteas sarsi* capturing *Pseudoboeckella silvestri*. The carnivore generally assumed a near vertical position in the water with head uppermost, the body slowly sinking with its limbs apparently motionless. Periodically the animal would swim jerkily upwards. In every case the prey passed in front of and above the predator, which made a single vigorous dart upwards and seized the prey with its extended maxillipeds. There appeared to be no prior contact and the predator may have been made aware of its prey by water movement or by visual stimulus.

Some information on how the carnivore handles its prey has been gained from a study of the musculature of the mouthparts and sections of animals killed in the process of eating. The prey is seized in a scoop formed by the setae of the extended maxillipeds and maxillae. By flexion and a forward and inward movement, the limbs draw the prey close to the body. In some instances the prey appears to have been orientated so that its main axis lay along the median line of the carnivore. The manipulation is presumably carried out by a co-ordinated effort of the maxillipeds, maxillae and maxillules similar to that described for *Calanus hyperboreus* by Conover (1966). When so orientated the prey is held by the maxillae and maxillipeds in a cage of inter-digitate setae. The prey is pushed towards the mouth by setae of the maxillu-lary gnathobases, the second and third maxillary segments and the basal maxilliped segments (Fig. 5). The "push" is achieved by rotation of these segments. Whether all segments of the maxillae or maxillipeds rotate, alter-nately loosening and tightening the retaining "cage" of setae, or whether the distal segments of these limbs rotate against the movement of the proximal segments to maintain the "cage" is not known. Sectioned material does show that each limb can work independently of the rest and that the endites of the second and third maxillary segments do move independently of each other. The median setae of these endites are mainly used to push the prey forward, but some leverage may be given by their long outer setae. These long setae, which form the lateral walls of the retaining cage, extend into the oral cavity, where they assist the setae of the gnathobases in holding the prey against the "incisors" of the mandibular blades.

Although it would seem advantageous for *Parabroteas sarsi* to orientate its prey so that either the head or anal end entered the mouth first, the manoeuvre is not essential. In one case examined an adult *Pseudoboeckella silvestri* was being eaten from the latero-ventral surface in the metasomal wing region. Most of its body curled anterior to the carnivore. The main retaining force seemed to be exerted by the distal setae of the maxillae which were leaning so far forward that the distal setae were pushing almost verti-cally downwards. The very strong setae of the distal maxilliped segments, which point dorso-medially, anteriorly to the mouth, only formed a "pas-sive" retaining screen at that time, but presumably they would be used to move the body gradually backwards into the mouth region. A considerable amount of body tissue had been extruded and was being held against the mandibular teeth by the setae of the gnathobases and proximal segments of the maxillae. The extrusion of tissue was incidental and not a deliberate act prior to rejection of the cuticle; a leg and pieces of cuticle had already been ingested.

Parabroteas sarsi is very large for a freshwater copepod (females can be 7·5 mm long), and it is presumably the relative size of predator to prey (*Pseudoboeckella silvestri* may be 3·7 mm long) which determines how *Para-broteas sarsi* handles its food. Whereas nauplii and early copepodid stages may always have to be manipulated because they are small and therefore difficult to retain, later copepodid stages are of such a size that they can be handled in the second manner described above, should the need arise. It would be difficult for even an adult *Pseudoboeckella silvestri* to escape from this hold, because *Parabroteas sarsi* is so relatively large and strong.

B. PSEUDOBOECKELLA SILVESTRI

The mouthparts of *Pseudoboeckella silvestri* have some, but not all, the characteristics of a filter feeder and are therefore described by comparison with both *Boeckella titicaca*,* which has more typical filter feeding mouthparts, and *Parabroteas sarsi*. Antennae, mandibular palps and maxillules of both *Pseudoboeckella silvestri* and *Boeckella titicaca*, limbs used in the steady gliding movement common to most calanoids, and in the maintenance of feeding swirls (Gauld, 1966), bear very long plumose setae, which greatly increase their effective surface area. In comparison, the plumose setae of the antennae and mandibular palps of *Parabroteas sarsi*, which swims in a more jerky fashion and which does not rely on feeding swirls, are relatively short; the antennal exopod is short and only six segmented; the mandibular palp itself is very slender. The maxillae (Fig. 1) of *Pseudoboeckella silvestri* and *Boeckella titicaca* also have many long plumose setae which form an efficient filter for food particles. Much of the filtering screen in *Pseudoboeckella silvestri* must have spacing less than 3μ wide (less than 2μ in *Boeckella titicaca*). The unicuspid teeth of the mandibular blade of *Pseudoboeckella silvestri*, however, are more like the sharp, tearing teeth of *Parabroteas sarsi* than the blunt grinding teeth of *Boeckella titicaca* (Fig. 3). The gnathobase of the *Pseudoboeckella silvestri* maxillule is more developed, and its setae stronger, than that of *B. titicaca*. The maxillipeds of the two species are strikingly different. Most of the setae of *Boeckella titicaca* maxillipeds are moderately long and flexible, particularly those of the first segment (the feeding swirls are reinforced as they flow round the bases of the maxillipeds, by rotation of these limbs). The maxilliped of *Pseudoboeckella silvestri* is a comparatively stouter limb and certain setae of the first, third, fourth and fifth segments are long and strong (Fig. 2).

Gut content analyses show that *Pseudoboeckella silvestri* is herbivorous. The source of its food, however, is not immediately obvious. Algae, the only vegetation, form often luxuriant felts over boulders on the shelf areas of the lakes, but only a poor summer population of phytoplankton (Fogg and Horne, 1970). Although there is always plant debris floating in these wind-tossed lakes, there does not appear to be enough free-floating organic matter to support the large summer population of *Pseudoboeckella silvestri*. Although naupliar and early copepodid stages form part of the nektoplankton, the later stages (mainly IV–VI) are nektobenthic—at least during the summer. They swarm over the algae-covered rocks of shelf areas and are particularly numerous where algal felt debris has collected. The gut contents show that these stages are ingesting, almost exclusively, algal felt which is identifiable by the presence of abundant, compact bundles of blue-green algal filaments.

---

* *Pseudoboeckella* and *Boeckella* are very closely allied genera, their separation being taxonomically convenient rather than natural.

No mouthpart is adapted for scrapping living felt from rock, so the animals must be feeding off the debris. The long stout setae of the maxillipeds are probably used to stir up the debris into a suspension for filtration. Sectioned material shows that the animal also handles larger pieces of debris, using maxillipeds, maxillae and maxillulary gnathobases in the same manner as that adopted by *Parabroteas sarsi* when feeding.

Food supply must be limiting in the winter, because, when the shelf area freezes solid, practically all the vegetation is encased in ice. There can be very little activity in the photoautotrophic species of phytoplankton for most of this period, because the snow and ice layers reduce the amount of available light to a level at which photosynthesis is thought to cease. The small over-wintering population of *Pseudoboeckella silvestri* may have to rely on obtaining organic debris from the sides and floor of the trough. The importance of bacteria, fungi and heterotrophic phytoplankton as food sources during winter cannot yet be assessed.

C. Changes in the Feeding Habit of Pseudoboeckella silvestri

The maxillipeds do not appear until the sixth naupliar stage in both *Parabroteas sarsi* and *Pseudoboeckella silvestri*. By the first copepodid stage the limb consists of four segments which correspond to the first, second, sixth and seventh (terminal) segments of the adult limb (Fig. 4). The remaining stages appear on ecdysis through the second, third and fourth copepodid stages and are all formed from material contained within the original penulti-mate segment. The significance of this form of development differs between the species.

As each segment of the *Parabroteas sarsi* maxilliped bears one or more strong setae, the limb is raptorial even at the first copepodid stage. It is aided in seizing prey by the maxilla, of course, which is fully developed by the second copepodid stage. Gut-content analyses show that the early copepodid stages do utilize the same food source as the adults. I have not been able to identify much of the naupliar gut contents so far examined. Although there is little cuticle present, the cellular material appears to be of animal origin, and I presume the nauplii are feeding on *Pseudoboeckella silvestri* nauplii, using the large stout setae of the antennal and mandibular basal segments.

But in *Pseudoboeckella silvestri* only the maxillipeds are used in stirring up or lifting debris and, since the relevant setae are borne on segments three, four and five, the animal is ill equipped for feeding on bottom debris until at least the third copepodid stage. Gut analyses show that the naupliar and early copepodid stages of *Pseudoboeckella silvestri* feed on phytoplankton and whatever small organic particles have become suspended in the water by wind and current action. The peak in the number of nauplii occurs towards

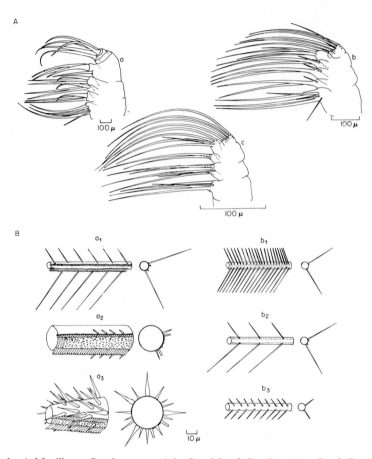

FIG. 1. *A.* Maxilla. a. *Parabroteas sarsi.* b. *Pseudoboeckella silvestri.* c. *Boeckella titicaca.*
B. Setulation of the maxilla. a. *Parabroteas sarsi.* b. *Pseudoboeckella silvestri* (Setulation in
Boeckella titicaca is identical to that in *Pseudoboeckella silvestri*). 1. proximal setae; 2. distal
setae; 3. median setae of second segment. Setules can indicate feeding habits. Stout, peg-
like setules enable carnivores to hold their prey firmly without risk of piercing the cuticle.
Long, slender setules assist the setae of particle feeders in forming filtering meshes (on
maxillae) and in maintaining water currents (on maxillipeds).

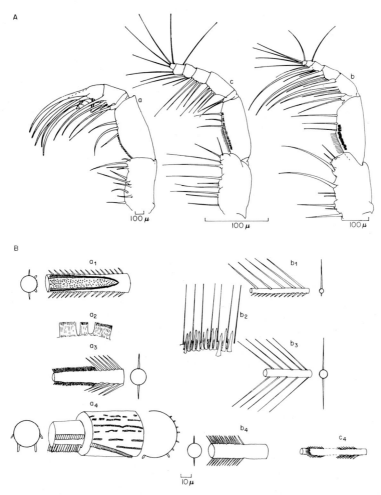

FIG. 2. *A*. Maxilliped. a. *Parabroteas sarsi*. b. *Pseudoboeckella silvestri*. c. *Boeckella titicaca*. *B*. Setulation of the maxilliped. a. *Parabroteas sarsi*. b. *Pseudoboeckella silvestri*. c. *Boeckella titicaca* (where it differs from *Pseudoboeckella silvestri*). 1. large setae of basal segment; 2. fringe of second segment; 3. seta of second segment; 4. large setae of distal segments. In *Parabroteas sarsi*, the base of the seta is covered with rows of small peg-like setules; this area is bare in *Pseudoboeckella silvestri*. The seta in *Boeckella titicaca* differ from the seta of *Pseudoboeckella silvestri* in that the distal region is also bare.

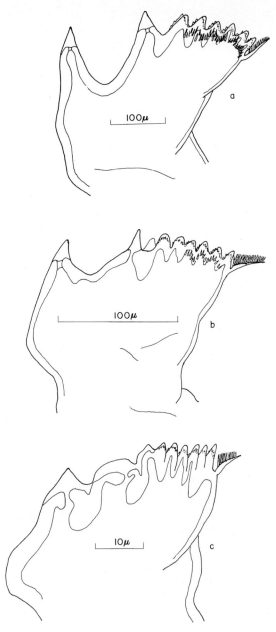

FIG. 3. Cutting edge of mandible. a. *Parabroteas sarsi*. b. *Pseudoboeckella silvestri*. c. *Boeckella titicaca*.

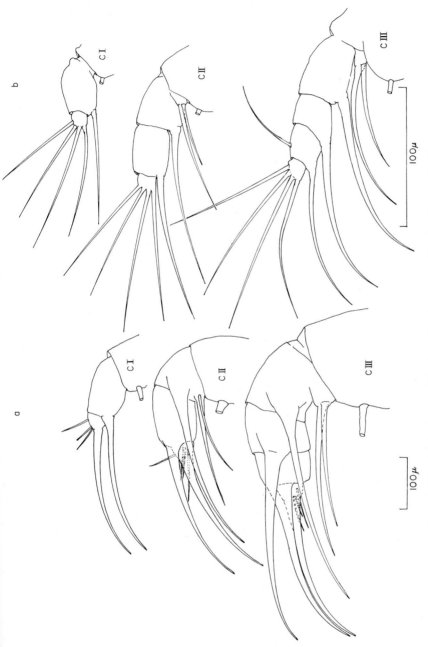

FIG. 4. The developing maxilliped. a. *Parabroteas sarsi.* b. *Pseudoboeckella silvestri.*

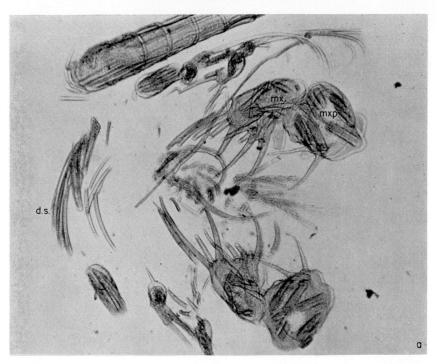

FIG. 5. Consecutive 140μ sections of C VI ♂ *Parabroteas sarsi* eating a C II *Pseudoboeckella silvestri* d.s. distal setae of maxilliped; lbr labrum; lm labium; mx maxilla (Fig. 5a 2nd and 3rd segment, Fig. 5b 2nd segment); mxl maxillule (gnathobase); mxp maxilliped (1st segment). (British Antarctic Survey Photo)

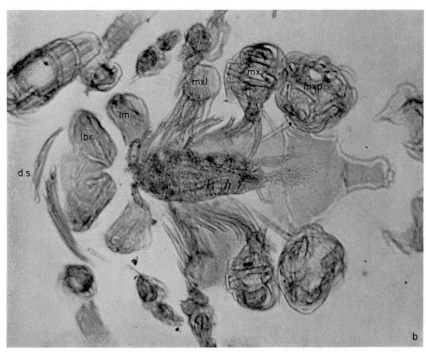

the end of winter before the lakes open and this suggests that there must be a bloom in the phytoplankton at this time. If photoautotrophic, the phytoplankters must be adapted to very low light intensities. Heterotrophic phytoplankton, bacteria and fungi may be very important sources of food for the early larval forms of *Pseudoboeckella silvestri*.

IV. Conclusion

A major ecological distinction which enables these two closely related species to coexist in an extreme environment is their feeding at different trophic levels. The highly successful colonization of these lakes by both species may be due to the ability of later copepodid stages of *Pseudoboeckella silvestri* to feed on algal felt debris produced by ice scour.

Acknowledgements

I am greatly indebted to Dr G. Fryer, Freshwater Biological Association, for guidance during the preliminary period of this study and for critically reading the manuscript, and to Miss Olive Forshaw, Freshwater Biological Association, for preparing some of the sectioned material. I am also most grateful to Dr K. G. McKenzie, for the loan of the *Boeckella titicaca* specimens from the Entomostracan section of the British Museum (Natural History).

References

Anraku, M. and Omori, M. (1963). Preliminary survey of the relationship between the feeding habit and the structure of the mouthparts of marine copepods. *Limnol. Oceanogr.* 8, No. 1, 116–26.
Beklemishev, K. V. (1959). The anatomy of the mastication apparatus in copepods: I. Masticating edge of the mandible in some Calanidae and Eucalanidae. *Trudy Inst. Okeanol.* 30, No. 1, 148–55.
Conover, R. J. (1966). Feeding on large particles by *Calanus hyperboreus* (Kröyer). *In* "Some Contemporary Studies in Marine Science" (Barnes, H., ed.), Allen and Unwin, London, pp. 187–94.
Daday, E. (1902). Mikroskopische süsswasserthiere aus Patagonien gesammelt von Dr. Filippo Silvestri. *Természetr. Füs.* 25, 201–310.
Fogg, G. E. and Horne, A. (1970). (This volume.) The Physiology of Antarctic Freshwater Algae.
Fryer, G. (1957). The feeding mechanism of some freshwater cyclopoid copepods. *Proc. zool. Soc. Lond.* 129, No. 1, 1–25.
Gauld, D. T. (1966). The swimming and feeding of planktonic copepods. *In* "Some

Contemporary Studies in Marine Science" (Barnes, H., ed.), Allen and Unwin, London, pp. 313–34.

Heywood, R. B. (1967). Ecology of the fresh-water lakes of Signy Island, South Orkney Islands: I. Catchment areas, drainage systems and lake morphology. *Br. Antarct. Surv. Bull.*, No. 14, pp. 25–43.

Heywood, R. B. (1968). Ecology of the fresh-water lakes of Signy Island, South Orkney Islands: II. Physical and chemical properties of the lakes. *Br. Antarct. Surv. Bull.* No. 18, 11–44.

Sars, G. O. (1909). Freshwater Entomostraca from South Georgia. *Arch. Math. Naturv.* 30, No. 5, 3–35.

Arctic Lake Ecosystems

J. KALFF

Department of Zoology, McGill University, Montreal, Canada

I. Introduction

Limnological research in the Arctic is of recent origin. Until well after World War II research was restricted by logistic problems to surveys of the flora and fauna (see Livingstone, 1963). Experimental studies on Arctic freshwater ecosystems date from 1953, when Comita and Edmondson reported on rates of primary production and copepod development in an Alaskan lake. With the exception of three largely unpublished dissertations (Hobbie, 1962; Kalff, 1965; Holmgren, 1968), no long-term studies, so essential to the understanding of any ecosystem, have been reported.

Although the environment in which Arctic lake organisms operate is at one extreme of the spectrum of conditions encountered in aquatic environments, it is not unique to the Arctic or Antarctic. For example, the low water temperatures characteristic of Arctic lakes, with a summer maximum below 10–15°C (Brewer, 1958; Hobbie, 1961; Oliver, 1964), are also encountered in north temperate zone lakes of southern Canada between November and May. Although Arctic lake organisms may have to live in virtual darkness for four to five months during winter, north temperate zone phytoplankton, too, may receive insufficient light for measurable photosynthesis for nearly two winter months (Kalff, unpublished data). The much-vaunted low nutrient levels of Arctic lakes also have their counterparts in North America on the Pre-Cambrian shield of the north temperate zone.

Arctic lakes are, however, ice covered much longer than those in the temperate zone. Lake Hazen on Ellesmere Island becomes ice free only in some years (McLaren, 1964), and even those lakes which become ice free regularly are still ice covered when the sun is at the summer solstice. Although the size of the heat budget calculated for a few lakes (Livingstone *et al.*, 1958; Hobbie, 1962) is comparable to that of temperate zone lakes (27,000–31,000 cal/cm²), most of the heat income is needed to melt the nearly 2 m thick ice (Brewer, 1958). The result is that little heat remains for warming the water. The substantial ice and snow cover severely restricts much of the radiation potentially available for photosynthesis (400–700mμ) from reaching the water and being utilized by the phytoplankton. Thus Hobbie (1962) found that less than 1% of the solar radiation in the visible range reached the water until late May, when the snow started to melt. At this time light transmission quickly rose beyond 30%.

II. Phytoplankton

Little is known about the species composing Arctic lake phytoplankton. The limited information indicates that most of the species encountered in the Arctic can also be found during the winter in north temperate zone lowland and mountain lakes (Skuja, 1964; Prescott and Vinyard, 1965; Hansen, 1967; Holmgren, 1968; Nauwerck, 1966; Pechlander, 1967; Kalff, unpublished data). However, whether a morphologically identical species found in both zones also exhibits an identical physiological response to environmental variables is unknown, but unlikely. There appears to be no automatic reduction in the number of algal species with latitude, because in Nedre Laksjön Lake, in northern Lapland (68°21′N, 18°49′E), 428 different phytoplankton species have been recorded (Holmgren, 1968), roughly equal to the number of species (approximately 440) recorded in Lake Erken in southern Sweden (Skuja, 1948). The variety of algae recorded is not so much a function of latitude as of the intensity of sampling and the environmental conditions in particular lakes. Thus in Nedre Laksjön Lake, Lapland, with a fairly high electrolyte content of the water, 428 largely planktonic species have been found, while Nauwerck (1968) has been able to find only about 200 phytoplankton species in near-by Latnjajaure Lake, which is characterized by a very much lower electrolyte content of the water.

Although practically all Arctic phytoplankton species can at times be found in the temperate zone as well, the commonly lower proportion of blue-green algae (Prescott, 1963a) in Arctic lakes may well indicate that nutrient levels are generally too low to permit the abundant blue-green development so characteristic of productive temperate zone lakes in summer. Circumstantial evidence in support of this view is that recently initiated work in our laboratory on two adjacent Subarctic lakes in northern Quebec (50°48′N, 60°49′W) indicates that organic pollution of the downstream lakes sharply raises the summer importance of blue-green algae in that lake.

The biomass of phytoplankton of different taxonomic groups at different seasons has been reported for only one lake with some Subarctic characteristics (Holmgren, 1968), demonstrating a seasonal succession in species composition (Fig. 1). In April the Chlorophyta species were the dominant group. They were displaced in May and June by the Cryptophyceae. In June the largest cryptomonad standing crop, found near the bottom, had three

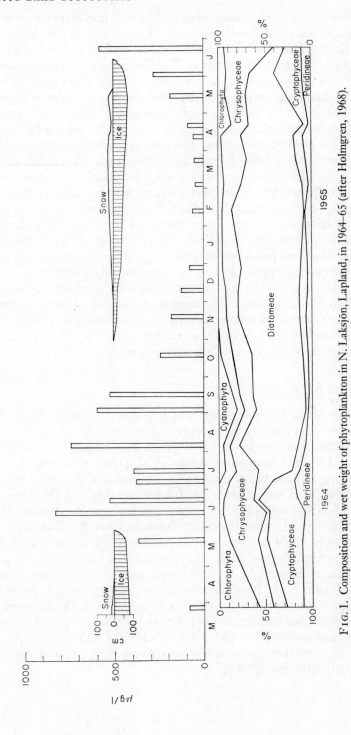

FIG. 1. Composition and wet weight of phytoplankton in N. Laksjön, Lapland, in 1964–65 (after Holmgren, 1968).

Cryptomonas spp. and *Rhodomonas minuta* as the most important components. The Chrysophyceae constituted nearly 50% of the volume in mid-June when *Ochromonas* and *Dinobryon* dominated near the surface and five other important species occupied deeper waters. The Cyanophyta were quantitatively important only in late summer and autumn, while the dinoflagellates were present throughout the year in generally small quantities. Except in May and June, the diatoms were the commonest algal group, with a total range in biomass between 10 and about 500 mg/m³ wet weight and *Cyclotella* spp. responsible for most of the volume. The predominance of diatoms is, however, not a universal feature of Arctic lakes (Nauwerck, 1967; Kalff, 1967b), where virtually all common species were small flagellates. In Imikpuk Lake, Alaska, approximately 80% of the phytoplankton were 10 μ or less in diameter and few cells were larger than 20μ (Kalff, 1967b). In a near-by tundra pond the ultraplankton (< 5μ) made up an average of 41% of the phytoplankton population during the summer (Kalff, 1967a). Pavoni (1963), working on some Swiss lakes, concluded that the percentage of nannoplankton species as well as their biomass appeared to be higher in the oligotrophic than in the eutrophic lakes studied. The high proportion of nannoplankton in the Arctic may similarly be a reflection of the extreme oligotrophy of these waters, in which the high surface-to-volume ratio of the nannoplankton, as well as the mobility of the flagellates, is likely to facilitate the uptake of nutrients and growth factors from the generally nutrient-poor waters.

III. Primary Production

In Arctic Alaska (Hobbie, 1964) and Lapland (Holmgren, 1968) algal photosynthesis was initiated in February when less than 1% of the solar radiation in the visible range penetrated the ice of an Alaskan lake, indicating an extreme low light adaptation. Rodhe *et al.* (1966) even recorded net photosynthesis at 40 m below the ice of a Lapland lake in June, when the energy flux at 30 m was estimated at 0·6 cal/cm² day, and Pechlaner (in Rodhe *et al.*, 1966) measured net carbon fixation near the bottom of an Austrian mountain lake when the energy flux there was only 0·2 cal/cm² day. Adaptation to low light conditions is not peculiar to the Arctic or high altitude, because primary production was recorded in a north temperate zone lake when the under-ice light was only approximately 0·07% of the incident radiation (Wright, 1964). Phytoplankton adapted to very low light levels are strongly light inhibited when this very low illumination is slightly increased on bright days. Thus a November population of *Cyclotella* sp. and *Synedra* sp. incorporated more carbon/cell at 1·5 m below the ice than immediately below the ice, even though the daily energy flux at the ice surface was only 14 cal/cm² day (Holmgren, 1968).

Increased light transmission accompanies the melting of the snow and ice in the spring, while at the same time the zone of maximum photosynthesis, moves farther away from the ice (Hobbie, 1962; Kalff, 1967b; Holmgren, 1968), until frequently a new population with a higher light optimum develops near the ice surface, resulting, temporarily, in two zones of relatively high photosynthesis (Holmgren, 1968; Holmgren et al., unpublished data). After the disappearance of the lake ice, algal distribution remains fairly uniform in non-stratified lakes with maximum photosynthesis commonly occurring at 1–2 m below the surface.

It is quite likely that the period of high photosynthesis recorded in two lakes at about the time these became ice free (Hobbie, 1964; Holmgren, 1968), was, as in temperature zone lakes, partially the result of a return of nutrients to the photic zone during the turnover. The absence of a distinct autumn bloom (Hobbie, 1964; Kalff, 1967b) in Arctic Alaska may be related to the only ephemeral summer stratification which does not allow the accumulation of nutrients in the hypolimnion. In contrast Nedre Laskjön Lake, in Lapland, which was stratified during most of the summer, did experience an autumnal bloom (Holmgren, 1968). In Imikpuk Lake, Alaska, those heterotrophic bacteria capable of growing on nutrient agar also demonstrated two population maxima (Boyd and Boyd, 1963). One major peak occurred during June and July, coinciding with the period of run-off and relatively high phytoplankton production, while a much smaller August peak occurred at the time of maximum water temperature.

A gradual autumn decline in primary production accompanies the decreasing light and water temperature even before the ice and snow covers the lakes in September or early October (Hobbie, 1964; Holmgren, 1968). The polar night lasting from early November to the end of February at 70°N does not allow photosynthesis. Yet an appreciable number of phytoplankton survive the darkness without any resting stages and it is these organisms which are responsible for the initiation of light assimilation in February (Hobbie, 1962; Holmgren, 1968). Vanhöffen (in Prescott, 1963a), working in Greenland in 1897 was the first to notice that algae persisted beneath the ice. However, it was not until 1955 that the question of algal survival was raised when Rodhe reported up to 10^6/l nannoplankton beneath the ice of a Lapland lake and suggested a heterotrophic existence in the dark. Since that time algal populations surviving in virtual darkness during the winter have also been found in north temperate zone, lowland and mountain lakes (Nauwerck, 1963; Wright, 1964; Pechlaner, 1967; Kalff, personal observation). From measurements of glucose uptake by a flagellate and by some bacteria Wright and Hobbie (1966) demonstrated that algae in the dark compete poorly with the bacteria for the normally low levels of glucose and acetate found in lake waters and suggested that phagotrophy and respiration of stored cell material might allow phytoplankton to survive long periods in the dark.

In Lake Peters (69°N, 145°W) primary production occurred in the upper few metres of water at least as late as 6 November 1960 and at least as early as 20 February 1961 (Hobbie, 1962). The sun remained below the local mountain valley horizon from mid-November to the beginning of February, indicating that net carbon fixation occurred approximately as long as the sun made its appearance above the local horizon and little or no snow covered the surface. Thus the period when light intensity was below the photo-synthetic compensation level of the phytoplankton, which were extremely adapted to low light intensities, was less than four months at the surface. Although it is not known how long Arctic lake phytoplankton might survive on the respiration of stored nutrients, there is some evidence that very low or even sub-compensating levels of photosynthesis, such as reach the surface waters during a portion of the Arctic winter, may aid in the survival of Arctic phytoplankton. Culture experiments (Hellebust and Terborgh, 1967) have demonstrated that a combination of low temperature (5°C) and sub-compensating levels of photosynthesis strongly retarded the loss of organic carbon from the cells of a marine flagellate and also permitted the organisms to maintain their photo-synthetic capacity for much longer than in total darkness. Very low light levels may also increase the limited heterotrophic capacity of some phytoplankton because work on tundra pond phytoplankton (Kalff, 1967a) indicated a greater velocity of glucose uptake under low light than in the dark. Conversely, the availability of organic substrates in laboratory cultures (Sen and Fogg, 1966) enhanced photosynthesis under a very low light regime and may possibly help to explain the observed net carbon fixation under the extremely low light regimes reported by Pechlaner and Rodhe (Rodhe, et al., 1966). Although phagotrophy has been observed in some dinoflagellates (Nauwerck, 1963, 1966) and may well occur among some other algal flagellates, it is not a plausible mechanism for survival among all the remaining algal groups that occur in Arctic lakes during the winter. Thus the very limited evidence suggests that Arctic lake phytoplankton may well utilize a variety of mechanisms to survive the winter.

Nearly all primary production in Arctic lakes takes place between the end of April and the end of September, and the rates recorded to date indicate that the sampled lakes are ultra oligotrophic, and considerably less productive than most oligotrophic lakes of the north temperate zone (Table 1). Of the reasons for this, a prime one is the short growing season. However, even during the growing season rates of production are low. Although a low water temperature may affect the species composition, it need not be an important reason for the low production rates, because the highest production of the year has been recorded when the water temperatures were near zero (Hobbie, 1964), and Holmgren (1968) has reported turnover times as short as 0·7 days

TABLE 1

Primary Productivity in Six Arctic and Two Temperate Zone Lakes

Lake	Annual Range (mgC/m² day)	Average June, July, August (mgC/m² day)	Annual Total (gC/m² year)	Authors
Imikpuk Alaska	0–120	70	8·5	Kalff (1967b)
Schrader, Alaska	0–167	72	7·5	Hobbie (1964)
Peters, Alaska	0–21	7	0·9	Hobbie (1964)
Latnjajaure, Lapland	0–80	—	6*	Nauwerck (1967)
Nedre Laksjon, Lapland	0–200	82	12·0	Holmgren (1968)
Lunzer Untersee, Austria	10–178	150*	30·0	Steemann Nielsen (1959)
Esrom, Denmark	30–1600	±1000	180·0	Jónasson and Mathiesen (1959)

* Estimated from very limited published data by the present author.

for a population in the m³ of maximum photosynthesis when the water temperature was close to 0°C. Similarly in the temperate zone the spring algal blooms occur shortly after the ice leaves the lakes.

The most important reason for the low production during the summer appears to be the low nutrient content of most Arctic waters. Chemical analysis of fifty-eight lakes and rivers in Arctic Alaska plus some in western Canada showed that two-thirds of the Alaskan lakes had a total alkalinity smaller than 40 mg/l as $CaCO_3$ (Kalff, 1968), and the few waters analysed across mainland Arctic Canada (Thomas, 1964) showed similarly low alkalinities. Moyle (1956) characterized lakes in northern Minnesota with such alkalinities as nutrient poor, producing scanty plankton crops. Further support for the view of a nutrient poverty is the observation that Spitsbergen lakes and ponds fertilized by breeding ducks were more productive than adjacent waters (Thomasson, 1956) and that a northern Quebec Subarctic lake at Schefferville fertilized by sewage produced a recorded daily maximum of 1400 mg/m³ (2570 mg/m²) on 22 July 1968. The maximum, recorded at the same time, in an unpolluted lake immediately upstream was only 19 mg/m^3 (98 mg/m^2) (Kalff, unpublished data). Reasons for the nutrient poverty of Arctic lakes include relatively poor development of the soil (Tedrow and Harries, 1960) and the low rate of bacterial decomposition of the organic matter in the soils during the summer (Douglas and Tedrow, 1959). In addition, when the surface soils are thawed the low precipitation prevents a significant nutrient flow from the land into the lakes. The nutrient consistently most deficient in some Alaska tundra ponds, as determined by bioassays, was PO$_4$, followed by NO$_3$ (Kalff, 1965). Other deficiencies, noted only during periods of increased photosynthesis, were one or more trace metals and vitamins. Recent work in Alaska even showed a PO$_4$ deficiency in early May when only about 0·25% of the incident solar radiation reached the lake organisms (Kalff, unpublished data), suggesting that the uptake velocity for PO$_4$ may to some extent be proportional to rates of photosynthesis at very low light levels. This PO$_4$ deficiency is a reflection of the low phosphorus content of Arctic Alaskan soil (Kelogg and Nygard, 1951).

Besides the phytoplankton some Arctic lakes have a significant benthic flora (Prescott, 1963*b*; Nauwerck, 1967) which may contribute appreciably to the annual primary production. In one such lake only 60% of the primary production was contributed by the phytoplankton, while the mosses produced 20% and the bottom diatoms and epiphytic algae the remaining 20% (Nauwerck, 1967).

IV. Fauna

I have spent so much time on the causes of the generally low primary productivity and low algal standing crops in Arctic lakes because it is the phytoplankton which in most cases directly affect the sustainable biomass at higher trophic levels. For example, the number of species and the standing crop of rotifers in north Lapland and Spitsbergen were greatest in the most productive waters (Pejler, 1957). Pejler also noted a reduction in rotifer species with increasing altitude and latitude, with the Arctic-Alpine lakes having an average of 6·4 species versus 16·2 in the Subalpine forest lakes. No more than six rotifer species were found in each of eight Spitsbergen lakes (Amren, 1964) while Lake Hazen at nearly 82°N contained only two rotifer and one copepod species (McLaren, 1964).

The turnover rate of the phytoplankton population is much greater than for the zooplankton herbivores and it is, therefore, quite possible to have a small grazed phytoplankton population supporting a much larger standing crop of herbivores. Thus the wet weight zooplankton to phytoplankton ratio in a Lapland lake varied between 1·7 to 6·4 at different times of the year. Only during a burst of phytoplankton growth in the spring did the ratio fall below unity (Holmgren, 1968).

Most crustacean zooplankton species are monocyclic in the Arctic (Tash and Armitage, 1967), where a short growing season results in a short period of abundant food. In a unusually favourable summer at least one copepod (*Cyclops scutifer*) becomes dicyclic, indicating some environmental control of the number of cycles (Nauwerck, 1967). In contrast to many temperate crustacean zooplankton, the Arctic lake species mature between one and three years after birth, with nearly all development restricted to the brief Arctic summer (Edmondson, 1955; Comita, 1956; McLaren, 1964; Nauwerck, 1967).

The copepod *Cyclops scutifer* in the temperate zone of Scandinavia has sufficient time and food available to reach maturity in one year (McLaren, 1964). In one high Arctic pond with sufficient food but a short growing season, the earliest maturation is at thirteen months, while in nearby oligotrophic Lake Hazen maturation occurs twenty-three months after birth (McLaren, 1964).

Mechanisms for winter survival in the crustaceans include the production of resting eggs in some species (Poulsen, 1940; Edmondson, 1955; Comita, 1956) and an active existence in the water column in other species (Nauwerck, 1967; Holmgren, 1968).

The zooplankton standing crop in most lakes is low. In such an ultra-oligotrophic lake as Lake Hazen (McLaren, 1964) the crop is roughly two orders of magnitude smaller than in one mildly eutrophic temperate zone lake (Wright, 1958).

The survival of salvelinid fish in high Arctic lakes would be problematic in the absence of prey other than the zooplankton. Insect larvae form an important source of food and, during the summer period of most rapid fish growth, are quite likely more important than the zooplankton. An examination of Arctic char (*Salvelinus alpinus*) stomachs from Nettilling Lake, Baffin Island (Thomson, 1957), showed that about 85% of the fish caught with food in their stomachs were feeding predominantly on insect material and only 1% were feeding largely on zooplankton. However, zooplankton increased in importance as fish food in late summer and may well be very important during the winter for the larger fish and throughout the year for the young fish. Among the insect larvae the chironomids made up over 95% of the total number of benthic organisms in Nettilling Lake (Oliver, 1964) and in an Arctic-Alpine lake with a benthic invertebrate population varying between 500 and 2500 individuals/m² during the year, the chironomids were also the most abundant component (Nauwerck, 1967). Some aspects of the biology of the little-known Arctic chironomids were recently reviewed by Oliver (1968).

The North American landlocked char and the lake trout (*Salvelinus namaycush*) show a very small amount of annual growth, which occurs only during the summer months. The lake trout, which does not occur in the high Arctic, has a smaller annual growth and matures later in Great Bear Lake,

N.W.T., than in Great Slave Lake further south (Miller and Kennedy, 1948; Kennedy, 1954). The much slower growth in that portion of Great Slave Lake adjoined by the pre-Cambrian shield, where the waters are of much lower nutrient content, but also somewhat colder than in the rest of the lake, suggests that the amount of food available to the fish has a significant bearing on the growth rate. Heavy experimental fishing for char in a small virgin lake on Victoria Island also resulted in increased growth among the survivors (Hunter, 1968).

Most individuals in landlocked populations of char grow until about 16 to 18 years of age, when the fish have a forklength of 30 to 50 cm and a weight between approximately 0·5 and 1 kg (Thomson, 1957; Hunter, 1968; Hunter, personal communication). After growth terminates, the life span of the salvelinids can be considerable, because approximately 40-year-old trout and char have been collected (Hunter, personal communication). These generally late-maturing species apparently do not breed every year (Miller and Kennedy, 1948; Hunter, 1968), but those char breeding do so between August and November and the eggs hatch in the spring or early summer previous to the disintegration of the ice cover (Hunter, 1968).

By three different sampling techniques Hunter (1968) estimated that the landlocked char population of a previously unfished Victoria Island lake numbered 8000 fish over 6 years of age, with a total biomass of approximately 40 kg/ha, which is very similar to the 45 kg/ha estimated by netting, commercial fishing and angling, for an average oligotrophic northern Minnesota lake (Moyle, 1956). However, the rate of production is likely to be much smaller in Arctic than in temperate zone lakes. The char is being fished commercially in a few places, but as yet the maximum sustained yield is unknown. Personal observation added to the finding of Hunter (1968) that a small number of loons (*Colymbus* spp.) were the only natural predators noted on the Victoria Island lake, suggests that little energy flows from the fish to higher trophic levels.

V. Future

Many of the statements made in this paper are based on limited data and some are in the realm of conjecture. The greatest need in Arctic limnology is for comprehensive studies of lake ecosystems with individuals pooling their efforts. Only then will rapid advances be made in our understanding of the interactions between species and the flow of energy between trophic levels. This need has recently become recognized both in Sweden and in Canada. In Sweden a detailed study on an Arctic-Alpine lake without fish is in progress (Nauwerck, 1967). After a few years char will be introduced and their effect on the ecosystem studied.

In Canada we have, as part of the International Biological Programme, started a comprehensive study of a small high Arctic lake near Resolute Bay, Cornwallis Island, which contains a char population. Life histories as well as the energy flow through the ecosystem are being investigated, and ultimately the lake may be fertilized.

I am confident that these efforts will, over the next few years, lead to a very much better comprehension of Arctic lake ecosystems.

References

Amrén, H. (1964). Ecological and taxonomical studies on zooplankton from Spitsbergen. *Zool. Bidr. Upps.* **36**, 193–208.

Boyd, W. L. and Boyd, J. W. (1963). A bacteriological study of an Arctic coastal lake. *Ecology* **44**, 705–10.

Brewer, M. C. (1958). The thermal regime of an arctic lake. *Trans. Am. Geophys. Un.* **39**, 278–84.

Comita, G. W. (1956). A study of a calomoid copepod population in an arctic lake. *Ecology* **37**, 576–91.

Comita, G. W. and Edmondson, W. T. (1953). Some aspects of the limnology of an arctic lake. *Stanford Univ. Publs Biol. Sci.* **11**, 7–13.

Douglas, L. A. and Tedrow, J. C. F. (1959). Organic matter decomposition rates in Arctic soils. *Soil Sci.* **88**, 301–12.

Edmondson, W. T. (1955). The seasonal life history of *Daphnia* in an arctic lake. *Ecology* **36**; 439–55.

Hansen, K. (1967). The general limnology of arctic lakes as illustrated by examples from Greenland. *Meddr. Grønland* **178**, 1–77.

Hellebust, J. A. and Terborgh, J. (1967). Effects of environmental conditions on the rate of photosynthesis and some photosynthetic enzymes in *Dunaliella tertiolecta* Butcher. *Limnol. Oceanogr.* **12**, 559–67.

Hobbie, J. E. (1961). Summer temperatures in Lake Schrader, Alaska. *Limnol. Oceanogr.* **6**, 326–9.

Hobbie, J. E. (1962). Limnological cycles and primary productivity of two lakes in the Alaskan Arctic. Unpubl. Ph.D. thesis, Indiana Univ., 124 pp.

Hobbie, J. E. (1964). Carbon 14 measurements of primary production in two arctic Alaskan lakes. *Verh. int. Verein. theor. angew. Limnol.* **15**, 360–4.

Holmgren, S. (1968). Phytoplankton production in a lake north of the arctic circle. Unpubl. Lic. thesis. Uppsala Univ., 145 pp.

Hunter, J. G. (1968). Production of arctic char (*Salvelinus alpinus* Linnaeus) in a small Arctic lake. Unpubl. Ph.D. thesis, McGill Univ., 190 pp.

Jónasson, P. M. and Mathiesen, H. (1959). Measurements of primary production in two Danish eutrophic lakes, Esrom Sø and Furesø. *Oikos* **10**, 137–67.

Kalff, J. (1965). Primary production rates and the effect of some environmental factors on algal photosynthesis in small arctic tundra ponds. Unpubl. Ph.D. thesis. Indiana Univ., 122 pp.

Kalff, J. (1967a). Phytoplankton abundance and primary production rates in two arctic ponds. *Ecology* **48**, 558–65.

Kalff, J. (1967b). Phytoplankton dynamics in an Arctic lake. *J. Fish. Res. Bd. Can.* 24, 1861–71.

Kalff, J. (1968). Some physical and chemical characteristics of freshwaters in Alaska and northwestern Canada. *J. Fish. Res. Bd. Can.* 25, 2575–87.

Kelogg, C. E. and Nygard, I. J. (1951). Exploratory study on the principal soil groups of Alaska. *U.S.D.A. Agr. Monogr.* 7, 138 pp.

Kennedy, W. A. (1954). Growth, maturity and mortality in the relatively unexplored lake trout *Cristivomer namaycush*, of Great Slave Lake. *J. Fish. Res. Bd. Can.* 11, 827–52.

Livingstone, D. A. (1963a). Alaska, Yukon, Northwest Territories, and Greenland. *In* "Limnology of Northern America" (Frey, D. G. ed.), pp. 559–74. Univ. Wisc. Press, Madison, 734 pp.

Livingstone, D. A., Bryan, K., Jr., and Leaky, R. C. (1958). Effect of an arctic environment on the origin and development of freshwater lakes. *Limnol. Oceanogr.* 3, 192–214.

McLaren, I. A. (1964). Zooplankton of Lake Hazen, Ellesmere Island, and a near by pond, with special reference to the copepod *Cyclops scutifer* Sars. *Can. J. Zool.* 42, 613–29.

Miller, R. B. and Kennedy, W. A. (1948). Observations on the lake trout of Great Bear Lake. *J. Fish. Res. Bd. Can.* 7, 176–89.

Moyle, J. B. (1956). Relationships between the chemistry of Minnesota surface waters and wildlife management. *J. Wildl. Mgmt.* 20, 302–20.

Nauwerck, A. (1963). Die Beziehungen Zwischen Zooplankton und Phytoplankton im See Erken. *Sym. Bot. Upps.* 17, Ser. 5, 163 pp.

Nauwerck, A. (1966). Beobachtungen über das Phytoplankton klarer Hochgebirgsseen. *Schweiz Z. Hydrol.* 28, 4–28.

Nauwerck, A. (1967). Das Latnjajaure Projekt. Untersuchung eines fischfreien sees vor und nach Einsatz von Fisch. *Rep. Inst. Freshwat. Res. Drottningholm* 47, 56–75.

Nauwerck, A. (1968). Das phytoplankton des Latnajajauve, 1954–65. *Schweiz. Z. Hydrol.* 30, 188–216.

Oliver, D. R. (1964). A limnological investigation of a large arctic lake, Nettilling Lake, Baffin Island. *Arctic* 17, 69–83.

Oliver, D. R. (1968). Adaptations of arctic Chironomidae. *Ann. Zool. Fennici* 5, 111–18.

Pavoni, M. (1963). Die Bedeutung des Nannoplanktons im Vergleich zum Netzplankton. *Schweiz. Z. Hydrol.* 25, 219–341.

Pechlander, R. (1967). Die Finstertaler Seen (Kühtai, Osterreich) II. Das Phytoplankton. *Arch. Hydrobiol.* 63, 145–93.

Pejler, B. (1957). Taxonomical and ecological studies on planktonic Rotaria from northern Swedish Lapland. *K. svenska Vetensk-Akad. Handl.* Ser 4, 6, No. 5, 68 pp.

Poulsen, E. M. (1940). The Zoology of East Greenland, Freshwater Entomostraca. *Meddr Grønland* 121, 1–73.

Prescott, G. W. (1963a). Ecology of Alaskan freshwater algae: II. Introduction: General considerations. *Trans. Am. microsc. Soc.* 72, 83–98.

Prescott, G. W. (1963b). Ecology of Alaska freshwater algae: III–IV. III. Introduction. General features (additional notes). IV. Additional notes on *Pseudenoclovium*, and a transfer. *Trans. Am. microsc. Soc.* 82, 137–43.

Prescott, G. W. and Vinyard, W. C. (1965). Ecology of Alaskan freshwater algae: V. Limnology and flora of Malikpuk Lake. *Trans. Am. microsc. Soc.* 84, 427–78.

Rodhe, W. (1955). Can plankton production proceed during the winter darkness in subarctic lakes. *Verh. int. Verein. theor. angew Limnol.* 12, 117–22.

Rodhe, W., Hobbie, J. E. and Wright, R. T. (1966). Phototrophy and heterotrophy in high mountain lakes. *Verh. int. Verein. theor. angew Limnol.* 16, 302–13.

Sen, N. and Fogg, G. E. (1966). Effects of glycollate on the growth of a planktonic *Chlorella*. *J. exp. Bot.* 17, 417–25.

Skuja, H. (1948). Taxonomie des Phytoplankton einiger Seen in Uppland, Schweden. *Symp. Bot. Upps.* 9, No. 3, 399 pp.

Skuja, H. (1964). "Grundzüge der Algenflora und Algenvegetation der Fjeldgegenden um Abisko in Schwedisch-Lappland." Almquist and Wiksells, Uppsala, 465 pp.

Steemann Nielsen, E. (1959). Untersuchungen über die primärproducktion des Planktons in einigen Alpenseen Osterreichs. *Oikos* 10, 24–37.

Tash, J. C. and Armitage, K. B. (1967). Ecology of the zooplankton of the Cape Thompson area, Alaska. *Ecology* 48, 129–39.

Tedrow, J. C. F. and Harries, H. (1960). Tundra soil in relation to vegetation, permafrost and glaciation. *Oikos* 11, 237–49.

Thomas, J. F. J. (1964). Surface water quality in major drainage basins and northern areas of Canada. *J. Am. Wat. Wks Ass.* 56, 1173–93.

Thomasson, K. (1956). Reflections on Arctic and Alpine lakes. *Oikos* 7, 117–43.

Thomson, J. A. C. (1957). On the biology of the Arctic Char, *Salvelinus alpinus* (L) of Nettilling Lake, Baffin Island, N.W.T. Unpubl. M.Sc. thesis, McGill Univ., 95 pp.

Wright, J. C. (1958). The limnology of Canyon Ferry Reservoir: I. Phytoplankton-Zooplankton relationships in the euphotic zone during September and October. *Limnol. Oceanogr.* 3, 150–9.

Wright, R. T. (1964). Dynamics of a phytoplankton community in an ice-covered lake. *Limnol. Oceanogr.* 9, 163–78.

Wright, R. T. and Hobbie, J. E. (1966). The use of glucose and acetate by bacteria in aquatic ecosystems. *Ecology* 47, 447–64.

Discussion

Freshwater Ecosystems

E. B. WORTHINGTON

Dr Kalff has strikingly demonstrated the magnitude of the differences between Arctic and Antarctic. We may ask how much of the endemism and species poverty of the Antarctic is due to its isolation throughout the recent ice-retreat period. The presence of marine diatoms in fresh water also parallels a well-known oceanic island situation.

I have one question. What role is played by bacteria in primary production? Bacterial chemosynthesis has been said by some Soviet and Japanese workers to provide as much as one-third the primary production in certain lakes. What is its role in Antarctica?

THE ROLE OF BACTERIA

G. E. FOGG

Plankton algae may release 40% of their photosynthetic products in extracellular form and bacteria must be the main utilizers of this dissolved organic matter.

C. R. GOLDMAN

The high rate of uptake in dark conditions in Lake Vanda and Lake Bonney probably result from bacterial action. Glucose and acetate are also taken up. There are high bacterial counts in Lake Vanda at the level where the water gets warm and salty, and when a $5–10\mu$ membrane filter is used 80% of the active organisms pass through, so bacteria are obviously very important. Signy Island would be a good place to look at the role of bacteria as food for zooplankters.

E. D. RUDOLPH

Were all autotrophic bacteria eliminated from Professor Fogg's leakage data?

A. HORNE

An HA Millipore filter was used (pore size 0.45μ): anything that got through would have to be very small!

PHYTOPLANKTON AND BENTHIC ALGAL FELTS

C. R. GOLDMAN

May I emphasize the danger of considering standing-crop figures only, without data on turnover? In 1963 I added molybdenum to an Alpine lake in California and this fertilization produced only a small increase in phytoplankton, but substantial increases in numbers of zooplankton and fish. The explanation was that primary production rates were improved, but that the primary production was consumed as fast as it appeared.

The relationship between blue-green algal felts and phytoplankton is interesting. At Skua Lake we have little felt and much phytoplankton, while at Alga Lake the position is reversed. When the lakes were both drawn down and salt concentration increased, production in Skua Lake shot up, but not that in Alga Lake. There is some relationship between phytoplankton and benthic felt: perhaps the former is suppressed by the latter.

S. Z. EL-SAYED

How were the phytoplankton turnover rates cited by Dr Kalff obtained?

J. KALFF

The Swedish author who obtained these data made regular phytoplankton counts and ^{14}C measurements, and from these he calculated the time necessary for production to equal the standing crop. An extreme value in the optimum M^3 was as high as 0·7 of the standing crop per day, while on average there was complete turnover in three to five days during spring and early summer. In winter there was very little production.

G. E. FOGG

Blue-green algal felts may well release an antibiotic and suppress the phytoplankton. In the poorer lakes, however, ultraviolet radiation may also have an inhibiting effect: this would be screened out by the water and the carotenoid pigments which are conspicuous in the felt algae and have less influence on the benthic felts than on the plankton.

C. R. GOLDMAN

In Alga Lake the felt has a stronger development of the protective screen of orange carotenoid pigment on its surface than in Skua Lake, whose dense phytoplankton bloom shades the underlying algal mat.

V. AHMADJIAN

Have you determined the presence and quantity of heterotrophic organisms in or on the algae felts? If so, what do they do?

G. E. FOGG

A few rotifers are conspicuous in the felts, but I have no measurements of the overall role of heterotrophs.

R. DELEPINE

It is interesting to report the discovery of a marine green alga found by Dr Lamb 30–40 m below low-water mark at Melchior Island. *Lambia* has been cultured in Paris at 0–1°C for three years in zero or near zero illumination. Clearly this marine form resembles freshwater algae in these respects.

HERBIVORES AND PREDATORS

M. W. HOLDGATE

Mr Heywood's account of a simple predator-prey interaction in a small lake reminded me of some of the classic experiments with protozoan species described by Gause, Lotka and Volterra. In such simple, confined systems oscillations in predator and prey numbers, and even extinctions, might be expected. Are there any indications of these? Has Mr Heywood considered smaller-scale tank experiments on this theme?

R. B. HEYWOOD

The population of the predator *Parabroteas sarsi* is small; only two or three adults are often caught in four vertical net hauls from 6 m. The impact of this predator on the abundant *Pseudoboeckella silvestri* must be very small.

M. W. HOLDGATE

But something must limit its numbers? If prey is always abundant, what controls the predator?

E. B. WORTHINGTON

How long did the observations continue?

R. B. HEYWOOD

Continuously over between two and three years. I have one observation that may help us solve this problem. The herbivorous copepod has an extended life cycle, and females with eggs and nauplii may be found in most months. The nauplii of the carnivore, on the other hand, appear in October when the herbivore larvae are at a peak, and the two cycles may be geared together through the interaction of the youngest stages. I hope to get more information on this when I have material in culture in this country. Dr Kalff said that copepods in the Arctic extend their life cycle over three years when food supplies are short. Under similar conditions *Pseudoboeckella silvestri* varies in body size. This is what seems to happen. During a mild winter food supplies remain good and more individuals survive to the adult stage. Numbers of nauplii become excessive at the October "bloom", and consequently the amount of food available to each individual is small, although the total amount of food remains high. The resulting adults are small. But in a harsh winter only a relatively few adults are available to contribute to the "bloom". The amount of food per individual after this time is therefore large and the nauplii grow into a larger-mode adult.

E. B. WORTHINGTON

Dr Kalff mentioned an Arctic situation where the biomass of copepods was greater than that of their food organisms. Surely wild oscillations in the population would result?

J. KALFF

No, because the phytoplankton was reproducing very rapidly. There appeared to be only a relatively low phytoplankton biomass, but what was happening was that the production was being grazed off as fast as it was renewed. Hence a large herbivore population could be supported.

K. G. McKENZIE

What other arthropods occur in Signy Island lakes, and what role do they play in the ecosystem?

R. B. HEYWOOD

There are three Cladocera, two Ostracods and one Anostracan—*Branchinecta gaini*. All are benthic and all seem to be connected with the blue-green algal felt. *Branchinecta* seems to grasp the living felt, and can be seen over it, with its limbs stirring the felt surface. Examination of gut contents reveals that quite large pieces of blue-green algae are ingested.

K. G. MCKENZIE

Cypridopsis frigogena, one of the two ostracods which occurs in the Signy Island lakes, is an active swimmer and, since it is a scavenger, may well play a completely complementary role to that of *Parabroteas sarsii* in the plankton community.

P. K. DAYTON

Are predators significant in the dry-valley lakes?

C. R. GOLDMAN

Only three or four individual Heliozon protozoa have been found in Lake Bonney. They must have a negligible impact. There is, of course, very little food supply for them.

R. B. HEYWOOD

The lakes on Signy Island do fluctuate very much from year to year in such parameters as the duration of ice cover, which depends especially on the pattern of snow accumulation. The number of herbivorous organisms also fluctuates and when these are sparse their rarity may restrict carnivore populations, which may not be able to breed fast enough to catch up in a year with abundant herbivores.

CONCLUSIONS

E. B. WORTHINGTON

To sum up I would like to make two or three generalizations. What strikes me, as a tropical limnologist, about these polar systems is the limitation imposed in the Arctic by a shortage of nutrients and in both regions by the ice regime. The concept of "solid limnology" is a new and entertaining one for me. It is also intriguing to learn of lakes that concentrate salts and perhaps organic matter as the water freezes out. The contrast between the poor, but endemic diatom flora of Antarctica and the abundant plankton in the Arctic is striking. So is the question of competition between the primary producers of the phytoplankton and the benthic felts. Clearly we have a lot to learn about the role of bacteria in these lakes. Among the secondary producers, it is clear that we have very simple systems, especially in the Antarctic, and it was striking to attend a session where the uppermost, terminal trophic level— fish—that normally dominate limnological discussion were nowhere mentioned. These fresh waters obviously have a high potential as laboratories and we shall look forward to learning more from them in future.

Part XI

SOILS

Soils

Research on the soils and soil-forming processes in Antarctica has developed greatly in the interval between the two SCAR Symposia on Antarctic Biology. The work of United States and New Zealand scientists, especially in Victoria Land, is reviewed comprehensively by F. C. Ugolini in this section and has been the subject of a special volume in the Antarctic Research Series (1966). This research has revealed the desert character of the soils in inland continental Antarctica, with their low moisture content and high salinity, and correspondingly sparse, or even non-existent microbiota, described in the papers in the present section by Cameron *et al.* and by Benoit and Hall. The arthropod fauna inhabiting these inland soils is also impoverished, as H. Janetschek reports in his paper in Section 13, and is critically dependent upon the availability of liquid water.

Parallel studies of the more highly developed soils of the Maritime Antarctic by United Kingdom workers have been reported in a series of papers by M. J. G. Chambers and by S. E. Allen and his collaborators, briefly reviewed by S. E. Allen and O. W. Heal in this section. Associated microbiological and mycological research has been described more fully by Heal *et al.* in the proceedings of a discussion on the terrestrial Antarctic ecosystem (Smith, 1967). J. Baker, in the section, reports some recent findings, while the larger soil fauna is discussed by P. J. Tilbrook in Section 13 of this volume.

The maritime Antarctic soils differ in many respects from those of the continental zone, largely because of the much higher availability of water, coupled with less intense cold. They lack desert characteristics, and include accumulations of organic matter of vegetable origin as well as those produced by birds and seals which are the only organic soils to be widespread on the coast of continental Antarctica. There are even a few local patches of "brown earth" type soils associated with higher plants. An outline classification for these maritime Antarctica soils is provided by Allen and Heal, but their precise interrelationships with the soils of the continental interior are not clear, although coastal areas of East Antarctica are evidently intermediate in their pedological characteristics. Future research will no doubt elucidate the whole complex of intergradation and show the subtle variation in soil type and weathering characteristics in relation to source, circumstances of origin and present climate, and within the next five years an interpretative account of the pedology of the whole Antarctic region should be possible.

In the papers by Ugolini and by Allen and Heal in this section reference is made to various zones and sub-zones into which the Antarctic has been divided by ecologists. This classification is discussed in the Introduction to Section 12.

References

Antarctic Research Series, Vol. 8 (1966). *Antarctic soils and soil forming processes.* American Geophysical Union.

Smith, J. E. (Leader) (1967). A discussion on the terrestrial Antarctic ecosystem. *Phil. Trans. R. Soc.* B **252**, No. 777, pp. 167–392.

Antarctic Soils and their Ecology

F. C. UGOLINI
College of Forest Resources, University of Washington,
Seattle, Washington, U.S.A.

I. Introduction

Soil formation in Antarctica is limited by scarcity of ice-free areas (Fig. 1), by low temperatures, and by paucity of liquid water. These conditions are also effective in preventing establishment of an extensive flora and fauna; thus the conventional definition of soil as a body supporting, or capable of supporting, a living phase is no longer tenable for this environment. Soil formation in much of Antarctica occurs virtually under abiotic conditions except for microflora and microfauna. Penguin guano, concentrated along restricted coastal areas, is not only the largest accumulation of organic material on the continent, but also represents the introduction of material from the rich marine ecosystem to the depauperated terrestrial system. Under the prevailing desert conditions, Antarctic soils, excluding those of the Antarctic Peninsula and of some coastal areas, are generally poorly developed, have coarse textures, contain soluble salts, have a neutral reaction and display little biological activity. A few acid soils occur locally. Except in penguin colonies where guano has accumulated, or in areas where mosses grow, barren conditions prevail.

Various subdivisions of the Antarctic biological zone have been proposed, on ecological and climatological grounds (e.g. Holdgate, 1964; Sabbagh, 1962; Markov and Bodina, 1960). In this paper the classification of Weyant (1966), who recognized four climatological regions: oceanic Antarctica, Antarctic coast, Antarctic slopes and the interior Antarctic plateau, will be used, and the pedology of each discussed in turn.

II. Oceanic Antarctica

A. CLIMATE

Oceanic Antarctica includes the South Shetland Islands, South Orkney Islands, Palmer Archipelago and the west coast of the Antarctic Peninsula. It has an oceanic climate and lies between two regions of frequent disturbance activity, the Ross Sea and the Weddell Sea (Sabbagh, 1962). The mean annual temperature for the oceanic Antarctic is not below $-10°C$, and the means for the summer are above $0°C$ or close to it. Total annual precipitation (in cm of water) varies from 36 cm (Marguerite Bay, 68°11'S, 67°01'W) to 116·9 cm (Melchior Island, 64°20'S, 62°59'W).

B. BIOLOGY AND SOILS

The ice-free coastal areas of oceanic Antarctica support dense mats of mosses and harbour the only two vascular plants of the continent (Gimingham and Smith, 1970; this symposium). Invertebrates are quite abundant (Gressitt, 1965), and the microbial population is more abundant and varied than that of the Ross Sea area (coastal Antarctica) (Boyd and Rothenberg, 1968). The numbers of micro-organisms in similar soils on Signy Island and in northern England are comparable (Heal et al., 1967).

During summer, mean soil temperature is above zero in many areas, due to radiation warming, and moss mats have temperatures higher than the soil (Longton and Holdgate, 1967; Greene and Longton, 1970; this symposium). Holdgate et al. (1967) showed that the 0–5 cm, 10–15 cm and 50–200 cm soil layers undergo, respectively: a diurnal, seasonal and annual freeze-thaw cycle. Processes of solifluction, formation of sorted patterned ground, and ice-wedge polygons occur at Signy Island (Holdgate, 1964; Chambers, 1966) and in the Antarctic Peninsula (Berg, 1965).

Pedological information collected by Allen and Northover (1967) and by Holdgate et al. (1967) for Signy Island is summarized by Allen and Heal (1970; this symposium). Mature soils comparable to "brown earths" develop only in small areas on north-facing slopes where conditions are especially favourable, and where grass (Deschampsia antarctica) and the herb (Colobanthus quitensis) are dominant. Most Signy Island soils are underlain by permafrost, poorly drained and disturbed by solifluction, and they are locally covered with a poorly decomposed moss mat that rests sharply on the mineral soil. There are no soil invertebrates (such as earthworms and myriapods) that might mix the organic matter in the soil.

Soils of the younger Signy Island moraines are almost completely devoid of vegetation, have a very alkaline reaction (pH = 9) and considerable clay content. The soils of the older moraines are colonized by mosses, and have a pH about 6·0 and some organic matter (0·5% carbon), but the nutrient status is low. The gleyed material in these soils shows some resemblance to the soils of Macquarie Island and perhaps other Subantarctic areas (Taylor, 1955). Soils developed over stable schist outcrops are limited to pockets of fines among rock projections, and to debris derived from decomposition of the schists. Soils developed on marble outcrops have high calcium content and moderately high sodium and magnesium.

Organic soils tend to develop under the combined influence of the various mosses and the close proximity of permafrost. The deeper peats are sub-acid, and show little mixing with the mineral matter below. Bacterial and fungal populations, in addition to protozoa, are present but biological activity is low. Among the extractable nutrients of the peat, sodium and magnesium are high relative to potassium and calcium, and readily extract-able. Analyses of rain water, snow and sea water collected at Signy Island clearly show that the ocean is the major source of mineral ions in the precipita-tion. Total nitrogen and phosphorus in the peat are similar to the quantities present in the living moss (Allen *et al.*, 1967). Northover and Allen (1966) have reported that extractable phosphorus and ammonium-nitrogen of these peats vary seasonally and Allen *et al.* (1967) have suggested that the marine mammal and bird fauna is the source of these two elements. Soils developed under the influence of penguins and seals are rich in potassium, phosphorous and ammonium-nitrogen. According to Allen and Northover (1966), soil nutrient levels are above the requirements of the existing flora and fauna.

III. Coastal Antarctica

A. CLIMATE

The climate of coastal Antarctica is influenced by latitude, the type of land surface, and by the vicinity of the slopes to the polar plateau (Weyant, 1966). There is more cyclonic activity, more complex air mass structure, stronger aperiodic temperature fluctuations, higher cloudiness, more precipitation and in general higher temperatures than in the Antarctic slopes and interior plateau regions. Mean annual temperatures, and means for the austral summer, are broadly related to latitude, being higher at stations along the coasts of East Antarctica than on the Ross Sea coasts (Table 1). In contrast

TABLE 1

Climatic Data for Some Stations in Coastal Antarctica

Station	Lat.	Long.	Mean annual	Mean summer temp.	Max. temp.	Precipt (water eq.)
Hallett	72°18′S	170°18′E	−15·5°C	−2·4°C	8·3°C	12 cm
Scott	77°51′S	166°45′E	−20·8°C	−5·6°C	5·0°C	15 cm
Port Martin	66°40′S	141°24′E	−11·8°C	−3·2°C	—	—
Dumont D'Urville	66°40′S	140°01′E	−10·9°C	−3·3°C	—	—
Wilkes	66°16′S	110°34′E	− 9·9°C	−1·5°C	8·0°C	36 cm
Mirny	66°33′S	93°01′E	−10·2°C	−1·5°C	5·0°C	85 cm
Mawson	67°36′S	62°53′E	−10·6°C	−1·8°C	7·3°C	—
Showa	69°00′S	39°35′E	−11·4°C	−2·6°C	6·5°C	—

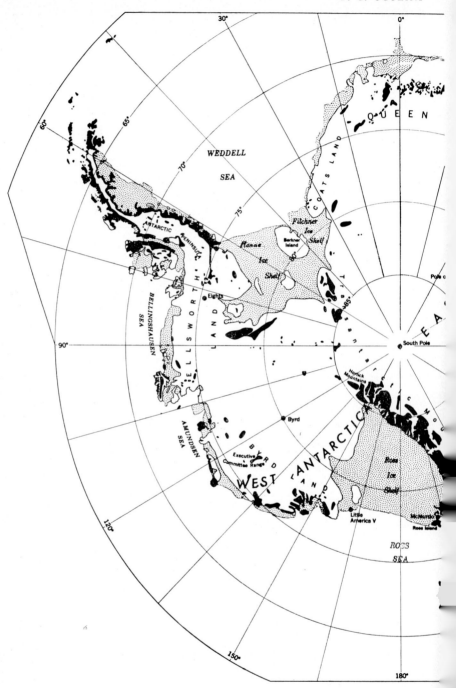

FIG. 1. Map of Antarctica. The dark area

(From Tedrow a

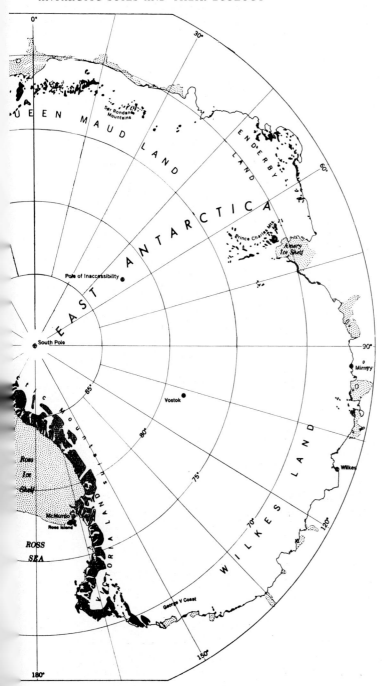

present ice-free regions including mountains.
golini, 1966.)

stations in Queen Maud Land have a mean annual temperature similar to the Ross Sea stations. Precipitation (cm of water equivalents) in coastal East Antarctica is from three- to eightfold higher than in the Ross Sea region.

Extensive ice-free dry valleys or oases are found in Victoria Land, Knox Coast, Queen Mary Coast, Pravda Coast and Queen Maud Coast. Southern Victoria Land contains an essentially ice-free area of 4000 km² (Bull, 1966), which is probably one of the largest on the continent. The climate is characterized by low temperatures ($-18°C$ mean annual) and light precipitation (about 10g/cm²). The highest temperature recorded, $12\cdot3°$ at Lake Vashka, Victoria Valley, on December 20, 1959, exceeds any other temperature recorded in continental Antarctica (Bull, 1966). A minimum of $-62°$ for the winter of 1960 was recorded near Lake Vida (Bull, 1966). January is the warmest month and August the coldest. The ice-free area west of McMurdo Sound is warmer and drier than Ross Island and the coast of the Sound. Easterly winds coming from the Sound are colder and wetter than the westerly katabatic winds from the Polar Plateau, and consequently precipitation is greatest in the eastern ends of the valleys. Geomorphic evidence shows that strong westerly winds blow during the winter. The annual heat balance for the ice-free area is estimated to be 29,000 cal/cm² compared with a loss of heat energy of 4000 cal/cm² for the nearby ice-covered terrain (Ugolini and Bull, 1965).

Daily and seasonal fluctuations in temperatures were observed by the author and by Berg and Black (1966). In the Wright Valley at the beginning of November 1962 the soil surface was still below or at $0°C$; at 30 cm the soil temperature was $-15°C$. By January 19, 1963, the soil surface had reached a temperature of $10°C$ and a layer approximately 15 cm thick was above $0°C$. During the winter a reverse temperature gradient occurs with temperatures approaching $-40°C$ at the surface and increasing to $-20°C$ at a depth of 5 m (Berg and Black, 1966).

Nichols and Ball (1964) found that along the coast of McMurdo Sound at Marble Point the maximum depth of thaw was $40\cdot6$ cm in January 1959, and $67\cdot1$ cm during the same month in 1958. In Taylor Valley and on Ross Island, Black and Berg (1963) reported an active layer from 15 cm to more than 1 m deep. They recognized that local factors may alter the depth of thawing. A preliminary estimate is that about 20–60 freeze-thaw cycles affect portions of the active layer during the year (Black and Berg, 1963).

B. SOIL BIOLOGY

Plant life is scarce and local in coastal Antarctica, consisting chiefly of crustose lichens and patches of moss where water is available (Llano, 1962). Microbial activity is in general limited, and in a few areas of Taylor and Wright Valleys no microbes at all could be detected (Boyd et al., 1966);

however, with favourable edaphic conditions, an abundant population of micro-organisms was found whose characteristics are described in this volume (Cameron *et al.*). Most of the microbial population occurs in places where free water is available, but in the dry soils of Taylor Valley more organisms occur at the surface of the ice-cemented permafrost than at the soil surface. Free-living land arthropods occur locally where ecological conditions are favourable (Janetschek, 1967 and 1970; this symposium).

C. SOILS OF VICTORIA LAND

Soils from Southern Victoria Land were first collected during Shackleton's 1907–09 expedition and analysed by Jensen (1916), who recognized their main characters: his findings were confirmed by McCraw (1960). The soils of the Ross Dependency were considered to be of the desert type, with low moisture, cold temperatures, slow rate of weathering, dominance of physical weathering, coarse textures, and containing soluble salts and calcium carbonate on or near the surface. They were divided into four groups on the basis of topography and parent material. In this preliminary field-work it was implied that a secondary carbonate horizon tends to develop with time, but may be destroyed in the older surfaces (McGraw, 1960).

Ugolini (1963) studied morphological, chemical and physical parameters of a number of soils along a chronosequence in the Lower Wright Valley, Southern Victoria Land (Fig. 2). The moisture regimen of soils uninfluenced by snow patches was shown to be dictated by the proximity of the ice-cemented layer to the soil surface. Where the ice-cemented layer or the ice-cemented permafrost is within about 15 cm of the surface, some melting of the ice occurs in summer and the soil above it becomes moist. The melt water moves upwards under a strong evaporating gradient and is eventually lost to the atmosphere. In such places where there is a net transfer of water from the ice-cemented layer to the atmosphere, the ice-cemented surface should recede and older soils should have thicker unconsolidated layers resting on the ice-cemented surface. Field evidence obtained by this author and others (Black and Berg, 1963; G. Linkletter, *personal communication*; R. Behling, *personal communication*) from moraines of varying age in Taylor and Wright Valleys show that this mechanism is operating. However, other factors such as exposure to solar radiation, underground seepage and topographical position may destroy the precise relationship. Ultimately the ice-cemented surface comes to lie below the permafrost table and part of the permafrost is "dry permafrost".

Using some of the observations of the author and the concept that the ice-cemented layer is the source of soil moisture, Janetschek (1967) produced a very interesting diagram of Southern Victoria Land. In this model, climatologic and pedologic factors are related to the soil-moisture regimen, which in turn determines the occurrence of life in the soil. This simple ecological model may break down in places, but still provides a valid generalization.

Ugolini and Bull (1965) discussed soil formation in relation to the glacial history of ice-free areas and the mechanics of glaciation and deglaciation. They concluded that parameters such as moisture content, depth to the ice-cemented layer, percentage of silt and clay, salt concentration, and free-iron oxides could be used, cautiously, as criteria for soil development and as indexes of the relative age of moraines. The soils considered were from the Upper and South Fork of Wright Valley and were derived from three

F IG. 2. Ahumic soil profile in the Lower Wright Valley, Antarctica. The measuring tape rests on the ice-cemented permafrost at 28 cm. The maximum depth of thawing was about 15 cm as recorded on 19 January 1963.

chronologically different land surfaces. The soil on the youngest moraines was grey to pale yellow in colour, had a coarse sandy texture, was low in soluble salts and in free iron oxides. The ice-cemented layer was at a depth of 8 cm and had a moisture content of about 15%. The soil from the older moraines (Fig. 3) near the east end of the South Fork, Wright Valley, showed a strong brown colour, had a sandy texture but contained 6% clay, was high in soluble salts, contained carbonates and had about 1% of free iron oxide. The ice-cemented permafrost was more than 70 cm from the surface and had a moisture content of about 1·5%.

During the 1968–69 austral summer the author continued studies of the hydrothermal regimen of some soils from Southern Victoria Land. Radio-active sodium chloride was used as a tracer to establish movement of ions and

FIG. 3. Ahumic soil profile at the east end of the South Fork, Wright Valley, Antarctica. This soil is developed from old moraines and the ice-cemented permafrost is below 70 cm.

liquid water. Sodium chloride ions were shown to move upward in the soil at temperatures continuously below freezing. This indicates that ionic migration occurs and that liquid water may also move in the upward direction. These findings are of considerable interest for the formation of polar soils and have important bearing on plant life in cold environments (Ugolini and Grier, in preparation).

1. Composition of soils

A number of soils from Southern Victoria Land derived from different parent materials or from different geomorphologic features were analysed by

Claridge (1965). The soil on granite showed an olive yellow colour typical of soils derived from this rock in Antarctica. Clay content ranged from 3·5% to insignificant amounts, extractable iron varied from 0·4% to 0·8%, and calcium carbonate varied from 24% to none. The clay minerals included mica, hydrous mica, vermiculite and montmorillonite. Soil derived from marble (Marble Point) has a low clay content, high percentage of carbonates (12·9%), and 0·06–0·23% of free iron oxides. The clay composition showed mica and hydrous mica at the surface, but montmorillonite at the permafrost level. The soils of dolorite debris in Victoria Valley were rich in soluble salts, had neutral or alkaline pH and a high clay content (2–5%) consisting of mica and montmorillonite. Recent soils from alluvium showed low content (0·6–1%) of soluble salts and calcium carbonates, high pH (9 and 10) and low clay content. The clay minerals present in alluvial soils included mostly mica, with some vermiculite B and a little chlorite. Electron micrographs showed a few halloysite tubes. The soils on low-level moraines have more soluble salts and carbonates at the surface than at the permafrost table. The clay consisted mainly of micas and vermiculite A and B. By contrast the soils on high level moraines that are derived from dolorite and Beacon sandstone showed a concentration of soluble salts at the permafrost table. No carbonates were present and the soil had a pH of *circa* 8. The clay was mainly micaceous.

2. Weathering processes

According to Claridge (1965), the dominant process of clay formation in Antarctic soils under the present climate is the weathering of mica. As the chemical weathering processes proceed, micas tend to expand and become vermiculite A (hydrated mica) or vermiculite B (non–collapsing after potassium saturation). Montmorillonite is mainly present in soils derived from marble, dolomite and greywacke. The formation of this mineral is interpreted as the result of aridity and high pH.

Different results were obtained by Kelly and Zumberge (1961) at Marble Point. After an intensive study of exposed quartz-diorite rocks, they found that no clays are being formed and that the only chemical alteration was the oxidation of ferrous iron in biotite and pyrrhotite to ferric hydroxides.

A weathering study conducted by the author on a soil derived from granite bedrock and located on the north shoulder of Wright Valley near Bull Pass shows that this soil was not entirely derived *in situ*, but that probably only the surface was contaminated. A number of chemical and mineralogical analyses, including optical, X-ray and differential thermal methods, showed that the feldspars of the granitic rocks were altered and clay minerals had formed. The site is dry at present, but it may have been wetter in the past, as suggested by the substantial weathering observed, and it was concluded that some of the alteration may be relict. This study demonstrates that one of the difficulties of evaluating weathering in Antarctica is that relict weathering may be erroneously attributed to present conditions. The other difficulty is that the soil may not have been derived *in situ*. Studies made on glacially or fluvially transported material may be vitiated by the fact that some of the minerals may have been weathered prior to transportation. Lack of a vegetation cover coupled with strong winds favours wind erosion and deposition. Therefore, it may be difficult to find substrata that are strictly *in situ*, free from contamination, and reflecting present weathering conditions.

D. SOILS OF ROSS ISLAND

Local glaciers cover most of Ross Island except for coastal areas, where an older sequence of olivine basalt, basalt and trachyte and a younger basalt sequence are exposed (Treves, 1967). Moraine deposits contain granitic and sandstone erratics derived from the mainland. Soils derived from penguin guano (ornithogenic, Syroechkovsky, 1959) as well as ahumic soils formed outside the penguin colonies occur at Cape Royds. Samples of the ahumic mineral soils collected by the British Antarctic Expedition 1907–09 were analysed by Jensen (1916), who discovered that they were rich in soluble salts and lime, that they had an alkaline reaction, and that mirabilite was present. His results have been confirmed during more recent studies by Ugolini (1964), Claridge (1965), Tedrow and Ugolini (1966) and McCraw (1967). These soils have high pH values (8·0–9·0), 0·5–2·0% of calcium carbonates and high concentration of chlorides and sulphates. The clay mineralogy is dominated by mica, vermiculite and feldspars (Ugolini, 1964; Claridge, 1965).

Among Antarctic soils, those derived from guano are by far the richest in organic matter. In such ornithogenic soils the layer of guano rests sharply on a mineral layer. The guano is rich in ammonia-nitrogen and the C/N ratio is extremely narrow (1 or 2). Soluble salt content of the guano is high, as is phosphorus (5%), which is mainly in inorganic form. Among the anions, chlorides and sulphates predominate. The impact of guano on clay alteration appears to be negligible (Ugolini, 1965).

Mineral soils from Cape Evans and Scott Base are similar to soils outside the Cape Royds rookery. They have an alkaline pH and are well supplied with soluble salts, especially sodium chloride. Mica is the clay mineral reported. Samples collected in the vicinity of Scott Base had lower concentrations of soluble salts than the soils at Cape Evans and Cape Royds (Claridge, 1965). A soil near Scott Base analysed by Blakemore and Swindale (1958) had a coarse texture, high pH value, high inorganic phosphorus, and relatively high cation exchange capacity in spite of the small amount of organic and mineral colloids. Mica was the main clay mineral; interstratified swelling and non-swelling micaceous minerals, and feldspars and kaolin were present but scarce.

The soils of Mount Erebus, the only known active volcano on the continent of Antarctica, were examined by Ugolini and Starkey (1966) and Ugolini (1967); contrary to the ubiquitous alkaline conditions, these soils have an acid reaction. A soil sample collected at about 3600 m in an area of fumaroles displayed considerable microbiological activity. The presence of allophane and gibbsite was interpreted as the result of hydrothermal processes (Ugolini, 1967).

E. SOILS OF INEXPRESSIBLE ISLAND

Inexpressible Island (75°S and 163°45′E) lies in Terra Nova Bay on the west coast of Ross Sea. Campbell and Claridge (1966), in order to examine the effect of penguins on soil studied a sequence of soils from Adélie penguin colonies, ranging from a site presently occupied to a site which had probably not been inhabited for a considerable time. Occupied sites show high concentrations of carbon and nitrogen with C/N ratios of 1 and 2. These values agree with data obtained by the author at Cape Royds. The presence of penguins increased the quantity of pebbles, silt and clay, soluble salts and phosphate. The clay minerals, however, do not seem to be affected by the presence of penguin guano. The changes brought about by the penguin occupancy tend to disappear after the sites are abandoned. The oldest sites have little organic matter and little of the fine-size fractions remain. Leaching of the salts has also taken place. The only long-lasting effect of penguin occupancy is the pebble concentration at the abandoned nest.

F. SOILS OF CAPE HALLETT

Hallett Station at Cape Hallett (72°19′S, 170°18′E), Northern Victoria Land, is located on Seabee Hook, a small gravel spit largely occupied by an Adélie penguin colony. A scree apron rests against the high cliffs (McCraw, 1967; Rudolph, 1966). Due to the northern position, Cape Hallett is warmer than McMurdo Sound area (Table 1). In December and January the mean monthly temperatures are above 0°C at a depth of 10 cm, but the soils remain continuously below 0°C at a depth of 50 cm (Benes, 1960). Absolute maximum and minimum temperatures for rock surfaces during the 1963–64 austral summer indicate a daily freeze-thaw cycle. Comparison of surface rock temperatures with the air temperatures at 2 and 5 feet above the ground demonstrates that the actual environmental conditions under which the small Antarctic cryptogams live are much milder than would appear from the standard weather reports (Rudolph, 1966). According to Rudolph (1963, 1966), the vegetation of Cape Hallett is luxuriant compared with inland regions and the McMurdo Sound sector, and it consists of algae (12·8%), mosses (2·4%) and lichens (0·2%). Pryor (1962) discovered four species of free-living mites.

The soils on scree slopes are very pebbly, contain some organic matter and are low in soluble salts. The clay fraction is poorly crystalline and dominated by mica and feldspars (Claridge, 1965). Soils under mosses and in the lichen areas are also very coarse, poor in clay, have an acid pH (4·6–4·2) and are low in soluble salts (Rudolph, 1966). There are ornithogenic soils with typical morphology, which contain 3·5% of soluble salts and have a slightly alkaline pH (McCraw, 1967).

Specimens of basaltic and volcanic rocks collected for the writer by Dr. E. Rudolph at Cape Hallett were used by Ugolini and Perdue (1968) to investigate the role of lichens in weathering of rocks. Eleven elements were determined in rock layers cut parallel to and below the surface containing the lichen crust. Similar rock layers were cut below a surface without lichens. The analyses show that *Xanthoria mawsoni* and *Polycauliona pulvinata* tend to deplete silica and iron from the rock, whereas alkaline and alkaline earth elements tend to accumulate slightly. Phosphorus increases, but not consistently. Where lichens are absent the depletion of silica is less and there is an increase of iron and some aluminium. There is no increase of phosphorus, but some calcium, magnesium and sodium may accumulate.

G. Weathering Conditions near Mirny and in Bunger Hills

Avsyuk *et al.* (1956) visited the Bunger Hills and the surrounding areas in Queen Mary Land Coast and Kaiser Wilhelm II Coast. Bunger Hills is an ice-free area of about 775 km², located at about 66°S and 101°E. The Mirny base is situated on the coast at 66°33′S and 93°E.

During about two months in summer the soil surface there is warmed to above freezing during the afternoon. A soil-surface temperature of 12·5°C has been recorded in December (Weyant, 1966). The soil begins to thaw in early November and the thaw reaches a maximum depth of about 2 m at the end of January (Grigor'ev, 1959). At Oazis Station in the Bunger Hills the air is very dry with summer humidity values as low as 10–15%. The soil is also very dry and warm, temperatures of 35°C having been measured at the surface. These coastal areas are influenced by the Antarctic anticyclone, and atmospheric precipitation averages about 85 cm water equivalent (Rudolph, 1966).

Avsyuk *et al.* (1956) reported considerable exfoliation of rocks and honeycomb surfaces. These features were attributed to thermal weathering rather than frost action. Chemical weathering was considered widespread in the oasis, as evidenced by desert varnish and salt efflorescences on the surface of rocks and boulders. The weathering processes of this Antarctic oasis were thought to be very similar to those observed in the cold desert of eastern

Pamirs. Specimens analysed by Glazovskaia (1958) show that the varnish crusts have concentrations of oxides of iron and manganese. The more visible products of weathering (carbonate) accumulate within the cracks and beneath the surface of these exfoliated crusts. Thin sections of bedrock with various degrees of weathering show alteration of the feldspars, hornblende, chlorites and garnets in granite and granite-gneisses. In the considerably weathered rock, primary chlorite disappears first, then hornblende and biotite. The feldspar grains are covered by a film of secondary minerals, including clay minerals and iron hydroxides. Some of these secondary minerals are translocated along bedrock cracks. Once mobilized, some of the oxides of iron and manganese may move toward the surface of the rocks and form the desert varnish following evaporation and dehydration.

H. Soils in Enderby Land

Pedological investigations conducted by MacNamara (1969) at the Soviet base of Molodezhnaya in Enderby Land, East Antarctica (67°40'S, 45° 51'E), reveal degrees of soil development not yet reported for the rest of continental Antarctica. A Red Ahumisol described by MacNamara shows clay translocation, the formation of cutans, and considerable horizon differentiation. The depth of thawing is about 70 cm. The ice-free areas near Molodezhnaya receive considerable precipitation (65 cm water equivalent) and experience a very moderate Antarctic climate, having a mean annual temperature of $-11.5°C$. According to MacNamara, the area is biologically richer than the ice-free areas of McMurdo Sound.

IV. The Antarctic Slopes

A. Climate

The climatic conditions of the Antarctic slopes are intermediate between those of the plateau and those along the coasts. Continuous meteorological observations for this climatic zone are scarce; by first approximation it seems that parts of the Antarctic slopes may coincide with some of the Marginal Climatic Regions of Sabbagh (1962); however, without knowing the exact geographical boundaries of the slope areas it is difficult to propose any correlation.

Micrometeorological observations made by Dr. H. Janetschek (1963) at about 2600 m on 6 December, 1961, showed a fluctuation in the air temperature (1 m above the ground) between $-17°C$ and $-10°C$. Although warmer than the air $(-3°C)$, the surface soil temperature remained continuously below the freezing-point. As deduced from Rubin's maps (Rubin, 1965), the mean annual temperature at Plunket Point should be $-35°C$ and the average annual snow accumulation should be 20 cm (water equivalent). This area appeared devoid of both macroscopic and microscopic life (Janetschek, 1963; Meyer *et al.*, 1963).

B. SOILS OF DOMINION RANGE AND CLOUDMAKER

Soil studies in this area are very limited. Ugolini (1964) briefly described and partially analysed a soil profile from a dolorite still at 3320 m at Plunkett Point, Dominion Range (approx. 85°05′S, 167°3′E), which was considered typical for soils derived from this rock. The soil consists of an 8 cm surface layer which is drier, more sandy and more coloured than the layer below it. The soil temperature at a depth of 5 cm was −12°C (5 p.m., 6 December, 1961) whereas the air temperature was −22°C. Partial chemical analysis performed on the samples showed definite saline conditions, an alkaline pH, and abundance of chlorides: 30·0 millequivalents per litre of extractable solution were present in the 0–8 cm layer, and 82·2 millequivalents per litre in the layer extending from 8 to 20 cm. Cursory X-ray analysis of the clay showed a strong 14Å reflection for either vermiculite or chlorite and one at 10Å for illite.

During a cursory visit to the Cloudmaker (Beardmore Glacier area) a soil profile was opened on glacial till (Ugolini, 1964). The soil appeared dry, with temperatures below 0°C (−6·0°C at 1 cm) and was yellowish and sandy in texture. Partial chemical analysis of the 1:1 soil water extract showed an alkaline pH (7·8) and a high chloride content near the surface (116·5 millequivalent per litre of extracting solution).

C. SOILS OF DARWIN GLACIER REGION

Campbell and Claridge (1967) explored a sequence of soils in the Brown Hills region of the Darwin Glacier. A gross climatic picture of the area can be broadly deduced from Rubin's (1965) maps: the mean annual temperature should be about −30°C and the average annual snow accumulation 10–15 cm of water equivalent. In January 1965 Campbell and Claridge measured soil surface temperatures of up to 7°C with an air temperature of 2°C. Moisture from melting snow penetrates only the top inch of soil. This study of Campbell and Claridge (1967) emphasizes the influence of topography on the morphological, chemical and mineralogical properties of the soils. Soils at the bottom of the slope were moister, had more salts and displayed a clay mineral assemblage different from the soils along, and on top of the slope. Small amounts of montmorillonite were detected in the lower soils. No montmorillonite was found in the other soils of the toposequence.

D. SOILS OF ROBERTS MASSIF AND MCGREGOR GLACIER AREA

Analyses of water-soluble salts in soils from the Roberts Massif at the head of Shackleton Glacier (85°11′S, 174°05′W) show that the chloride to nitrate ratio is low in the Roberts Massif (1:15,000), but it approaches 1:1 in the McGregor area (Claridge and Campbell, 1968). Difference in salt composition was explained in terms of different climatic conditions at the two sites. The Roberts Massif region is at the edge of the Polar Plateau and it is affected by cold and dry katabatic winds from the south; precipitation is low and little melting occurs. Consequently the salts contained in the snow tend to remain in the soil. The McGregor Glacier area is affected by warm and wet air masses coming from the Ross Sea which bring more precipitation and more melting. The precipitation in this area should be rich in chloride supplied by the ocean, whereas the Roberts Massif receives snow blown off the Polar Plateau. This "continental" snow should be rich in nitrate and depleted in chloride; chloride is more hydroscopic than the nitrate and percolates downward into the snow of the Plateau, leaving the nitrate at the surface to be carried by the wind (Claridge and Campbell, 1968).

The slopes of Antarctica have been searched for plants and for free-living organisms. Mosses were collected at Garden Spur, Shackleton Glacier area (84°35′S, 174°52′W) and east of Barratt Glacier (Wise and Gressitt, 1965). Lichens were reported in the Horlick Mountains (86°09′S, 131°14′W) at an altitude of 1980 m. Mites were reported at Point Durham (Robert Scott Glacier, 85°32′S, 153°W); springtails near the Shackleton Glacier (84°47′S 176°W) and rotifers in the Shackleton Glacier area. These represent, except for mosses, the southernmost known occurrences of these organisms. The collection localities are mapped by Greene et al. (1967). Although there are still ice-free areas to be visited, in general the geographical occurrence of organisms in this sector of Antarctica is limited and spotty.

V. Interior Antarctic Plateau

A. CLIMATE

This climatic zone, which includes nearly all of East Antarctica, consists of a high plateau, about 2500 m in elevation, covered by snow and ice and devoid of known ice-free areas. It has considerable sunshine, a precipitation of 5 cm (water equivalent) or even less, light winds and extremely low temperatures. Due to heat loss from the snow surface, a steep inversion prevails in the 300 m surface layer of air above the Pole for about 80% of the year (Sabbagh, 1962). The lowest temperature so far recorded on the earth, −88·3°C, was observed at Vostok (78°27′S, 106°53′E).

B. COMPOSITION OF SNOW

A study made by Wilson and House (1965) on chemical composition of fresh snow and snow collected at a depth of 13 m at the South Pole revealed an annual infall of 10^{-7} g/cm^2 for sodium, 5×10^{-8} g/cm^2 for potassium,

2×10^{-7} g/cm² for chloride and 5×10^{-2} g/cm² for nitrogen (nitrate plus nitrite). According to these authors the ocean supplies the sodium, potassium and chlorides, whereas the auroral activity is responsible for the fixation of nitrogen. Using this evidence and additional data from salt composition in the soils of the Roberts Massif, Claridge and Campbell (1968) support the idea that nitrates and iodates in the soils of Antarctica have been accumulated by precipitation. Therefore the interior Antarctic plateau, in spite of being devoid of life, may play an important role in the ecology of the bordering ice-free areas. If the mechanism suggested by Claridge and Campbell (1968) occurs, where the nitrates are left at the surface of the plateau as the snow sublimes, then nitrogen could be available in the ice-free areas and only temperature and moisture would be the limiting factors for plant growth.

VI. Conclusions

Terrestrial life in Antarctica develops under one of the most hostile known environments of the earth. Among the spectrum of abiotic factors involved in the relatively simple Antarctic ecosystem, soil occupies a relevant position. Because liquid water, rather than temperature, is the most important limiting factor for terrestrial life in Antarctica, soil moisture correlates very well with the occurrences of microorganisms, bryophytes and arthropods. The most reliable source of soil moisture is the ice-cemented permafrost or the ice-cemented layer, provided it is within the maximum depth of thawing. An ideal situation is obtained when a zone of clay material exists between the ice-cemented layer and the soil surface; this situation was originally observed by the writer in the summer of 1962 at Springtail Point, Mackay Glacier, where numerous Collembola were collected.

The generally dark desert pavement covering the surface of the soil has, during the summer, a positive heat balance, and it allows the creation of a particular microenvironment much milder than the air temperature would suggest.

Other things being equal, high salinity of some soils of Antarctica may constitute a limiting factor for life. If, indeed, this is so, the older terrains with the best-developed soils would be less suitable for life, because in general these areas show high salt content. A confirmation of this implication is apparent in the scheme produced by Janetschek (1967) for the Antarctic terrestrial ecosystem. The chalikosystem or bare gravel system is the poorest in terms of biological activity, but it may be the most developed from the pedological point of view. The bryosystem, the ecosystem with an open macrophytic vegetation made of mosses and lichens, represents the climax vegetation for continental Antarctica. The bryosystem is more biologically active than the chalikosystem, but it is not the most pedologically developed system. In Antarctica, therefore, it seems that there is an inverse relationship between pedologic evolution and life succession.

Acknowledgements

The researches conducted by the author in Antarctica have been supported by the National Science Foundation, Antarctic Research Program, through Grants G-17212, G-23787, GA-74, GA-1186 and GA-1476.

The author wishes to thank the United States Navy Task Force 43 for logistic support while in Antarctica. Thanks are extended to Dr A. L. Washburn for reviewing the manuscript.

References

Allen, S. E. and Northover, M. J. (1967). Soil Types and Nutrients on Signy Island. *Phil. Trans. R. Soc.* Ser. B **252**, No. 777, 179–85.

Allen, S. E. and Heal, O. W. (1970). Soils of the Maritime Antarctic Zone. This Symposium, 693–96.

Allen, S. E., Grimshaw, H. M. and Holdgate, M. W. (1967). Factors Affecting the Availability of Plant Nutrients on an Antarctic Island. *J. Ecol.* **55**, 381–96.

Avsyuk, G. A., Markov, K. K. and Shumskii, P. A. (1956). Geographical Observations in an Antarctic "Oasis". *Izv. Vses. Geogr. Obshch.* **88**, No. 4, 316–50.

Benes, N. S. (1960). Soil Temperatures at Cape Hallett, Antarctica. *Mon. Weath. Rev.* **88**, 223–7.

Berg, T. E. (1965). Observations of Patterned Ground on the Antarctic Peninsula. International Association for Quaternary Research, VII International Congress, Abstracts. Boulder and Denver, Colorado, 24 pp.

Berg, T. E. and Black, R. F. (1966). Preliminary Measurements of Growth of Nonsorted Polygons, Victoria Land, Antarctica. Antarctic Soils and Soil Forming Processes. *Antarct. Res. Ser.* **8**, 61–108.

Black, R. F. and Berg, T. E. (1963). Hydrothermal Regimen of Patterned Ground, Victoria Land, Antarctica. *I.A.S.H. Commission of Snow and Ice* **61**, 121–7.

Blakemore, L. C. and Swindale, L. D. (1958). Chemistry and Clay Mineralogy of a Soil Sample from Antarctica. *Nature, Lond.* **182**, 47–48.

Boyd, W. L. and Rothenberg, I. (1968). Ecology of Soil Microorganisms in the Vicinity of Almirante Brown Base. *Antarct. J. U.S.* **3**, No. 3, 60–63.

Boyd, W. L., Staley, J. T. and Boyd, J. W. (1966). Ecology of Soil Microorganisms of Antarctica. Antarctic Soils and Soil Forming Processes. *Antarct. Res. Ser.* **8**, 125–59.

Bull, C. (1966). Climatological Observations in Ice-free Areas of Southern Victoria Land, Antarctica. Studies in Antarctic Meteorology. *Antarct. Res. Ser.* **9**, 177–94.

Campbell, I. B. and Claridge, G. G. C. (1966). A Sequence of Soils from a Penguin Rookery, Inexpressible Island, Antarctica. *N.Z. Jl. Sci.* **9**, No. 21, 361–72.

Campbell, I. B. and Claridge, G. G. C. (1967). Site and Soil Differences in the Brown Hills Region of the Darwin Glacier, Antarctica. *N.Z. Jl. Sci.* **10**, No. 2, 563–77.

Chambers, M. J. (1966). Investigations of Patterned Ground at Signy Island, South

ANTARCTIC SOILS AND THEIR ECOLOGY

Orkney Islands. I. Interpretation of Mechanical Analyses. *Br. Antarct. Surv. Bull.* **9**, 21–40.

Claridge, G. G. C. (1965). The Clay Mineralogy and Chemistry of some Soils from the Ross Dependency, Antarctica. *N.Z. Jl. Geol. Geophys.* **8**, No. 2, 186–220.

Claridge, G. G. C. and Campbell, I. B. (1968). Origin of Nitrate Deposits. *Nature, Lond.* **217**, No. 5127, 428–30.

Gimingham, C. H. and Smith, R. I. L. (1970). Bryophyte and Lichen Communities in the Maritime Antarctic. This Symposium, 752–85.

Glazovskaia, M. A. (1958). Weathering and Primary Soil Formations in Antarctica. *Scientific Paper of the Inst., Moscow Univ., Faculty of Geog.*, No. 1, 63–76. (In Russian).

Greene, S. W. and Longton, R. E. (1970). The Effects of Climate on Antarctic Plants. This Symposium, 786–800.

Greene, S. W., Gressitt, J. L., Koob, K., Llano, G. A., Rudolph, E. I., Singer, R., Steere, W. C. and Ugolini, F. C. (1967). Terrestrial Life of Antarctica. Antarctic Map Folio Series, Folio 5. *Am. Geogr. Soc., New York.*

Gressitt, J. L. (1965). Entomological Field Research in Antarctica. *BioScience* **15**, No. 4, 271–4.

Girgor'ev, N. F. (1959). Some Results of Permafrost Investigations in East Antarctica. *Inf. Byull. sov. antarkt. Eksped.* **7**, 288–98.

Heal, O. W., Bailey, A. D. and Latter, P. M. (1967). Bacteria, Fungi and Protozoa in Signy Island Soils compared with those from a Temperate Moorland. *Phil. Trans. R. Soc.*, Ser. B. **252**, No. 777, 191–9.

Holdgate, M. W. (1964). Terrestrial Ecology in the Maritime Antarctic. "Biologie Antarctique: Antarctic Biology", (Carrick, R., Holdgate, M. and Prévost, J., eds) pp. 181–94. Hermann, Paris.

Holdgate, M. W., Allen, S. E. and Chambers, M. J. G. (1967). A Preliminary Investigation of the Soils of Signy Island, South Orkney Island. *Br. Antarct. Surv. Bull.* **12**, 53–71.

Janetschek, H. (1963). On the Terrestrial Fauna of the Ross Sea Area, Antarctica. *Pacific Insects* **5**, No. 1, 305–11.

Janetschek, H. (1967). Arthropod Ecology of South Victoria Land. Entomology of Antarctica. *Antarct. Res. Ser.* **10**, 205–93.

Janetschek, H. (1970). Environment and Ecology of Terrestrial Arthropods in the High Antarctic. This Symposium, 871–85.

Jensen, H. I. (1916). Report on Antarctic Soils. *Br. Antarct. Exped. 1907–1909.* Reports on Scientific Investigations. Geology 2, Part VI. pp. 89–92.

Kelly, W. C. and Zumberge, J. H. (1961). Weathering of a Quartz Diorite at Marble Point, McMurdo Sound, Antarctica. *J. Geol.* **69**, No. 4, 433–46.

Llano, G. A. (1962). The Terrestrial Life of the Antarctic. *Scient. Am.* **207**, No. 3, 213–30.

Longton, R. E. and Holdgate, M. W. (1967). Temperature Relationships of Antarctic Vegetation. *Phil. Trans. R. Soc.* B **252**, No. 777, 237–50.

MacNamara, E. E. (1969). Biological Research Opportunities at the Soviet Antarctic Station Molodezhnaya. Antarct. J. of the U.S. **4**, No. 3, 8–12.

Markov, K. K. and Bodina, E. L. (1960). Map of Periglacial Formations in Antarctica. *Antarctica Commission Reports, 1960.* Akademiya Nauk SSSR. Isreal Program for Scientific Translations. Jerusalem, 1966. pp. 49–59.

McCraw, J. D. (1960). Soils of the Ross Dependency, Antarctica, A Preliminary Note. *N.Z. Soc. Soil Sci. Proc.* **4**, 30–35.

McCraw, J. D. (1967). Soils of Taylor Dry Valley, Victoria Land, Antarctica, with Notes on Soils from other Localities in Victoria Land. *N.Z. Jl. Geol. Geophys.* **10**, No. 2, 498–539.

Meyer, G. H., Morrow, M.B. and Wyss, O. (1963). Incidence of Soil Microorganisms in Antarctica (abstract). *Bull. Ecol. Soc. Am.* **44**, No. 2, 38.

Nichols, R. L. and Ball, D. G. (1964). Soil Temperatures, Marble Point, McMurdo Sound, Antarctica. *J. Glaciol.* **5**, No. 39, 357–9.

Northover, M. J. and Allen, S. E. (1966). Seasonal Availability of Chemical Nutrients on Signy Island. *Phil. Trans. R. Soc.*, Ser B **252**, No. 777, 187–9.

Pryor, M. E. (1962). Some Environmental Features of Hallett Station, Antarctica, with Special Reference to Soil Arthropods. *Pacific Insects* **4**, No. 3, 681–728.

Rubin, M. J. (1965). Antarctic Climatology. "Monographiae Biologicae", Vol. 15, Biogeography and Ecology in Antarctica. pp. 72–96.

Rudolph, E. D. (1963). Vegetation of Hallett Station Area, Victoria Land, Antarctica. *Ecology* **44**, No. 3, 585–6.

Rudolph, E. D. (1965). Antarctic Lichens and Vascular Plants: their Significance. *BioScience* **15**, No. 4, 285–7.

Rudolph, E. D. (1966). Terrestrial Vegetation of Antarctica: Past and Present Studies. Antarctic Soils and Soil Forming Processes. *Antarct. Res. Ser.* **8**, 109–24.

Sabbagh, M. E. (1962). A Preliminary Regional Dynamic Climatology of the Antarctic Continent. *Erdkunde* **16**, 94–111.

Syroechkovsky, E. E. (1959). The Role of Animals in the Formation of Primary Soils Under the Conditions of Circumpolar Regions of the Earth (Antarctica). *Zool. Zh.* **38**, 1770–5.

Taylor, B. W. (1955). The Flora, Vegetation and Soils of Macquarie Island. *A.N.A.R.E. Reports*, Ser. B **2**, 192 pp.

Tedrow, J. C. F. and Ugolini, F. C. (1966). Antarctic Soils. Antarctic Soils and Soil Forming Processes. *Antarct. Res. Ser.* **8**, 161–77.

Treves, S. B. (1967). Volcanic Rocks from the Ross Island, Marguerite Bay and Mt. Weaver Areas, Antarctica. *Proc. Symp. Pacific-Antarct. Sci.* No. 1, pp. 136–49.

Ugolini, F. C. (1963). Soil Investigations in the Lower Wright Valley, Antarctica. *Permafrost International Conference.* NAS-NRC Pub. No. 1287. pp. 55–61.

Ugolini, F. C. (1964). A Study of Pedologic Processes in Antarctica. Final Report to the National Science Foundation, 1964. 82 pp.

Ugolini, F. C. (1965). Ornithogenic Soils of Antarctica. Agronomy Abstracts. 1965 Annual Meeting, Columbus, Ohio. 109 pp. (abstract).

Ugolini, F. C. (1967). Soils of Mount Erebus, Antarctica. *N.Z. Jl. Geol. Geophys.* **10**, No. 2, 431–42.

Ugolini, F. C. and Bull, C. (1965). Soil Development and Glacial Events in Antarctica. *Quaternaria* **7**, 251–69.

Ugolini, F. C. and Perdue, M. J. (1968). Biological Weathering in Antarctica. *Antarct. J. U.S.* **3**, No. 5, 166.

Ugolini, F. C. and Starkey, R. L. (1966). Soils and Microorganisms from Mount Erebus, Antarctica. *Nature, Lond.* **211**, No. 5047, 440–1.

Weyant, W. S. (1966). The Antarctic Climate. Antarctic Soils and Soil Forming Processes, *Antarct. Res. Ser.* **8**, 47–59.

Wilson, A. T. and House, D. A. (1965). Chemical Composition of the South Pole Snow. *J. Geophys. Res.* **70**, No. 22, 5515–18.

Wise, K. A. J. and Gressitt, J. L. (1965). Far Southern Animals and Plants. *Nature, Lond.* **207**, No. 4992, 101–2.

Soils of the Maritime Antarctic Zone

S. E. ALLEN AND O. W. HEAL
The Nature Conservancy, Merlewood Research Station,
Grange-over-Sands, Lancashire, England

I. Introduction

This brief report is based on the examination of vegetation and soil from Signy Island in the South Orkney Islands (Allen *et al.*, 1967; Allen and Northover, 1967; Heal, 1965; Heal *et al.*, 1967; Holdgate *et al.*, 1967; Tilbrook, 1967) and to a lesser extent from several of the South Sandwich Islands and from sites along the Antarctic Peninsula.

On these islands primitive soils which are essentially lithosols and regosols, and ornithogenic soils, appear to be similar to those reported for continental Antarctica (Tedrow and Ugolini, 1966). The sea and its associated bird and mammal populations accounts for a high income of chemical nutrients and organic matter to the relatively small land areas. However, the relatively milder, although still cold maritime conditions in the summer months and the less extreme continental winter climate clearly influence soil-forming processes. The marked increases in higher plants, and soil organisms, provides for the formation of more mature soils similar to those of temperate regions.

The soils on these islands may be conveniently placed in four groups:

II. Mineral Soils

These raw soils range from lithosols to fine glacial debris. The coarser material is particularly unstable, showing frost-pattern phenomena and solifluction. Physical breakdown is dominant, although chemical weathering also takes place. Moraine and valley deposits show considerable size gradation down to clay, beds of which have been recorded up to 30 m thick. Marked salt accumulation is not a feature of maritime sites, although they are usually base rich (pH 7–9) the degree depending on parent rock material. All these soils have negligible organic content ($<1.0\%$) and lichens and mosses only appear locally as the soils become more stable. A sparse soil flora and fauna is present, but in older moraine the numbers increase.

III. Organic Soils

This group may be further divided into two types, although there is an intermediate gradation.

A. Moss Peat

Under some bryophtes, notably *Polytrichum* and *Dicranum* species, peat up to 2 m thick has developed. The loosely packed moss remains overlie compact fibrous peat similar to Arctic moss peats, but unlike the gelatinous amorphous peats common in temperate blanket bogs. Below about 25 cm these peats are permanently frozen. The pH and nutrient contents appear to be generally higher than in Arctic and temperate peats. Numbers of fauna and microflora in the upper layers are similar to those in similar temperate soils, but species composition is restricted. Some peat beds have largely dead and eroding surface layers, suggesting that the peat-forming communities reach a point of instability and thereafter decline.

B. Protoranker

These are felt-like pads of organic material, a few centimetres thick, which form under many mosses. They are found in areas of less stability and often permeated with ground water. The mineral content (notably phosphorus) is usually higher and they are less acid (pH 5·5–7·0) than the deeper moss peats.

IV. Brown-earths

These loam-like soils are usually found on north-facing slopes and are associated with the small colonies of *Deschampsia antarctica* and *Colobanthus quitensis*. They show general similarities to the temperate brown earths, but their precise nature is influenced, among other factors, by the parent material. Chemical nutrient availability is high and the C/N ratio of approximately 12 indicates an active population of soil organisms. This is supported by the lack of accumulated organic matter and by information on numbers of fauna and microflora which are similar to brown earth soils in temperate regions, although the number of species is restricted. However, the rate of decomposition is much slower than in temperate soils and the fauna lacks earthworms, which are usually regarded as important in the formation of brown earths.

V. Ornithogenic Soils

The term suggested by Syroechkovsky (1959) is used to classify the excretory deposists which have accumulated around the colonies of sea birds and mammals. This material is particularly rich in organic matter, nitrogen compounds, calcium and phosphate. The alga *Prasiola* and various lichens are tolerant of these conditions, but little information is available on associated microflora and fauna. A real importance of these colonies is that they are the source of organic matter and nutrients which are distributed by wind, spray, melt water and bird droppings.

The range of soils described above for maritime Antarctica is greater than than that reported for continental Antarctica by Tedrow and Ugolini (1966). This is clearly due to the biotic influences which are present in the maritime sites in association with the milder summers. Two of the soil types in particular, the brown earths and peats, result from biotic influences. In the first the rate of primary production and decomposition appears to be in balance, as indicated by C/N ratios of about 12. However, in the peats, production exceeds decomposition (C/N ratio about 40). The differences are related to changes in micro-climate which influence soil aeration and water availability, and to plant growth habit and the nutrient content of the vegetation. However, the relative importance of these is not clear.

Our examination of these soils, together with descriptions of similar materials found on other islands, leads us to suppose that this classification is typical of the maritime Antarctic.

Acknowledgements

We were greatly indebted to the British Antarctic Survey for providing samples and to many members of B.A.S. and the Nature Conservancy for information and discussion.

References

Allen, S. E., Grimshaw, H. M. and Holdgate, M. W. (1967). Factors affecting the availability of plant nutrients on an Antarctic Island. *J. Ecol.* 55, 381–96.

Allen, S. E. and Northover, M. J. (1967). Soil types and nutrients on Signy Island. *Phil. Trans. R. Soc.* B 252, 179–85.

Heal, O. W. (1965). Observations on testate amoebae (Protozoa: Rhizopoda) from Signy Island, South Orkney Islands. *Bull. Br. antarc. Surv.* 6, 43–47.

Heal, O. W., Bailey, A. D. and Latter, Pamela M. (1967). Bacteria, fungi and protozoa in Signy Island Soils compared with those from a temperate moorland. *Phil. Trans. R. Soc.* B 252, 191–7.

Holdgate, M. W., Allen, S.E. and Chambers, M. J. G. (1967). A preliminary investigation of the soils of Signy Island, South Orkney Islands. *Bull. Br. antarc. Surv.* 12, 53–71.

Syroechkovsky, E. E. (1959). The role of animals in primary soil formation under conditions of pre-polar region of the globe. (Exemplified by the Antarctic). *Zool. Zh.*
Tedrow, J. C. F. and Ugolini, F. C. (1966). Antarctic soils. *Antarctic Res. Series* 8, 161–77.
Tilbrook, P. J. (1967). The terrestrial invertebrate fauna of the maritime Antarctic. *Phil. Trans. R. Soc.* B 252, 261–78.

The Microbiology of Some Dry Valley Soils of Victoria Land, Antarctica

R. E. BENOIT AND C. L. HALL, JR.
Virginia Polytechnic Institute, Blacksburg, U.S.A.

I. Introduction

During the 1966–67 and 1967–68 austral summers a comprehensive study of the soil micro-organisms in the McMurdo dry valley area was initiated. Over 400 soil samples have been obtained from nearly every possible type of ecological niche in the region and in selected areas the microclimate and soil chemistry have been examined. Classical soil microbiological isolation techniques and media were not suitable, as demonstrated by the fact that few or no micro-organisms were detected in some of these soils. Other workers in the dry valleys have previously observed the same phenomenon. However, when we made several modifications of classical isolation procedures, we were able to show that some areas in the dry valleys have a unique microflora which is abundant and psychrophilic in character.

II. Isolation and Culture Procedure

All soil samples were kept at $-40°C$ from the time they were obtained until they were processed. In our isolation procedure soil or soil dilutions were spread uniformly over the surface of various media pretempered at the desired incubation temperature (2°, 15°, or 20°C), and the samples were processed in a 4°C environment. Media which possess a low substrate concentration and contain soil extract were the most suitable for isolation studies. Typically, the highest bacterial counts on the twenty-eight media tested were obtained using either a peptone (0·5%)-yeast extract (0·1%)-soil extract (20% by volume) or a Trypticase Soy medium (15 gm per litre) with soil extract (20% volume). The aerobic bacterial count was usually greater by a factor of ten on the former medium, but at some sites the reverse was true. These differences have been shown in pure culture studies to be related to the nutrition of different bacteria at different locations. The majority of these bacteria either require or grow best in media containing soil extract.

The soil-extract effect can be duplicated in media without soil extract if a critical concentration of sodium, or a combination of several salts, is added. Mesophilic and psychrophilic bacteria were isolated at 20°C and 2°C respectively. No thermophilic bacteria were detected at any inland dry valley location, although thermophilic bacilli were isolated from soil which was recently contaminated by human or animal waste.

III. Results

A. RATE OF GROWTH OF COLONIES

There is a correlation between the time a colony is visible on an isolation medium and the time interval since conditions were last favourable for growth in a given soil. For example, in soils near glacial melt-water pools where conditions are favourable for microbial growth frequently during the austral summer, there was a 1:1 ratio between psychrophilic and mesophilic bacteria observed on isolation plates; in soils where growth conditions are favourable infrequently, the ratio was 1:3 or greater. In those locations where conditions have not been favourable for many years few psychrophils were detected. Psychrophilic bacteria appear on isolation plates in seven to fourteen days from soils where the environment is biologically favourable, but in soils where bacteria have been dormant for long periods the psychrophils may have a lag period of four weeks to three months. The majority of bacteria isolated at 2° and 20°C were capable of growth at either temperature, but a number of strict psychrophils have been isolated. Most bacterial isolates have an optimum temperature near 15°C under static culture conditions, but under shake culture conditions the optimum temperature may be extended above 20°C.

B. ABIOTIC SOILS

At those soil sites which receive the least amount of water the surface inch of soil was often abiotic (i.e. no detectable life) or had less than 10 bacteria per gram of soil. At one site in Taylor Valley no bacteria were detected in the surface 2 cm of soil on any medium at any temperature, but at the 15 cm depth in the soil profile 8×10^3 mesophilic bacteria/gm of soil were detected, and at the 25 cm depth in the permafrost of this soil profile 1.8×10^4 mesophilic bacteria/gm of soil were detected. The soil surface temperature was 13·5°C and the permafrost temperature was 8·5°C. Similar bacterial profiles have been obtained in other soils in the dry valleys. But at a site on the south side of Taylor Valley area near Nussbaum Regal, at an altitude of 430 m, no bacteria were detected in the soil from the surface to a depth of 1 m. The soil surface temperature was 13°C, the temperature was −8°C at the 1 m level and no permafrost was detected. Both areas were sampled on 5 December 1967.

C. MICROFLORA OF MOIST AREAS

The bulk of the microbial life in the dry valleys is located in stream beds or ponds originating from alpine glaciers, or soils in the immediate vicinity of glaciers. In the soil near a small pond located half a mile west of the Lacroix glacier in Taylor Valley 1.4×10^6 mesophilic bacteria/gm of soil were isolated; 1.2×10^5 mesophilic bacteria/gm soil were detected in a pond in the Labyrinth near the Upper Wright Glacier, and 1.1×10^6 mesophilic bacteria/gm of soil were found in the soil near the shore of the lake in Upper Victoria Valley. In each case the psychrophilic count was equal to or slightly greater than, the mesophilic count. The mesophilic bacterial soil surface count 50 m from these eutrophic ponds decreased to 3.6×10^4, 4.5×10^3, and 7.8×10^3 bacteria per gram of soil respectively at the above sites. Numerous surface-soil bacterial counts 400 m from these locations on typical desert soils indicated less than 10 bacteria per gram of soil. The bulk of the bacteria which were found in the soil near the ponds consisted of a mixture of gram positive cocci and rods, gram negative cocci and rods and yeasts; the majority of the bacteria isolated were chromogenic and capsulated. Those bacteria in the typical desert soils were usually gram positive cocci and the majority were chromogenic (*Micrococcus* spp.), but other gram positive non-spore forming rods were observed. The bacilli and gram negative rods were isolated from various soils, but they comprise only a minor part of the microflora. It was observed in nearly all soil samples taken from below the 3 cm surface layer that chromogenic bacteria were rare. In the dry valley system the soil algae (especially the blue-green algae) are the primary producers of organic substrates for the heterotrophic bacteria; in nearly all cases organic matter cannot be detected in the typical soil. Numerous diatoms, blue-green algae and green algae were isolated in areas where water is available even for brief periods. Thick algae mats were observed around many ponds such as those in Bull Pass, Taylor Valley, Balham Valley and Labyrinth; and where moisture accumulates in very isolated soil microhabitats, such as a slight depression or under a rock, algae were isolated. Selected areas near the summit of Knobhead Matterhorn and Castle Rock illustrate these restricted habitats. Few algae were observed along the edges of Lakes Bonney, Vanda and Vida, but at those points where small streams flow into the lakes an increased algal production was noted. The concentration of nitrate in the melt water appears to be the limiting factor affecting algal growth.

D. MOULDS

Filamentous moulds were detected infrequently in soils, but in the vicinity of mosses at Marble Point and in the highland between Miers and Marshall valleys, psychrophilic moulds were isolated. These moulds have a maximum temperature near 28°C and appear to have an optimum temperature near

18°C. Actinomycetes were isolated in soils at the Sulfur Cones (Ross Island) and also in the proximity of glaciers near the Suess Glacier in Taylor Valley, the Labyrinth near the Upper Wright Glacier, Knobhead Mountain near the Ferrar Glacier and soils along the shore of Don Juan pond. At some sites they were the dominant type of micro-organism in the soil, but they were absent in soil several metres away. These actinomycetes were primarily *Streptomycetes* spp.; all isolates were capable of slow growth at 2°C but rapid growth at 20°C.

E. CHEMOAUTOTROPHIC BACTERIA

The chemoautotrophic bacteria were seldom detected in dry valley soils, although recently nitrifying activity was observed in soil enrichments taken from soil near eutrophic ponds. The sulphate-reducing bacteria and some of the photoautotrophic bacteria were observed in high numbers in many small ponds. During the mid-summer period the maximum water temperature in such a pond may reach as high as 13°C (Marble Point, 17 January 1967) under conditions of continuous sunlight even when the air temperature is slightly below 0°C. *Azotobacter chroococcum* was isolated from soil near small streams in Miers Valley and Marble Point, but not from other dry valley sites. Probably the bulk of the nitrogen-fixing activity in the dry valleys can be attributed to the blue-green algae and the anaerobic bacteria.

F. MICROFLORA OF SALINE HABITATS

The saline nature of many soils in the dry valley system is well known, but we were not successful in isolating any strict halophilic bacteria from soil in a saline depression in Taylor Valley or an extreme halophilic environment at Don Juan Pond (31% soluble salt); in fact, no viable bacteria were detected in Don Juan Pond. In the soil in the salt flat around the pond an abundant nonhalophilic mesophilic bacterial population was observed. At the Taylor Valley site the number of mesophilic bacteria per gram of soil on peptone-yeast extract-soil extract media, which contained either 0, 5, 15 or 20% NaCl (w/v), was 7.2×10^4, 2.0×10^5, 1.4×10^3 and less than 40 bacteria respectively. Psychrophilic growth was detected only on the media containing 0 and 5% NaCl. The combined effect of salinity and low temperature seem to have precluded the development of a strict halophilic population in Don Juan Pond or in saline soils.

IV. Discussion

Many different types of micro-organisms have not been observed in the dry valleys, but this may be more of a reflection of failure to develop a satisfactory isolation procedure, or failure to appreciate the effect of the variable environment within the valley system. Preliminary evidence indicates that the soil flora is quite different in the mountain highlands of the dry valley region from that found on the floor of the various valleys. For example, lichens are detected infrequently in the dry valleys, but various types have been observed in restricted areas near Marble Point, Mt. Discovery, Miers Valley, Upper Wright Valley and in the vicinity of glaciers in the highlands around Knobhead and the Royal Society Range. Similar trends have been observed with micro-organisms.

The combination of environmental factors prevailing in the dry valleys; desiccation, frequent freeze-thaw cycles, limited maximum temperature, salinity, short growth periods, high ultraviolet radiation levels and low organic matter severely limit the types of micro-organisms which can survive and multiply. The lack of available water is clearly the most critical factor. The low level of higher plant and animal life further simplifies the soil biology. The dry valleys represent a unique biological system which is almost exclusively microbiological, but the life in the system is well adapted to one of the world's most hostile environments.

Microbiology, Ecology and Microclimatology of Soil Sites in Dry Valleys of Southern Victoria Land, Antarctica*

R. E. CAMERON, J. KING AND C. N. DAVID
Bioscience Section, Jet Propulsion Laboratory, California Institute of Technology, Pasadena, California, U.S.A.

I. Introduction

The investigation of Antarctic dry valleys has been undertaken in preparation for detection of life in extraterrestrial environments. These valleys are useful study areas prior to searching for life in Martian soils because of low temperature, low humidities, diurnal freeze-thaw cycles even during daylight hours, low annual precipitation, desiccating winds, high sublimation and evaporation, high radiation, low magnetic field, absence of higher life forms, and the irregular distribution and low abundance of soil micro-organisms. However, the environment of the Antarctic dry valleys is more favourable than Mars because of the large quantity and proximity of water (ocean and sea ice, lakes, glaciers, snow and ice fields and the shallow depth to permafrost), comparatively lower solar radiation flux, abundance of oxygen, higher barometric pressure, and the proximity of sources of microbial colonists and greater opportunity for their influx, although man has only relatively recently arrived in Antarctica. The dry valleys also provide a wider variety of ecological habitats, which are expected to be more limited in the harsher Martian environment.

For our study in Antarctica, five sites were established for approximately one-week periods during austral summers 1966–67 and 1967–68 in McKelvey, Victoria, Taylor, Wheeler, King and David Valleys. Environmental measurements of soil and air temperature, relative humidity, dew point, wind direction and velocity, solar and environmental radiation flux, net thermal exchange, evaporation rate, light intensity, barometric pressure and cloud cover, were made either continuously or every three hours. Additional sites

* This paper presents the results of one phase of research carried out at the Jet Propulsion Laboratory, California Institute of Technology, under Contract No. NAS 7–100, sponsored by the National Aeronautics and Space Administration. Logistic support and facilities for this study in Antarctica were provided by the Office of Antarctic Programs, National Science Foundation.

in these and other dry valleys were investigated during both summers, and approximately 150 samples were collected from seventy-five sites.* Samples were collected from the surface to depths of hard, icy permafrost (ice-cemented soil) using aseptic techniques developed for sampling, handling, and processing of desert soils (Cameron 1968a; Cameron et al., 1966).

Soil physical, physico-chemical and chemical analyses were performed for many of the samples, including mineralogy, mechanical analysis, bulk density, porosity, reflectivity, in situ moisture and moisture constants, gases, weight loss on ignition, cation exchange capacity, buffer capacity, pH, Eh, electrical conductivity, elemental abundance, ionic concentrations, inorganic and organic C, H, N and their ratios.

Abundance and distribution of general and specific groups of soil microorganisms were determined by direct inoculation of soil on to agar plates, or by spread plate and dilution culture techniques designed for the investigation and study of low abundances of desert soil micro-flora (Cameron, 1967, 1968b; Hall, 1968; Benoit and Hall, 1970, this symposium). Tests were performed at various temperatures (ranging from $+ 2°C$ to $+ 55°C$) for aerobic, microaerophilic and anaerobic bacteria, lactose fermenters, nitrate reducers and coliforms. Additional media were used to detect and enumerate actinomycetes (streptomycetes), fungi and algae.

II. Results and Discussion

A. ENVIRONMENTAL

During the summer months, when there is a period of continuous daylight, there are diurnal fluctuations in environmental parameters for most of the area within the valleys, not only because of the low angle of incident solar radiation, but because of the interference of mountains surrounding the valleys, which have also been deepened by glaciation. Typical midsummer diurnal temperature, relative humidity, and incident light intensity curves for Wheeler Valley, a North-South oriented valley at 1000 to 1500 m are shown in Fig. 1. Air temperatures were below freezing, although the soil, which absorbed radiation, was above freezing to a depth of approximately 8 cm during periods of incident radiation. Soil thaw was not observed below approximately 10 cm. Although the air frequently had a low relative humidity, the relative humidity of the soil generally increased with proximity to the boundary of hard, icy permafrost and was correlated to some extent with the abundance of microflora. Air relative humidity was correlated with wind velocity and direction. For example, in King and David Valleys a decrease in air and soil surface relative humidity followed a shift in wind direction and

---

* Some sites were investigated in co-operation with Prof. Robert E. Benoit, Virginia Polytechnic Institute, Blacksburg, Virginia (Benoit and Cameron, 1967).

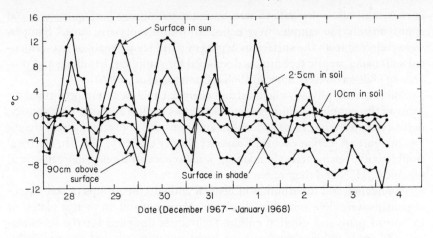

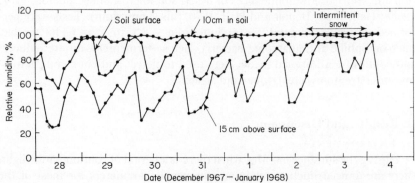

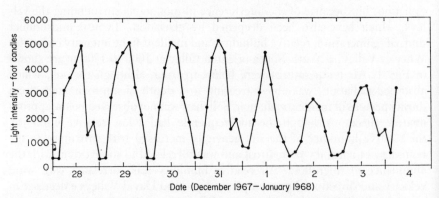

FIG. 1. Diurnal temperature (upper), relative humidity (centre) and light intensity (lower) curves in Wheeler Dry Valley at 1000–1500 m between December 28 1967, and January 4 1968.

an increase in wind velocity (Fig. 2.). Additional information about dry valley climatology has been given by Bull (1966).

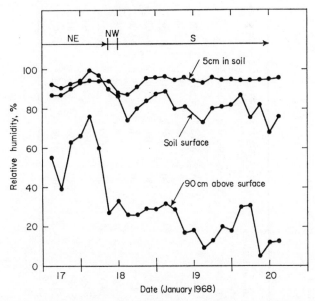

FIG. 2. Changes in air and soil relative humidity in King and David Valleys following a change in wind direction. Wind velocities increased during the period of observation.

B. SOIL PROPERTIES

Soils in the valleys are primarily oxidized desertic saline or alkaline sands and loams with pH values above 7. They are generally overlain by desert pavement, are shallow and show little, if any, profile development. A hard, icy permafrost layer of ice-cemented soil usually occurs at 10–30 cm. Salts, primarily of Na, Ca, Mg, Cl, SO_4, CO_3 and NO_3, may accumulate. Electrical conductivity, buffer capacity and cation exchange capacities are variable, but are within the range of values obtained for other coarse-textured desert soils (Cameron, 1966). Organic N and C levels are the lowest to have been reported for desert soils (Cameron and Blank, 1963). The nature of this organic matter and its origin is not well understood, although it may be old carbon, such as coal. Typical values of ten soil samples collected along a traverse east of the Matterhorn Glacier are cited in Table 1. Available moisture is a limiting factor in most of these soils, although the concentration and balance of ions, and solubility of trace elements, such as boron, are also detrimental, e.g. soil sample No. 664 (Cameron *et al.*, 1968a). Additional information and a discussion of Antarctic dry valley soils has been given by Claridge (1965), Tedrow and Ugolini (1966) and by Ugolini (1970, this symposium).

TABLE 1

Properties of Samples from Ten Sites east of Matterhorn Glacier

Sample No.	Sample depth	Texture	H_2O in situ %	pH Sat. Paste	Electrical conductivity $EC \times 10^6$ mhos/cm² at 25°C Sat. paste	H_2O soluble ions in 1:5 Extract ppm*			Organic %†	
						Nitrate	Sulphate	Chloride	N	C
661	Surface 2 cm	Sand	0·6	7·6	640	3	72	14	0·008	0·02
662	2→10 cm	Sand	1·0	8·0	520	0	48	18	0·005	0·01
663	Surface 2 cm	Sand	1·4	7·8	1360	10	380	41	0·006	0·04
664	Surface 2 cm	Sandy loam	5·0	8·9	10,000	130	450	2340	0·007	0·04
665	Surface 2 cm	Sand	0·6	7·9	128	0	6	9	0·006	0·04
666	2→10 cm	Sand	0·8	8·0	91	0	4	4	0·006	0·02
667	Surface 2 cm	Sand	1·8	7·5	1420	56	660	496	0·002	0·02
668	2→10 cm	Sand	1·5	7·5	3280	80	950	798	0·003	0·02
669	Surface 2 cm	Loamy Sand	0·8	7·7	5440	640	980	1575	0·001	0·03
670	2→10 cm	Sandy loam	1·5	7·7	5120	400	1160	1525	0·002	0·02

*Analyses by E. S. Babcock and Sons, Riverside, California.
†Analyses by Elek Microanalytical Labs, Torrance, California.

C. MICROBIOLOGY

The number of micro-organisms in samples from the various valleys varied widely from essentially zero to approximately 10^7 per gram of soil. The level of abundance was usually low compared with previously investigated desert soils (Cameron, 1966). The absence or presence of microflora in a number of samples was substantiated by ^{14}C substrate enrichment and radio-respirometric techniques (Hubbard *et al.*, 1968). The highest abundances were generally found at sites in Wheeler Valley (Table 2). Typical values for the Matterhorn Valley are shown in Table 3. Pertinent data concerning plating, media composition, incubation temperatures and the halophilic and psychrophilic nature of Antarctic microflora have been presented previously (Hall, 1968; Benoit and Hall 1970, this symposium). Results of prolonged incubation at high humidities for psychrophilic micro-organisms in these same samples are shown in Table 4.

As also shown previously (Cameron, 1967; Cameron *et al.*, 1968; Benoit and Hall, 1970, this symposium), as many, if not more, micro-organisms were found in subsurface soils, especially at the level of hard, icy permafrost, as in the surface layers. The ratio of surface to subsurface abundance for eighteen sites is shown in Fig. 3. For five sites, shown above the diagonal line, the abundance of micro-organisms was greater at the surface. For thirteen sites, shown below the diagonal line, the abundance of micro-organisms was greater below the surface. The subsurface bacteria were predominantly white, opaque translucent or non-pigmented colonies, whereas the chromogenic bacteria were most abundant at the surface. This abundance ratio is expressed in Fig. 4. The subsurface micro-organisms may represent an ancient "freeze-dried" microflora. Their dormancy is indicated by results of metabolic studies in which the subsurface soils were considerably less effective in dissimilating ^{14}C-labelled substrates than were the surface soils (Hubbard *et al.*, 1968).

The microflora populations were composed primarily of bacteria and included the following major groups: (1) gram positive cocci, *Micrococcus* and *Mycococcus* sp., (2) soil diphtheroids, *Corynebacterium*, *Brevibacterium*, *Arthrobacter* and related sp., (3) gram positive and negative rods, *Bacillus* and *Pseudomonas* sp., and (4) actinomycetes, primarily *Streptomyces* sp.* The opaque or white colonies were usually soil diphtheroids or micrococci, and the translucent or non-pigmented colonies were gram positive or negative rods. Pigmented colonies were generally micrococci. Algal populations were composed of coccoid blue-green algae (*Anacystis* and *Coccochloris* sp.), oscillator-ioid blue-green algae (*Schizothrix*, *Microcoleus*, and *Oscillatoria* sp.), and coccoid green algae such as *Protococcus grevillei*, resembling *Chlorococcum* sp. The fungi included various ascomycetes, e.g. *Penicillum* sp., and a few

---

* Bollen, W. B. and Byers, K. Microorganism Study of Bacteria and Actinomycetes from Harsh Environments, JPL Contract No. 950783.

TABLE 2

Numbers of Micro-organisms in Soil Samples from Wheeler Dry Valley (per gm soil)

Soil No.	Sample depth	Aerobic bacteria				Anaerobes		Fungi				Protozoa		Algae
								Moulds		Yeasts				
		+2°C	+20°C	+2°C	+20°C	+20°C	Room temp.	+20°C	Room temp.	+2°C	+20°C	+20°C	Room temp.	Room temp.
609	Surface 2 cm	1.8×10^{4}	2×10^{4}	2×10^{4}	3.2×10^{4}	0	0	20	0	0	0	0	200	2×10^{3}
610	2→15 cm	4.4×10^{4}	4.8×10^{4}	6.4×10^{4}	1.2×10^{5}	0	0	0	0	0	0	0	0	2×10^{3}
611	30 cm	4.8×10^{3}	7.8×10^{3}	6.2×10^{3}	5.8×10^{3}	0	1·5	0	0	0	0	0	0	20
612	60 cm	100	1.3×10^{3}	200	2.2×10^{3}	0	1	0	0	0	0	0	0	200
613	Surface 2 cm	4×10^{4}	2×10^{4}	1×10^{4}	3×10^{5}	0	0	0	0	0	0	0	40	800
614	2→10 cm	1×10^{3}	1×10^{4}	3×10^{3}	2×10^{4}	0	0	0	0	0	0	0	0	800
615	Surface 2 cm	1.5×10^{5}	1.2×10^{5}	9.6×10^{4}	1.5×10^{5}	0	0	200	0	0	2	0	40	6.4×10^{6}
616	2→10 cm	1×10^{5}	2×10^{5}	2×10^{5}	2×10^{5}	0	0	25	0	2	12	0	2	800
617	Surface 2 cm	200	3×10^{3}	2×10^{3}	2×10^{3}	0	0	35	0	0	0	0	0	2
618	2→10 cm	6×10^{3}	1×10^{4}	1×10^{4}	2×10^{4}	0	0	15	0	0	0	0	0	40
619	Surface 2 cm	1×10^{3}	8×10^{3}	8×10^{3}	1×10^{4}	0	0	50	0	0	0	0	0	40
620	2→10 cm	2×10^{3}	2×10^{4}	2×10^{4}	1×10^{5}	0	0	200	0	0	0	0	0	1.6×10^{3}
621	Surface 2 cm	1×10^{3}	3×10^{3}	4×10^{3}	2×10^{4}	0	0	0	0	0	4	0	2	1.6×10^{3}
622	2→15 cm	1×10^{4}	2×10^{4}	4×10^{4}	6×10^{4}	0	0	0	0	0	0	0	0	800
623	18→33 cm	500	1×10^{3}	1×10^{3}	3×10^{3}	0	0	0	0	0	0	0	0	40
Media		Trypticase soy agar		Salts (simulated Taylor Valley)+ yeast extract+ neopeptone		TSA in CO₂		Rose Bengal Agar		Dextrose-neopeptone agar pH 4·5		Thornton's salt medium		

TABLE 3

Numbers of Micro-organisms in Soil Samples from Matterhorn Valley (per gm soil)

Sample No.	Sample depth	Aerobic bacteria				Anaerobes	Fungi	Algae
		$+2°C$	$+20°C$	$+2°C$	$+20°C$	Room temp.		
661	Surface 2 cm	$3·7 \times 10^2$	3×10^3	$3·2 \times 10^2$	$1·8 \times 10^4$	0	$2·5 \times 10^2$	2×10^2
662	2→10 cm	20	4×10^4	<10	$1·7 \times 10^5$	0	3×10^3	20
663	Surface 2 cm	0	$1·6 \times 10^2$	$\sim10^2$	2×10^3	0	0	20
664	Surface 2 cm	0	<10	0	<10	0	0	0
665	Surface 2 cm	<10	$2·8 \times 10^3$	<10	$2·5 \times 10^4$	0	0	20
666	2→10 cm	<10	$2·7 \times 10^3$	<10	$1·1 \times 10^3$	0	0	20
667	Surface 2 cm	<10	30	0	40	0	0	0
668	2→10 cm	<10	<10	0	<10	0	0	0
669	Surface 2 cm	180	90	<10	$2·7 \times 10^2$	0	0	0
670	2→10 cm	$3·5 \times 10^4$	$1·4 \times 10^4$	<10	$4·4 \times 10^2$	0	0	0
		Trypticase soy agar		Salts (Simulated Taylor Valley) + Yeast extract + Peptone		TSA in CO_2	Rose Bengal Agar	Thornton's Salt medium

TABLE 4

Results of Prolonged Incubation of Samples at High Humidities (numbers per gm soil)

Sample No.	Sample depth	Incubation period					
		6 weeks	3 months	6 weeks	3 months	6 weeks	3 months
661 (VPI 555)	Surface 2 cm	NGD	$2 \cdot 3 \times 10^4$	NGD	$3 \cdot 6 \times 10^2$	NGD	NGD
662 (VPI 556)	2→10 cm	NGD	$1 \cdot 1 \times 10^6$	$1 \cdot 1 \times 10^{2*}$	$3 \cdot 5 \times 10^5$	$1 \cdot 1 \times 10^{2*}$	$1 \times 10^{3*}$
663 (VPI 557)	Surface 2 cm	NGD	$1 \cdot 5 \times 10^3$	NGD	$5 \cdot 2 \times 10^3$	NGD	NGD
664 (VPI 558)	Surface 2 cm	NGD	NGD	NGD	NGD	NGD	NGD
665 (VPI 559)	Surface 2 cm	NGD	$1 \cdot 2 \times 10^4$	NGD	$3 \cdot 2 \times 10^3$	NGD	NGD
666 (VPI 560)	2→10 cm	NGD	$1 \cdot 8 \times 10^4$	NGD	6×10^3	NGD	NGD
667 (VPI 561)	Surface 2 cm	NGD	NGD	NGD	NGD	NGD	NGD
668 (VPI 562)	2→10 cm	NGD	NGD	NGD	NGD	NGD	NGD
669 -	Surface 2 cm	NGD	NGD	2×10^3	$7 \cdot 2 \times 10^3$	NGD	NGD
670 -	2→ 10 cm	NGD	$7 \cdot 6 \times 10^2$	$6 \cdot 2 \times 10^3$	$2 \cdot 4 \times 10^4$	NGD	NGD
Media		M 12 (Taylor Valley soil extract + peptone + yeast extract)		Trypticase soy agar + Taylor Valley soil e2 sct		M 12+5% NaCI	

*=all counts refer to fungi only.
NGD=<40 bacteria/gm soil.
(Determinations by Prof. Robert E. Benoit, Virginia Polytechnic Institute, Blacksburg, Virginia. Results used with permission of Prof. R.E. Benoit.)

yeasts, e.g. *Candida* sp. No bacteriophages were found by means of the bacterial plaque technique. There was a positive correlation between the abundance of micro-organisms in a sample and the number of species represented (Fig. 4).

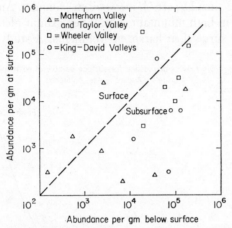

F I G. 3*a*. Relative abundance of micro-organisms in surface and subsurface soils.

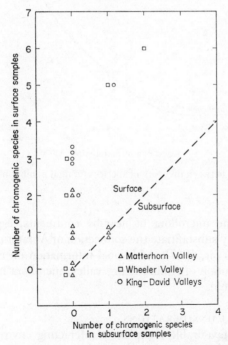

F I G. 3*b*. Relative abundance of chromogenic bacteria in surface and subsurface soils.

Neither coccoid blue-green algae nor coccoid bacteria have been found to be as abundant or as predominant in the soil microbial community in other desert soils. Characteristics of the Antarctic soil bacterial species are not easily resolved, but they appear to be most similar to those isolated from soils of the Chilean Atacama Desert. *Mycococcus* sp., found in Antarctica as well as Chile, also occur in high mountain soils. They exhibit pleomorphism which may possibly aid survival in harsh environments. A study of Antarctic soil

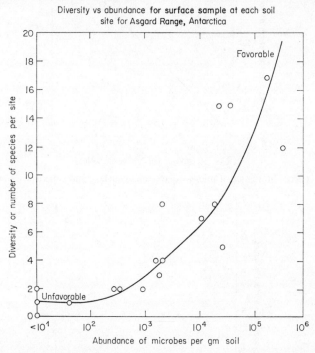

FIG. 4. Relationship between diversity of species and total number of micro-organisms in soil samples.

microflora and the microflora of near-by continents, especially in harsh environments, may substantiate the connection of Antarctica with other land masses (Science Year, 1967). Additional information on the general abundance and distribution of Antarctic dry valley microflora has been provided by Boyd, *et al.* (1966).

D. ECOLOGICAL CONSIDERATIONS

In general, a favourable complex of interacting environmental (microclimatic and edaphic) factors was necessary to obtain an abundance of mixed populations of micro-organisms. Regardless of elevation, a north-south valley orientation was extremely important, as were slope, drainage and exposure, so as to obtain maximum duration, frequency and quantity of insolation and available moisture and protection from wind, (Table 5). However, it was

TABLE 5

Ecological Factors determining Distribution of Life in Antarctic Dry Valleys

Favourable	*Unfavourable*
N-S orientation	E-W orientation
Northern exposure	Southern exposure
Gentle, north-facing slopes	Flat or south-facing slopes
High solar radiation	Low solar radiation
Microclimate above freezing	Microclimate below freezing
Absence of wind	High winds
Northerly winds	Southerly winds
High humidities	Low humidities
Slow or impeded drainage	Rapid drainage
Lengthy duration of available H_2O (presence of glaciers, lakes, streams, snow and ice fields)	Short duration of available H_2O (absence of glaciers, lakes, streams, snow and ice fields)
Translucent pebbles	Opaque pebbles
Non-salty soils, balanced ionic composition	Salty soils, unbalanced ionic composition
Approx. neutral pH	High (or low) pH
Organic contamination (skuas, seals, etc.)	No organic contamination (no large increments of organic matter)

found that an otherwise favourable environment could be limiting for micro-organisms because of one or more soil properties, such as unfavourable mineralogy, texture, structure, salts, pH or moisture relationships. For example, samples with increasing concentrations of salts, as shown by electrical conductivity measurements, generally had lower abundances of micro-organisms (Fig. 5). With an organic carbon content less than 0·5%, there was no apparent correlation with abundance of micro-organisms in the samples. Also, there was no obvious relationship between abundance of micro-organisms and *in situ* moisture content except that there were more micro-organisms in proximity to the more moist layer of hard, icy permafrost. The diurnal cycling of moisture and heat in the Antarctic dry valleys (Fig. 1), are not advantageous for growth and reproduction of soil micro-organisms. As shown by laboratory and other desert field studies, a relative humidity above ~80% and temperatures above ~15°C for extended time periods are more favourable for most micro-organisms.

Based on the above factors, it was postulated as to which high-altitude valleys would be favourable or unfavourable for life. Subsequently, additional valleys were investigated and it was substantiated that the abundance or absence of life in the valleys was indeed dependent upon specific climatic, topographic, and edaphic characteristics with respect to valley orientation, slope, drainage, exposure, wind, insolation, moisture supply and soil physical and chemical properties. This was found to be true for King and David Valleys.

With progression from extremely harsh to more favourable environments, especially with increase in quality, quantity, duration and frequency of

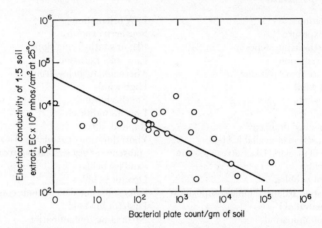

FIG. 5. Relationship between salt concentration and bacterial abundance in soil samples.

available moisture, it was found that there was a sequential increase in abundance, diversity and complexity of organisms. In general, the following sequence was observed: (1) heterotrophic, aerobic, non-pigmented, white, translucent or opaque bacteria, (2) heterotrophic, microaerophilic and chromogenic bacteria, (3) actinomycetes, (4) coccoid blue-green and green algae, and oscillatorioid blue-green algae, (5) moulds, yeasts and protozoa, (6) lichens containing coccoid green algae, and (7) mosses and other algae (filamentous green, nitrogen-fixing blue-green and diatoms) (Fig. 6). More specialized microflora, e.g. sulphate reducers and nitrogen-fixing bacteria, were generally not found unless algae were also present. Anaerobes, obligate psychrophiles, thermophiles, obligate halophiles, photosynthetic bacteria and coliforms were generally not detected. The absence of anaerobes and photosynthetic bacteria is especially significant, since this observation also has been made in investigations of other harsh desert soils, e.g. the Atacama and parts of the Sahara.

The increasing complexity of the life forms encountered as one passes from the harshest to the less harsh habitats is also important in the food chain of lower organisms (Janetschek, 1970, this symposium). The more complex organisms, which are found in relatively favourable habitats, have more requirements on both the biotic (organismal and communal) level and the environmental level. Although difficult to quantify on an ecological and physiological basis at present, it is more than coincidental that the greater exigency, size and complexity of an organism, the less likely it will gain a foothold and become established in the dry valleys.

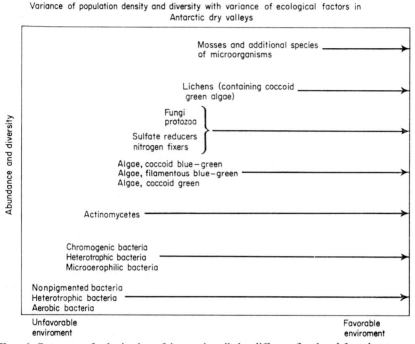

Variance of population density and diversity with variance of ecological factors in Antarctic dry valleys

FIG. 6. Sequence of colonization of Antarctic soils by different floral and faunal groups.

III. Conclusion

A favourable complex of interacting topographic, climatic and edaphic factors must be present before there is an abundance of populations of micro-organisms, whether broadly distributed throughout an area or at a local site. Consideration of these factors allows the prediction of the abundance and nature of the microflora likely to be encountered in a characterized environment. The investigation and study of Antarctic Dry Valleys has contributed substantially to an understanding of desert soil microbial ecology in a harsh environment prior to the search for life in extraterrestrial environments. The irregular distribution and low abundance of life in the dry valleys provides a valuable test area for life-detection methods (David and King, 1968).

References

Benoit, R. E. and Cameron, R. E. (1967). Microbial Ecology of Some Dry Valley Soils of Antarctica. *Bacteriological Proceedings*, 1967. Abstract A13, p. 3.

Benoit, R. E. and Hall, C. L., Jr. (1970). The Microbiology of Some Dry Valley Soils of Victoria Land, Antarctica. This symposium, pp. 697–701.

Boyd, W. L., Staley, J. T. and Boyd, J. W. (1966). Ecology of Soil Micro-organisms of Antarctica. *In* "Antarctic Soils and Soil Forming Processes." (Tedrow, J. C. F., ed.) *Antarct. Res. Ser.* 8, 125–59.

Bull, C. (1966). Climatological Observations in Ice-Free Areas of Southern Victoria Land, Antarctica. *In* "Studies in Antarctic Meteorology." (Rubin, M. J., ed.) *Antarct. Res. Ser.* 9, 177–94.

Cameron, R.E. (1966). Soil Sampling Parameters for Extraterrestrial Life Detection. *J. Ariz. Acad. Sci.* 4, 3–27.

Cameron, R. E. (1967). "Soil Studies—Desert Microflora." XIV. Soil Properties and Abundance of Microflora from a Soil Profile in McKelvey Valley, Antarctica. Space Programs Summary 37–44, Vol. IV, pp. 224–36, Jet Propulsion Laboratory, California Institute of Technology, Pasadena, California, April 30.

Cameron, R. E. (ed.) (1968a). "Soil Investigations of Antarctic Dry Valleys." 16 mm colour Motion Picture. JPL Internal. Jet Propulsion Laboratory, California Institute of Technology, Pasadena, California, April 22.

Cameron, R. E. (1968b). Soil Microbial Ecology of Valley of 10,000 Smokes, Alaska. *J. Ariz. Acad. Sci.* (In press.)

Cameron, R. E. and Blank, G. B. (1963). "Soil Organic Matter." Technical Report 32–443, Jet Propulsion Laboratory, Pasadena, California, May 23.

Cameron, R. E., Blank, G. B. and Gensel, D. R. (1966). "Sampling and Handling of Desert Soils". Technical Report 32–908. Jet Propulsion Laboratory, California Institute of Technology, Pasadena, California, April 15.

Cameron, R. E., David, C. N. and King, J. (1968a). Antarctic Soil Toxicity. *Antarct. J. U.S.* 3, 154–66.

Cameron, R. E., King, J. and David, C. N. (1968). Soil Microbial and Ecological Studies in Southern Victoria Land. *Antarct. J.U.S.* 3, 121–3.

Claridge, G. G. C. (1965). The Clay Mineralogy and Chemistry of Some Soils from the Ross Dependency, Antarctica. *N.Z. J. Geol. Geophys.* Third Special Antarctic Issue 8, 186–220.

David, C. N. and King, J. (1968). Searching for Life in Antarctica. *Eng. Sci.* 31, 14–18.

Hall, C. L., Jr. (1968). Isolation of Psychrophilic Halophiles from the Antarctic Polar Desert. M. S. Thesis, unpublished. 55 pp. Department of Biology, Virginia Polytechnic Institute, Blacksburg, Virginia.

Hubbard, J. S., Cameron, R. E. and Miller, A. B. (1968). "Soil studies—Desert Microflora." XV. Analysis of Antarctic Dry Valley Soils by Cultural and Radiorespirometric Methods. Space Programs *Summary*, No. 37–52, Vol. 3, April 30. Jet Propulsion Laboratory, California Institute of Technology, Pasadena, California. 172–5.

Janetschek, H. (1970). Arthropod Ecology of South Victoria Land. This symposium, 871–85.

Science Year, The World Book Science Annual, Microbiology, p. 327. Field Enterprises Educational Corporation. Chicago. 434 pp. 1967.

Tedrow, J. C. F. and Ugolini, F. C. (1966). Antarctic Soils. *In* "Antarctic Soils and Soil Forming Processes." (Tedrow, J. C. F., ed.) *Antarct. Res. Ser.* 8, 161–77.

Ugolini, F. (1970). Antarctic Soils and Their Ecology. This symposium, 673–92.

Yeasts, Moulds and Bacteria from an Acid Peat on Signy Island

J. H. BAKER
British Antarctic Survey Biological Unit, Monks Wood Experimental Station, Abbots Ripton, Huntingdon, England

I. Introduction

The 1901–03 Swedish South Polar Expedition spent an enforced winter on Snow Hill Island off the east coast of the Antarctic Peninsula. The disaster enabled the medical officer, Ekelöf, to study the numbers of bacteria in different environments including the soil and the seasonal variation in their abundance (Ekelöf, 1908). This appears to be the only account published dealing with the population of soil bacteria during the Antarctic winter.

II. Materials and Methods

The present research was done on Signy Island in the South Orkney Islands, which lie within the "maritime Antarctic" region (Holdgate, 1964), and the experimental material chosen was a fibrous acid peat of loose texture which occurred in banks in the coastal region. Fig. 1 shows the experimental site during December, at the beginning of the short austral summer. The marking stakes are approximately 130 cm high and the growing moss shoots can be seen in the partly snow-free area between them. Some bare peat is exposed in the left foreground. The vegetation of the site is almost wholly composed of the moss *Dicranum aciphyllum*, with very occasional tufts of another moss, *Pohlia nutans*. The underlying peat extends to a depth of almost 2 m in places, although the thaw on this site often only penetrates to about 30 cm.

The same site in winter is shown in Fig. 2, which also shows the winter sampling technique. Whereas in summer the unfrozen peat could easily be sampled by means of a simple soil corer, in winter it was necessary to use a hardened-steel hollow cylindrical drill attached to a modified carpenters' brace. The peat was sampled monthly at three depths, 1–2 cm, 6–7 cm and 11–12 cm, and the numbers of yeasts and aerobic bacteria at all three depths were counted. The filamentous microfungi were not investigated seasonally, but a washing technique was employed in order to separate the resting spore forms from the active mycelium, and both the washed particles and the washings were plated out on to Czapek doz agar with added yeast extract and rose bengal. A modified Sabouraud agar (Di Menna, 1957) was used for the yeasts and it was necessary to count them after only ten days' incubation, because they tended to become overgrown by the faster-growing fungi. Oxoid tryptone soya, with added actidione to inhibit fungal growth, was the isolation medium used for the bacteria. The pour plate method, which subjects the organisms momentarily to a temperature around 45°C, might kill

F IG. 1. General view of a peat bank on Signy Island, South Orkney Islands, composed almost entirely of *Dicranum aciphyllum*. The marker stakes are approximately 130 cm high.
(*British Antarctic Survey photo*)

any psychrophiles which were likely to be present. Therefore the serial dilutions of peat were absorbed on to plates which had been previously dried for one hour at 70°C. This method was also used for the yeasts, and all the isolates were incubated at 10°C; moreover, all samples were completely plated out within twelve hours of collection.

III. Results and Discussion

The yeasts showed no apparent seasonal variation at any of the three depths, but it is interesting to note that the numbers of yeasts in the uppermost layer was high, of the order of 10^6 per gm dry weight. This was considerably higher than the highest count recorded from preserved material from continental Antarctica (Di Menna, 1966). Yeast numbers, like those of the filamentous fungi, decreased rapidly going down the profile, so that at 11–12 cm depth there were only approximately 5×10^4 per gm dry weight; the pH at these depths was 4·1 and 4·4 respectively. Nevertheless, these results are only preliminary and a more detailed account is in preparation.

The numbers of bacteria are also of interest. In contrast to the situation in

FIG. 2. The peat bank illustrated in FIG. 1, in winter. The man is using the portable hand-operated boring device used for obtaining frozen cores.

(British Antarctic Survey photo)

most other soils, their numbers increased down the profile from approximately 3×10^5 in the 1–2 cm layer to of the order of 10^6 in the 11–12 cm layer. These counts compare favourably with those recorded by Heal *et al.* (1967), also from Signy Island.

The respiration rate of the peat was determined once every fortnight using a Dixon manometer (Dixon, 1951), attached to respiration flasks (Parkinson and Coups, 1963) as described by Howard (1967).

Figure 3 records the number of bacteria per gm of dry soil in the surface layer throughout the year, in relation to temperature and respiration rate. It shows that the numbers of bacteria did not decline during the long winter as

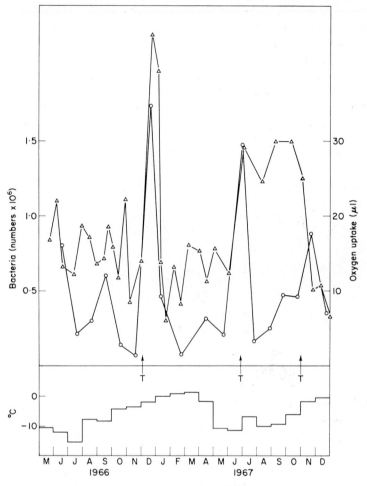

F IG. 3. Monthly counts of aerobic bacteria and concurrent oxygen uptake estimates, with the mean monthly screen temperature. T=time of thaw, circles=bacterial counts, triangles=oxygen uptake readings.

might be expected, and also that the numbers of bacteria correlated quite well with the laboratory respiration readings despite the unusually high readings of August and September 1967. A similar correlation, between carbon-dioxide evolution and plate counts, was found by Gray and Wallace (1957) in an arable soil, but such a relationship has not been commonly reported in the literature and has been shown not to exist in decomposing leaf litter (P. J. A. Howard, *personal communication*). The arrows indicate the time of the big thaw, generally in early summer, when the temperature was consistently above 0°C for several days, and when the snow on the surface of the experimental area disappeared. Each of the two major peaks in numbers of bacteria occurred just after a thaw, when the soil was very wet. The thaw of July 1967 is particularly interesting because it occurred in the middle of winter; it was, in fact, the warmest July at Signy Island since records began in 1947. From the microbiological point of view this is important because the reaction of the microflora to this thaw in winter was the same, on a slightly reduced scale, as that during the major spring thaw in the previous December. In contrast the bacteria did not show a big increase in number after the thaw at the beginning of the 1967–68 season. This may be explained in terms of the way in which this thaw occurred. The first two thaws were very sudden, allowing the more rapidly growing bacteria to increase greatly in number, whereas the third thaw was slow and discontinuous. Under the latter conditions predators, e.g. protozoa (Heal, 1965), were able to multiply sufficiently to check the increasing bacterial population.

The bacterial population declined after the spring thaw, although the mean monthly temperature, as shown in the histogram, continued to increase; thus the size of the bacterial population was not limited entirely by temperature. It is possible that the transient peak was controlled by nutrients contained in the snow and accumulated during the winter, but quickly used up when the snow melted at the beginning of summer. However, Allen *et al.* (1967) stated that standard chemical analyses of the peat indicated no lack of any of the major nutrients.

An alternative explanation, for which there is some positive evidence, is that the supply of available moisture governs the number of bacteria, as has been shown for temperate soils (Jensen, 1934). Just after the thaw the peat is saturated and water runs freely over its surface, but the annual precipitation is very low (estimated by Holdgate *et al.*, 1967, to be approximately 400 mm per annum, compared with an average of 650 to 1000 mm per annum in the U.K.), so that it is conceivable that later in the season the water supply becomes inadequate. Certainly the amount of water in the peat visibly declines during the summer months. To test this hypothesis, sterile distilled water was added to duplicate respirometry samples taken in summer. Oxygen uptake per gm dry weight by the sample with the added water was very much higher than by the sample in its field state.

IV. Conclusions

It has been shown that in an acid peat on Signy Island the numbers of aerobic bacteria increase down the profile to a depth of 12 cm, whereas the yeasts and filamentous fungi decrease in number with increasing depth. Also the yeasts show no apparent seasonal variation, but the bacteria in the surface layer do exhibit a short-lived peak after a big thaw which generally occurs in the spring. Moreover, the numbers of bacteria in the peat are positively correlated with its oxygen uptake.

Acknowledgements

My thanks are due to the British Antarctic Survey, the Director and Staff of Merlewood Research Station, Grange-over-Sands, and my colleagues on Signy Island, without whose assistance and forbearance this work would not have been possible.

References

Allen, S. E., Grimshaw, H. M. and Holdgate, M. W. (1967). Factors affecting the availability of plant nutrients on an Antarctic island. *J. Ecol.* **55**, 381–96.

Dixon, M. (1951). "Manometric methods as applied to the measurement of cell respiration and other processes." Cambridge University Press.

Ekelöf, E. (1908). Bakteriologische Studien während der Schwedischen Südpolar-Expedition. *Wiss. Ergebn. schwed. Südpolarexped.* **7**, 120.

Gray, P. H. H. and Wallace, R. H. (1957). Correlation between bacterial numbers and carbon dioxide in a field soil. *Can. J. Microbiol.* **3**, 191–4.

Heal, O. W. (1965). Observations on testate Amoebae (Protozoa: Rhizopoda) from Signy Island. *Br. Antarct. Surv. Bull.* **6**, 43–47.

Heal, O. W., Bailey, A. D. and Latter, Pamela M. (1967). Bacteria, fungi and protozoa in Signy Island soils compared with those from a temperate moorland. *Phil. Trans. R. Soc.* **252**, No. 777, 191–7.

Holdgate, M. W. (1964). Terrestrial ecology in the maritime Antarctic. *In* "Biologie Antarctique: Antarctic Biology". (Carrick, R., Holdgate, M. and Prévost, J., eds) 181–94. Hermann, Paris.

Holdgate, M. W., Allen, S. E. and Chambers, M. J. (1967). A preliminary investigation of the soils of Signy Island, South Orkney Islands. *Br. Antarct. Surv. Bull.* **12**, 53–71.

Howard, P. J. A. (1967). A method for studying the respiration and decomposition of litter. *In* "Progress in Soil Biology" (Graff, O. and Satchell, J. E., eds) Verlag Friedr. Vieweg & Sohn, West Germany.

Jensen, H. L. (1934). Contributions to the microbiology of Australian soils. I. *Proc. Linn. Soc. N.S.W.* **59**, 101–17.

Menna, Margaret E. di (1957). The isolation of yeasts from soil. *J. gen. Microbiol.* **17**, 678–88.

Menna, Margaret E. di (1966). Yeasts in Antarctic soils. *Antonie van Leeuwenhoek.* **32**, 29–38.

Parkinson, D. and Coups, E. (1963). Microbial activity in a podsol. *In* "Soil Organisms" (Doeksen, J. and van der Drift, J. eds). North Holland Publishing Company, Amsterdam.

Discussion

Soils

MINERAL SALTS IN ANTARCTIC SOILS
AND THEIR ORIGIN

A. T. Wilson

How was nitrate separated from chloride? Some soils have high nitrate and low chloride. Why?

F. C. Ugolini

Claridge and Campbell in the Shackleton region claimed that the atmospheric input of chloride was low, and that this was due to the distance of the area from the open sea. However, in lower slopes on moraines there were high chloride levels and this was discussed as evidence for higher salt influx and more leaching from above. But at Plunket Point I have found high chlorides and low nitrogen levels, which is the converse situation. It could be that this area, which now borders the Ross Ice Shelf, once was flanked by open sea and chloride was brought in by the coastal air circulation.

A. T. Wilson

Even at the South Pole, the precipitation contains five times as much chloride as nitrogen salts.

F. C. Ugolini

Claridge claims that the chloride, being far more soluble and mobile, is moved quickly down the snow column. While the nitrate stays on the surface and hence accumulates and is eventually blown to nunataks and ice-free areas. There are large areas of sulphate on the surface in the Victoria Land valleys, whereas in Wright and Taylor Valleys chlorides tend to prevail. This is another problem. Analysis of the inland snow by Belgian scientists, now being repeated at Scott Base, shows a continuous fall-off of chloride as one passes inland.

A. T. Wilson

Quite a lot of nitrate (5ppb) is present on the snow on the polar plateau. It is interesting to try to find out how much results from fixation by the aurora. Some organic nitrogen must have originated from the sea.

F. C. Ugolini

Work by Erickson on atmospheric deposition of salts has surely shown that where precipitation is low salt accumulation is high.

A. T. Wilson

Relative humidity gradients can be established passing uphill. NaCl passes into solution through hygroscopic absorbtion at 78% RH. At 80% RH. sodium chloride is mobilized, whereas sodium nitrate remains. Sodium nitrate is not removed until 80% RH. is reached. Bands of salt are present at different relative humidities. Calcium chloride moves down to the driest areas with a relative humidity as low as 45%.

F. C. UGOLINI

Jones and G. Faure have written a paper on the origin of the salt accumulations in the dry valleys and have analysed for strontium 87/86, and they found that the salts in the dry valleys could be produced by rock weathering.

A. T. WILSON

In this work the isotopic ratio of strontium in one sample of snow was compared to that of samples of glacier, stream and lake water. It was different and it was concluded that the Sr in the lake was not of marine origin. It is well known that the composition of precipitation varies considerably from sample to sample and from the ocean. More than one sample should have been analysed—especially as it is clear that the water in the glacier ice comes from snow fall, and since these glaciers do very little bottom cutting the glacial ice should have the same isotopic ratio as snow.

R. DELÉPINE

Near the coasts marine ecologists define a supralittoral belt which terrestrial ecologists sometimes call the adlittoral, where the green alga *Prasiola*, and its lichenized form *Mastodia*, are typical. Salt levels are high in the soils of this zone and it would be of interest to determine the physiological requirements, especially the tolerances of salt, nitrates and the humidity requirements of these species. In the Antarctic the supralittoral extends much higher than in other areas. This may be due to high salt deposition derived from sea spray and salt-laden precipitation.

H. JANETSCHEK

Sponge spicules are common on Observation Hill at McMurdo up to 100 m above sea-level and may be borne a long way inland by the strong prevailing winds.

G. A. LLANO

Finger-shaped siliceous sponges which are brought to the surface along Ross Island are blown inland so that it is impossible to collect mosses or lichens free of sponge spicules. As the sponges are tumbled inland they become smaller and more rounded, while the spicules are broken off. Sponge "balls" and small granite pebbles both occur on Crater and Observation Hill summits and both are believed to have been blown uphill by gales.

ORIGINS AND HABITAT PREFERENCES OF MICRO-ORGANISMS

W. J. L. SLADEN

Dr. Benoit said that the micro-organisms he studied might have had a marine origin. What about airborne immigration?

R. E. BENOIT

What I said was, of course, a speculation. Some most interesting micro-organisms have been reported, by Canadian workers from marine isolates, and these behave very like the Antarctic forms we observed. But airborne transport happens to some degree: a sticky plate exposed for four hours in a 70-knot wind caught a few organisms. Some of the airborne fungi observed were *Penicillium* spp., but we have not isolated these fungi from our soil samples. It is not clear why these forms die off very rapidly in Antarctic soils.

W. J. L. SLADEN

The medical microbiologist often finds marked morphological changes when culture media and methods are varied. How did Dr. Benoit's cultures from "dormant" micro-organisms behave?

R. E. BENOIT

Any one organism behaves consistently, but the longer it has been in culture the more variable it is. Some organisms do develop very odd forms. We need to look deeper into the microflora and see what the response to culture is. In the temperate zones the currently used isolation techniques are said to pull out only 10% of the organisms present. So far we have isolated few anaerobes in the Antarctic, but the high sulphide levels observed around some ponds in the dry valleys are clear proof that anaerobes are present and play an important role in the carbon cycle.

J. BAKER

I have found some anaerobes at Signy Island.

N. M. WACE

Is there any evidence of a distinct microflora around the manned bases as a result of contamination?

R. E. BENOIT

Boyd has shown that as one moves away from bases certain groups become less prominent, and this is an indication of contamination. The thermophils illustrate this contamination best.

V. A. GALLARDO

Would Dr. Cameron please explain his slide of abundance of species and individuals plotted together with habitat conditions. Were the favourable and unfavourable conditions assessed quantitatively?

R. E. CAMERON

The ecological variables were not measured exactly. Their excellent agreement with the curve just happens. The curve only relates individual abundance to species diversity and not either of these to specific environmental parameters. It might be possible roughly to quantify the degree of hostility of the environment and plot trial graphs to test correlations.

V. A. GALLARDO

Such an aproach might help to decide whether particular environmental factors are governing diversity.

R. E. CAMERON

We did try this subjectively in a predictive sense to seek collecting sites in which we anticipated biological diversity. Our first attempt succeeded: only 200 m from one favourable site we found diversity and abundance were contrastingly low. Another attempt in another valley gave us a site in which all factors were favourable except moisture and the soil texture and these deficiencies were sufficient to make the environment a poor one. In another case moisture, exposure, and texture were good, but the microbiota was poor because the soil contained seventeen parts per million of extractable boron, which was toxic. Thus any one of many variables can be limiting and the model is a complex one.

A. T. WILSON

Have counts been made right down into the permafrost zone to give us palaeoclimatic data? If there was a former mild period, there might be organisms from this period within the zone which is now permanently frozen.

R. E. CAMERON

At 3000–5000 ft in Wheeler Dry Valley many micro-organisms were found whenever samples were taken. We tried to sterilize a jackhammer and cut down 1 m in permafrost consisting of 50% ice. Algae, fungi and bacteria were present all the way down. It was interesting to note a concentration of chromogenic bacteria at the surface and white ones below. The Carbon 14 technique showed the subsurface organisms were definitely turning material over more slowly than those at the surface. Three-quarters of all sites had more organisms in the subsurface layers. There could be ancient organisms in an immobilized stage in the deeper layers, but we have no data.

R. E. BENOIT

There is one area in Taylor Valley where we dug down 1 m and found no organisms anywhere in the profile. Elsewhere we found sandy soils with bands of moisture and the organisms were restricted to those bands.

V. AHMADJIAN

Sieburth demonstrated multiple temperature optima, one low and one higher. Did Dr. Benoit find any parallels?

R. E. BENOIT

Not yet, but we have not really investigated this field deeply. In the determination of the optimum and maximum temperatures of a micro-organism the culture conditions may affect the results drastically; in static culture tubes oxygen may be the limiting factor and not temperature.

V. AHMADJIAN

Sieburth had one optimum at about 9–10°C, I believe.

R. E. BENOIT

Varying temperatures are always a problem in this work, and oscillations can even affect material in an incubator.

Part XII

VEGETATION

Vegetation*

Botanical observations and collections have been made by Antarctic expeditions since the mid-nineteenth century. Accounts of Antarctic vegetation by the earlier workers have been reviewed by Holdgate (1964), Greene (1964, 1967), Steere (1965), Longton (1967) and others. Greene (1967) appropriately describes an initial period of botanical studies as "the taxonomic phase", in which "the methods used were the collection, preservation and description of the specimens with the object of compiling a descriptive catalogue of the flora and determining the distribution patterns of its species". However, a marked change in the pattern of botanical studies in the Antarctic has taken place in the past twelve years, beginning with several more detailed floristic studies, particularly in the region defined by Holdgate (1964) as the Maritime Antarctic (Corte, 1961a, 1961b, 1962; Follmann, 1965; Longton, 1966, 1967; Smith, 1968). Greene (1967) points out that development of ecologically orientated research was greatly encouraged by the improved logistic facilities at the time of the IGY (1955–7) and subsequently.

Zones

Numerous workers on the terrestrial biology of the Antarctic have attempted to subdivide the region into zones and subzones with distinctive climatic and biotic features. All these classifications have one thing in common: they recognize the dominant influence of the oceanic circulation. Many workers have defined the Antarctic biological zone as the area to the south of the mean position of the Antarctic Convergence, while the Subantarctic has been considered to extend northward to the Subtropical Convergence. Very broadly, the latter corresponds with the southern limit of high forest, which has been considered as marking the northern limit of the Antarctic biological region by Godley (1960) and Skottsberg (1960).

The classifications of Wace (1960, 1965), Greene (1964), Holdgate (1964) and Weyant (1966) are all broadly compatible and have been used by most of the authors in the present symposium. For convenience and to prevent repetition, they are summarized here rather than in the individual papers.

Zone	Botanical definition	Region
Southern cold temperate	From the Subtropical Convergence southward to the southern limit of dwarf shrub vegetation	Western Magellanic Moorland of Chile, Falkland Islands, Tristan-Gough groups I. St Paul, Nouvelle Amsterdam, New Zealand Shelf Islands (Auckland, Campbell, Snares etc.)

* The papers submitted for this section overlapped one another considerably in introductory matter. For clarity and convenience, this material has been brought together here and this Introduction is a composite one, owing something to the thinking of most of the authors in the section.—Editor.

Zone	Botanical definition	Region
Subantarctic	From the southern limit of dwarf shrub vegetation to the southern limit of extensive, closed phanerogamic vegetation	South Georgia, Marion and Prince Edward Islands, Iles Crozet, Archipel de Kerguelen, Heard I., Macquarie Island
Maritime or Oceanic Antarctic	From the southern limit of extensive closed phanerogamic vegetation to the southern limit of extensive and relatively rich closed cryptogamic (expecially bryophyte) communities	South Sandwich, South Orkney, South Shetland Islands, Palmer Archipelago, Western coasts of Antarctic Peninsula south to Marguerite Bay, Bouvetøya, Peter I. Øy
Continental Antarctic	South from the southern limit of extensive diverse closed cryptogam communities	The main continental mass of Antarctica

The Continental Antarctic has been further divided (Weyant, 1966):

Coastal Antarctica	Areas with appreciable maritime influence: seabird (especially penguin) colonies: some bryophyte vegetation: relatively rich soil microfauna	The coastal fringes of East and parts of West Antarctica
Antarctic slopes	The mountain and glacier zone inland from the coast, with occasional snow petrel colonies, local lichen vegetation, arthropod fauna and soil microflora	A band about the margin of the Antarctic ice plateau
Antarctic ice plateau	The interior ice plateau of the continent. No biota except snow algae	Centre of Antarctica

Details of climate and soil in the Oceanic, coastal, slope and plateau areas of Antarctica are reviewed by Ugolini (1970: this symposium) in Part XI.

Because the taxonomy of most terrestrial groups of organisms represented in the Antarctic still requires critical revision, and because large tracts of land await exploration, no exact figures for the composition of the flora can be given, but the following estimates are the best now available.

Phanerogams	2 species
Mosses	72–75 species
Hepatics	9 genera
Lichens	350–400 species
Algae	360 species
Fungi	75 species

The reliability of these figures, and the composition of the flora is discussed in the review paper by I. M. Lamb in this section, and two different views as to the likely recent history of the biota in Antarctica are expressed by him and by V. Ahmadjian. Further critical taxonomic work, backed by quaternary studies (compare the paper by E. M. van Zinderen Bakker in Part I) and studies of direct dispersal like that by E. D. Rudolph in this section will be required before these uncertainties are ended.

In the extremely exacting habitats of the Antarctic, ecosystems are relatively simple owing to the restricted range of life-forms and species available. Consequently, unique opportunities are afforded for investigating the effects of certain environmental factors on the development and functional processes of plant species and communities, and examples are provided by the papers by V. Ahmadjian, S. W. Greene and R. E. Longton in this section. Experimental programmes, comparing the productivity of known genotypes in different polar regions and the growing of polar species under controlled conditions elsewhere, are also expanding and are illustrated by the papers by J. F. Jenkin and D. H. Ashton and by M. H. Lewis and S. W. Greene in this section. With the excellent facilities now available, Greene (1967) considers this rapidly expanding phase of Antarctic plant ecology to comprise "Vegetation Description, Environmental Analysis and Experimental Autecology". Such investigations are possible only when taxonomic understanding of the flora has progressed sufficiently. While nomenclatural problems remain and in many instances naming must still be provisional, the works of Lamb (1948, 1964, 1968) and Greene et al. (1968) have provided invaluable knowledge of the taxonomy, distribution patterns and behaviour of a number of species in the Scotia Ridge-Antarctic Peninsula sector. These have provided the essential foundations for detailed vegetational studies such as that by C. H. Gimingham and R. I. L. Smith which provides a classification for the plant communities of the maritime Antarctic far exceeding in detail anything that would have been possible only four or five years ago.

References

Corte, A. (1961a). La primera fanerogama adventicia hallada en el Continente Antartico. *Contr. Inst. Antart. Argent.*, No. 62, pp. 3–14.

Corte, A. (1961b). Fertilidad de las semillas en fanerogamas que crecen en Cabo Primavera (Costa de Danco), Peninsula Antartica. *Contr. Inst. Antart. Argent.*, No. 65, pp. 3–16.

Corte, A. (1962). Primera cita de la familia de Hepaticas "Marchantiaceae" para la Antartida. *Contr. Inst. Antart. Argent.*, No. 68, pp. 3–12.

Follmann, G. (1965). Una asociación nitrófila de líquenes epipétricos de la Antártica Occidental con *Ramalina terebrata* Tayl. et Hook. como especie caracterizante. *Instituto Antartico Chileno*, Publ. No. 4, pp. 3–18.

Godley, E. J. (1960). The botany of Southern Chile in relation to New Zealand and the Subantarctic. *Proc. R. Soc. B*, **152**, pp. 457–74.

Greene, S. W. (1964). Problems and Progress in Antarctic Bryology. *In* "Biologie Antarctique: Antarctic Biology" (Carrick, R., Holdgate, M. W. and Prévost, J. eds.) Hermann, Paris, pp. 173–9.

Greene, S. W. (1967). The Changing Pattern of Antarctic Botanical Studies. *JARE Scientific Reports*, Special Issue No. 1. Proceedings of the Symposium on Pacific Antarctic Sciences, pp. 236–44.

Greene, S. W., Greene, D. M., Brown, P. D. and Pacey, J. M. (1968). Antarctic Moss Flora. I. The genera *Andreaea, Pohlia, Polytrichum, Psilopilum* and *Sarconeurum. British Antarctic Survey Scientific Reports*, No. 64.

Holdgate, M. W. (1964). Terrestrial Ecology in the Maritime Antarctic, *In* "Biologie Antarctique: Antarctic Biology" (Carrick, R., Holdgate, M. W., and Prévost, J., eds), Hermann, Paris, pp. 181–94.

Lamb, I. M. (1948). Antarctic Pyrenocarp Lichens. *Discovery Reports*, No. 25, pp. 1–30.

Lamb, I. M. (1964). Antarctic Lichens. I. The genera *Usnea, Ramalina, Himantormia, Alectoria, Cornicularia. British Antarctic Survey Scientific Reports, No.* 38, pp. 1–34.

Lamb, I. M. (1968). Antarctic Lichens. II. The genera *Buellia* and *Rinodina. British Antarctic Survey Scientific Reports*, No. 61.

Longton, R. E. (1966). Botanical Studies in the Antarctic during the 1963–64 and 1964–65 seasons. *Br. Antarct. Surv. Bull.*, No. 10, pp. 85–95.

Longton, R. E. (1967). Vegetation in the Maritime Antarctic. *Phil. Trans. R. Soc.* B., **252**, pp. 213–35.

Skottsberg, C. J. F. (1960). Remarks on the plant geography of the southern cold temperate zone, *Proc. R. Soc.* B, **152**, pp. 447–50.

Smith, R. I. L. (1968). Ecology of the Vegetation of Signy Island, South Orkney Islands, British Antarctic Territory. Ph.D. thesis, University of Aberdeen. 228 pp. (Unpublished.)

Steere, W. C. (1965). Antarctic Bryophyta. *Bioscience*, **15**.

Wace, N. M. (1960). The botany of the southern oceanic islands. *Proc. R. Soc.* B., **152**, pp. 475–90.

Wace, N. M. (1965). Vascular plants. *In* "Biogeography and Ecology in Antarctica". Junk, Den Haag.

Watson, W. (1925). The Bryophytes and Lichens of Arctic-Alpine Vegetation. *J. Ecol.*, 13, pp. 1–26.

Weyant, W. S. (1966). The Antarctic Climate. *In* "Antarctic Soils and Soil Forming Processes". *Antarctic Research Series*, 8, pp. 47–59.

Antarctic Terrestrial Plants and Their Ecology

I. MACKENZIE LAMB

Farlow Herbarium, Harvard University, Cambridge, Massachusetts, U.S.A.

I. Introduction

The Antarctic continent, in the present interglacial phase, has an extent of nearly 14 million square kilometres, almost all of it covered by snow and ice. Apart from snow algae, plant life is established only in the ice-free areas, nunataks and coastal strips, which comprise approximately 4% of the total area. The purpose of the present paper is to review knowledge of Antarctic plants, particularly in relation to the edaphic environment.

II. Environmental Factors

The environmental factors controlling the present-day distribution of the terrestrial vegetation fall into three categories: climatic (temperature, availability of moisture, wind effect, etc.), edaphic (types of substratum available), and biotic (influence of other organisms, mainly animals). The factors influencing the terrestrial vegetation cannot, at least in coastal areas, be adequately studied without taking into consideration the influence of the marine ecosystem, which contributes to that of the land areas by wind-borne sea-spray and by the excreta of marine birds and seals (Holdgate, 1967b).

A. CLIMATE

It has been pointed out by Weber (1962) that environmental modification of forms of terrestrial vegetation is especially marked in areas with rigorous climates, such as the Arctic, the Antarctic, and major desert areas. "Sound taxonomic work in these regions", he writes, "requires an unusually clear understanding of field conditions as well as herbarium material of exceptional quality."

For the Antarctic Peninsula sector, the prevailing climatic conditions have been summarized by Longton (1967), who emphasizes the fact that the east side of the Peninsula is colder and drier than at comparable latitudes on the west side. Longton considers that while prevailing low temperatures are certainly of great importance in determining the general character of the vegetation, availability of water probably has even greater influence on the distribution of Antarctic cryptogamic plant communities. Micro-climatic studies in relation to the ecology of lichens have been made in the Cape Hallett area by Rudolph (1966b).

B. TEMPERATURE

In the Antarctic Botanical Zone there is, practically speaking, no month with a mean air temperature much above freezing. Thus the summer growing season is exceedingly short, and winter snow lies late. The west coast of the Peninsula and adjacent islands have the highest summer temperatures, with a mean around or slightly above 0°C; the east side of the Peninsula and nearly all the coastal areas of the rest of the continent have summer mean temperatures below freezing. Winter temperatures at coastal stations seldom go lower than −50°C, and on the Peninsula remain usually above −40°C (Greene, 1964; Greene et al., 1967; Sabbagh, 1962). Temperature conditions at plant level are, however, often much more favourable than at a few metres above the ground, as has been shown by Holdgate (1964) and Rudolph (in Greene et al., 1967). Aspect is also an important factor influencing the extent to which plants are warmed by radiation; this has been strikingly demonstrated by Longton and Holdgate (1967) by thermistor readings taken in moss cushions on Deception Island, on north and south-facing exposures respectively.

C. PRECIPITATION

Precipitation is difficult to measure in Antarctica because of the amount of wind-drifted snow. Recorded estimates indicate that for the continent as a whole, the total precipitation is relatively small. Rain occurs occasionally at most of the coastal stations, more frequently on the Peninsula (Rubin and Weyant, 1965).

D. RADIATION

Except for the northern part of the Peninsula, almost the whole of the Antarctic continent lies within the Antarctic Circle, with nearly continuous daylight in summer and continuous darkness in winter. Direct sunlight in many areas is relatively meagre. The coastal areas have an average cloud-cover of 5/8 to 3/4 of the sky; the interior of the continent has more continuous sunshine (Phillpot, 1964).

E. WIND

Katabatic winds reaching hurricane force are frequent in most coastal areas, and ice-crystals and granular snow, driven by these winds, can have a very destructive effect on exposed terrestrial vegetation. Crustose lichens, for instance, may have the outer cortical layers partly removed as if by a sand-blast and regenerate in states often very unlike the typical species in appearance.

F. EDAPHIC FACTORS

Edaphic factors of importance for the Antarctic terrestrial vegetation are rock-types (mainly for the epipetric lichens) and the presence of weathered mineral, or humic deposits which can be classed as soil (for mosses and higher plants). A variety of rock types are available for plant colonization in various ice-free areas: plutonic, metamorphic and sedimentary. The Antarctic Peninsula, where plant life is richest, consists of metamorphic rocks with granitic and dioritic instrusions, in places overlain by sedimentary strata.

Base-rich mineral substrata, such as limestone, marble outcrops and limpet-shell beds, are characterized by distinct communities of lichens and (as shown by Longton, 1967) mosses; the so-called calciphilous species. On calcareous sedimentary rocks around the Swedish Expedition base hut on Snow Hill Island (off the east side of the Antarctic Peninsula) one of the commonest lichens is *Lecanora mons-nivis* Darb., a species belonging to the obligately calciphilous *Lecanora dispersa*—assemblage. The terrestrial green alga *Prasiola* in the lichenized condition (*Mastodia*) is apparently quite sensitive to the pH of the substrate, for it has been observed to avoid more acid patches of granodioritic rock (Lamb, 1948).

The colour of rock substrata is of importance with regard to the production and retention of available moisture. I have observed that fine snow crystals blown on to the surface of dark basaltic rock will melt in bright sunshine, even when the air temperature is below freezing-point. Rudolph (1964) showed that, over a period of two months or more, during the austral summer at Cape Hallett, rock surfaces may have daily maximum temperatures well above 0°C, even up to 32°C on occasion, although the diurnal minimum temperatures remain below freezing, and a soil area, covered with a layer of mosses, underwent much less fluctuation in temperature.

The soil cover, where present, is usually quite shallow, in most cases not deep enough to extend down to the permafrost horizon. The daily fluctuations in temperature are naturally greatest at the surface and become negligible at a depth of about 15 cm. Generally speaking, Antarctic soils tend to contain soluble salts and have neutral or alkaline reaction, but humic deposits with an acid pH are also occasionally found (Rudolph, 1966). Like the vegetation, the soils of the Maritime Antarctic Zone are more diverse and more fully developed. What may be termed "ornithogenic" soil occurs around penguin colonies and at the base of birds' perching rocks, where it is well supplied with nitrogen in the form of ammonia. Formation of such soils from bird guano and mineral particles may be a very slow process, especially in Continental Antarctic areas, since the two layers are frequently sharply separated (Ugolini, 1965). Low temperatures and scarcity of water in the liquid state also slow down the formation of soil deposits. The mineral constituents may be sand or glacial till (silt or clay), and the organic moiety may be derived partly from decayed mosses or algae.

The investigations of Allen and Northover (1967) in the South Orkney Islands have shown that soil micro-organisms do not appear to be particularly active in chemical fixation or nutrient circulation; in fact, the waterlogged peaty substratum was found to encourage a mainly anaerobic soil-microflora which was relatively inactive in decomposition. It is interesting to note, however, that in tundra habitats of the Arctic, according to Cooke and Fournelle (1960), the soil microfungi, in spite of the permafrost, are quite active in the degradation of organic matter in the surface layers which thaw during the brief summer.

III. Habitats and Vegetation

Habitats for terrestrial plant life in ice-free areas of Antarctica comprise rocky coastlines, glacial moraines, scoria slopes of old volcanoes, lakes, freshwater ponds and puddles (either permanently or seasonally frozen over), and summer melt-water channels. A peculiar type of habitat occurs in local volcanically warmed areas, such as around fumaroles. Longton and Holdgate (1967) published some detailed studies on the rich bryophyte vegetation around fumaroles in the South Sandwich Islands. Janetschek (1963) found a soil flora consisting of microfungi, bacteria and blue-green algae in volcanically warmed detritus at an altitude of 3600 m on Mt Erebus, Ross Island, although no macroscopic vegetation was present.

The terrestrial vegetation of Antarctica, in order of decreasing abundance of representation, consists of lichens, mosses, algae, hepatics, fungi and bacteria, and flowering plants. Lichens extend furthest towards the pole, having been found on exposed rocks as far south as slightly over 86°S in the Horlick and Queen Maud mountain ranges. The most extensive vegetation, consisting of local patches of peat-forming moss tundra, is developed in the South Shetland Islands and localities on the west of the Antarctic Peninsula.

Holdgate (1964) reported three main bryophyte-lichen associations for Signy Island. Longton (1967) has formulated an ecological classification of the land vegetation of the Maritime Antarctic region as a whole and this is set out in full and discussed by Gimingham and Smith (1970: this symposium). Advanced phytosociological methods, such as those of Braun-Blanquet (1932), concerned with the establishment of a hierarchy of plant groupings based on the relative frequency and fidelity of occurrence of taxonomic units, have been only quite recently employed in the Antarctic Botanical Zone, by Follmann (1967), who distinguished, for example, in the Antarctic Peninsula sector associations named the *Ramalinetum terebratae*, the *Neuropogonion antarcticum*, and the *Lecideetum sciatraphae*. Phytosociological observations by statistical methods, based on quadrat analysis, have also been made recently in the South Orkney Islands by Gimingham (1967). The computerized results obtained from these observations were found to be in general accordance with the more subjective classification of physiognomic vegetational units made by Holdgate (1964).

The nature of vegetational succession in polar regions has not yet been satisfactorily elucidated. As pointed out by Rudolph (in Greene *et al.*, 1967), more than one type of terrestrial plant succession in Antarctica should be recognized. Llano (1965) has described one type of succession in unglaciated areas of the Ross Sea sector, initiated by algae on which soil micro-organisms develop and which, in turn, is followed by the invasion of various mosses and lichens. Some unpublished observations have indicated that, both in the Arctic and Antarctic regions, epipetric succession in lichens may begin with more highly evolved (foliose and fruticose) types, which may in certain circumstances later give way to lower (crustose) forms. In the Antarctic Peninsula sector we have noted that the crustose species *Buellia russa*, for instance, often develops in the shelter provided by tufts of *Usnea* (*Neuropogon*) *antarctica*; when the latter eventually dies off, new plants are unable to gain a foothold on the surface now entirely covered by the *Buellia*.

IV. The Flora of Antarctica

A. FLOWERING PLANTS

There are only two species of flowering plants native to Antarctica, *Colobanthus quitensis* (Kunth) Bartl. and *Deschampsia antarctica* Desv., both occurring only in the Peninsula sector; they are also present in the Subantarctic islands and southernmost South America. Their southernmost limit on the Peninsula is somewhat to the south of the Antarctic Circle (Neny Island, Marguerite Bay, lat. 68° 12′S); a detailed account of their distribution has been given by Skottsberg (1954). *Deschampsia antarctica* has been found subsequently in the South Sandwich Islands (Greene, 1964). Both species occur in localities with a favourable exposure and a fair accumulation of humic detritus (Holdgate, 1964).

Natural reproduction in *D. antarctica* was proved for the first time by Lamb, who collected seeds at Port Lockroy in 1944 and obtained their germination indoors (unpublished). Plants of both *D. antarctica* and *C. quitensis* have been grown in the phytotron of Birmingham University, and there is some evidence that different ecotypes may occur in various Antarctic and Subantarctic localities (Holtom and Greene, 1967).

Some alien phanerogams have also been introduced into Antarctica; the two *Poa* species, *P. pratensis* and *P. annua*, have succeeded in establishing themselves in places in the Antarctic Botanical Zone (Corte, 1961; Rudolph, 1965; Longton, 1966). I first observed *P. pratensis* on Deception Island in 1944; it formed some fairly luxuriant tufts on the cinder plain by the deserted factory at Whaler's Bay. Detailed observations on the population of *P. annua* on Deception Island were subsequently made by Longton (1966). Rudolph (1965) succeeded in getting seeds of *P. pratensis* to germinate in the open at Cape Hallett, Victoria Land, but the seedlings did not survive for long in that inhospitable environment.

By way of contrast, it is of interest to note that the Subantarctic island of South Georgia has fifty-six species of vascular plants, of which twenty-four are regarded as native, eight as naturalized aliens, and twenty-four as transient aliens (Greene, 1964*b*; Longton, 1965).

B. Mosses

Seventy-two species of mosses have been listed from the Antarctic Botanical Zone by Steere (1961). The southernmost known locality for mosses is in 87°37', at the southern edge of the Ross Ice Shelf (Greene *et al.*, 1967). Mosses are most frequently encountered in Antarctica in wetter areas of drainage channels or seepage slopes, on scree and morainic detritus and in crevices of rock-faces. Sexual reproduction appears to be exceedingly rare; *Polytrichum alpinum*, for instance, which produces capsules abundantly in South Georgia, has been found fruiting only a few times along the Antarctic Peninsula. It remains yet to be satisfactorily established whether this relative infertility is caused by low temperatures or by photoperiod factors, or a combination of both (Greene *et al.*, 1967; Longton and Holdgate, 1967). Among the commoner Antarctic mosses are *Polytrichum alpinum* (a bipolar species), *Drepanoeladus uncinatus*, *Bryum antarcticum*, *Pohlia nutans* and *Sarconeurum glaciale* (endemic genus and species).

Mats of mosses provide very effective insulation. Holdgate (1964), working at the South Orkneys, showed that the temperature 2·5 cm down inside a moss mat was considerably higher than that of the air above, whereas a soil surface not covered by moss, while still warmer than the surrounding air, remained relatively colder in the same locality. Fruticose lichens, such as *Usnea* (sect. *Neuropogon*) and *Stereocaulon*, frequently commence their develment in such moss mats, which obviously provide a more favoured environment, not only on account of the higher temperature but also by the provision of shelter from strong winds carrying detritus particles and ice crystals.

In the South Orkneys, as well as in several other localities on the west side of the Peninsula, banks of semi-decayed moss peat up to almost 2 m deep occur, usually underlying a turf of *Polytrichum* and *Dicranum*. The greater part of this deposit is, of course, permanently frozen (Holdgate, 1967*b*). Godwin and Switsur (1966) have shown by radiocarbon dating that the accumulation of some of these banks of moss peat has been going on for over 2000 years.

C. HEPATICS

Hepatics (liverworts) are considerably fewer in number than mosses and much less conspicuous, often occurring more or less concealed within moss tufts. Except for one, a species of *Cephaloziella*, which is known also from continental Antarctica, they are all restricted to the Peninsula sector, where some of them extend southwards to the latitude of Marguerite Bay (Steere in Greene *et al.*, 1967). Genera recorded from the Maritime Antarctic area are *Anthelia*, *Barbilophozia*, *Cephaloziella*, *Gymnomitrium*, *Lepidozia*, *Marchantia*, *Metzgeria*, *Pachyglossa* and *Riccardia* (Greene, 1964*a*, 1964*c*; Longton, 1967).

D. LICHENS

Lichens, which are, as mentioned above, the most successful and widespread of the plant groups occurring in Antarctica, are well fitted to polar habitats by virtue of their ability to colonize completely bare rock surfaces and their remarkably effective physiological adaptation to low temperatures. A number of lichen species, even in a saturated condition, have been found by Lange (1962) to be capable of surviving temperatures as low as $-75°C$ for prolonged periods. In the dry state their resistance to low temperatures is considerably greater. Polar and alpine lichens are therefore, facultatively or obligately, notably psychrophilic, according to the definition of Stokes (1963), who classes under this heading organisms which grow well at 0°C, optimally at temperatures below 20°C, and whose growth is inhibited by temperatures above 25°C. Lange showed that alpine lichens can carry on active assimilation down to $-23°C$, with the optimal temperature in some cases between 0°C and $+ 10°C$. Ahmadjian *et al.*, (1967), working at Hallett Station, found that the highest rate of gas exchange in the lichens studied took place at temperatures between $-1°C$ and $+16°C$, when the light intensity was below its maximum and the thalli were in a saturated condition; higher temperatures and light intensities were found actually to reduce the rate of gas exchange.

About 400 species of lichens have been recorded from Antarctica, about 200 from the Antarctic Peninsula sector and about 200 from the remainder of the continent. This number is, however, undoubtedly excessive, a result of inadequate or inept taxonomic treatments, and will be reduced by critical monographic revision. In the crustose genus *Buellia*, for instance, it has been shown by a study of type specimens and comparative observations on living populations in the field (Lamb, 1968), that many of the previously described taxa are superfluous synonyms.

The commonest and most conspicuous lichen genus in Antarctica is *Usnea* (sect. *Neuropogon*), with four or five species (Lamb, 1964). *U. antarctica* and *U. fasciata*, in the South Orkney and Shetland Islands and on the west side of the Peninsula, often cover the rocks with dense tufts or swards which from a distance may have been mistaken for grass by some casual or untrained observers; *U. sulphurea* gives a blackish colour to the landscape in some places on the east side of the Peninsula (Lamb, 1964, Plate V, Fig. a). The endemic genus *Himantormia* (Lamb, 1964), also belonging to the Usneaceae and related to *Ramalina*, occurs on the Antarctic Peninsula and the South Shetland and South Orkney Islands. Some bipolar species of *Alectoria* (*A. chalybeiformis*, *A. nigricans*) seem to be restricted in their Antarctic distribution to the South Orkney Islands.

Several species of Antarctic crustose lichens, e.g. *Verrucaria elaeoplaca* and *Staurothele gelida*, are markedly hydrophilic, growing in bands along seepage channels and around snow-melt water rock pools where they are seasonally inundated (Lamb, 1948). The melt water in these locations is usually heavily charged with organic matter in solution, derived from bird-excrement, which furnishes an important growth factor for the nitrophilous species. Even after actual inundation has ceased for the season and the lichen zones around pools are exposed to the air several centimetres above the water level, they may continue to receive nutrient substances by ascending capillarity in the rock surface. Scott (1967), in his studies of similar associations in Rhodesia, has shown that the rock surface actually affords separation of the ascending substances after the fashion of a thin-layer chromatogram, with a gradient in compounds having a growth promoting or retarding effect.

Mention should also be made in passing of the existence of several species of the crustose pyrenocarp genus *Verrucaria* in marine habitats in Antarctica. Some of these are bipolar, others endemic, and they occur in zones, characteristic for each species, in the supralittoral (spray zone), the intertidal, and the infralittoral (Lamb, 1948). One of them, *V. serpuloides*, is unique in being restricted to the infralittoral, where it descends to a depth of 10 m, as we found in 1964–5* by diving in the station inlet at the Melchior Islands; the only known marine lichen which passes its entire existence under water.

It is a peculiarity of the Antarctic lichen flora, especially in the Peninsula sector, that it contains endemic fruticulose representatives of some genera which are purely crustose in other parts of the world; examples are *Caloplaca* (*Thamnoma*) *regalis*, *Lecania* (*Thamnolecania*) *Brialmontii*, *Catillaria* (*Hypo-*

* Botanical Survey in West Antarctica, supported by National Science Foundation Grant No. GA–119 and the Argentine Service of Naval Hydrography.

caulon) *corymbosa*, and *Bacidia* (*Thamnopsis*) *stipata* (Lamb, 1954). These are obviously ancient and highly evolved taxa.

The growth of lichen thalli is in general extremely slow, and particularly so in polar and alpine regions (Beschel, 1961). The covering of bare rocks by lichens in Antarctica is obviously a process which takes a very long time, probably of the order of several centuries or even millennia. I have noticed that the lateral moraines of some glaciers on the Antarctic Peninsula, at Hope Bay and adjoining the Crown Prince Gustav Channel, are almost completely destitute of lichens, in spite of the potentially favourable growth conditions which they offer.

E. ALGAE

Approximately 360 species of non-marine algae have been recorded from Antarctica (Greene, *et al.*, 1967), but here, as with the lichens, the actual number is probably lower. The taxonomic revisions necessary to establish the real total will be difficult and time-consuming, as in most freshwater algae developmental studies of living material in culture are necessary. The groups represented belong to the divisions Cyanophyta, Chrysophyta, Xanthophyta, Bacillariophyta (Diatoms), and Chlorophyta, and display a variety of morphological organization including unicellular, colonial, filamentous, and thalloid types. The habitats which they occupy are terrestrial (rocks, detritus, sometimes also artificial solid substrata), aquatic (freshwater lakes, ponds and pools), or, in the case of the so-called cryoplankton, snow or ice. The terrestrial forms belong to the Cyanophyta (*Nostoc, Phormidium, Oscillatoria*, etc.) or the Chlorophyta (*Ulothrix, Prasiola*, etc.). The aquatic representatives are planktonic or attached; planktonic unicellular forms, such as *Chlamydomonas*, sometimes produce seasonal blooms and occur even beneath the ice of some permanently frozen lakes. In such cases, and also in those of the other freshwater lakes which are ice-free for only three or four months in the summer, the available light penetrating to the algae through the snow and ice layers is greatly diminished, to a level at which photosynthesis must be considerably reduced. Under such conditions, oxygen supplies become depleted and almost anaerobic conditions may prevail (Heywood, 1967). The benthic forms consist almost exclusively of blue-green algae, which form felted masses over rocks and stones on the bottom, or float on the surface; they become completely encased in ice during the winter months, but remain viable, although their metabolic activity must be severely curtailed. When the ponds thaw in the spring, the algae may suffer damage by scouring ice action. Damp gravelly areas surrounding lakes and ponds, and periodically inundated by melt water, often support extensive growths of blue-green algae, such as *Phormidium* in the South Orkney Islands (Heywood, 1967), and *Nostoc* on some of the islands off the east side of the Peninsula (personal observation).

Unicellular forms (cryoplankton) which give rise to reddish, yellow or green patches in snow are found only in the coastal areas of Antarctica, where permanent snowfields undergo extensive annual thawing (Follmann, 1964). They belong mainly to the Chlorophyta (*Chlamydomonas, Scotiella, Chodatella* and *Chlorosphaera*, etc.), but Fogg (1967) has found also a Chrysophycean species tentatively assigned to the genus *Ochromonas*. According to Fogg (op. cit.), the growth of these snow algae is, in general, quite slow.

Algae occur also, of course, inside the thalli of lichens, to which they are mostly peculiar, apparently very seldom occurring in the free-living condition. The commonest phycobiont of lichens in Antarctica, as elsewhere, is *Trebouxia*, a genus of the Chlorophyta, Chlorococcales. Ahmadjian (1958), has isolated and cultured the *Trebouxia* symbionts from Antarctic species of *Caloplaca* and *Physcia*; he found that they grew well at temperatures averaging 18°C.

Holm-Hansen (1963) has proved that some species of *Nostoc* occurring in Antarctica are capable of fixing atmospheric nitrogen. In areas where birds are scarce or absent this may represent a significant source of available nitrogen for other types of vegetation.

F. FUNGI

Fungi are few in Antarctica. One Myxomycete, three Ascomycetes, and six Basidiomycetes have been listed by Singer (in Greene *et al.*, 1967), from the west coast of the Peninsula and the South Shetland Islands. Most of them grow among mosses. Some of the Basidiomycetes are of bipolar distribution, others are endemic. These mushrooms belong to the genera *Galerina* and *Omphalina*. *Galerina antarctica* grows on tufts of *Deschampsia*, and *Omphalina antarctica*, growing among mosses on Deception Island, South Shetland Islands, was described by Singer (1957) as the first published record of a native Antarctic fungus. Certain boreal and arctic species of the genus *Omphalina* are symbiotic with green algae* to produce squamulose or glo-bulose lichen-like thalli which were formerly classified as the lichen genera *Coriscium* and *Botrydina* (Poelt and Oberwinkler, 1964). Such symbiotic lichenized basidiomycete forms have not yet been found in Antarctica and careful search should be made for similar structures in moss mats around the fruiting bodies of the Antarctic *Omphalina* species.

Detritus-inhabiting microfungi are, according to the observations of Heal *et al.* (1967) in the South Orkney Islands, representatives of the typical soil forms found in temperate regions. This seems to indicate widespread aerial distribution of spores. Trapping of air-borne spores on exposed sterile plates in the same locality yielded some species not present in the soil microflora. Wicklow (1968), working at Hallett Station, isolated *Aspergillus fumigatus*,

---

* *Coccomyxa* and *Polycoccus*, acc. to Zahlbruckner (1926).

which causes the respiratory disease known as aspergillosis among penguins in captivity, from ornithogenic soil in an Adélie colony and its presence at Hallett Station was considered to be possibly due to contamination by human agencies.

Bacteria have been isolated from lakes on Deception Island, South Shet-land Islands, by Stanley and Rose (1967), and were found in culture to be markedly adapted to low temperatures (psychrophilic). The same has been found with certain yeasts (species of *Candida*) isolated from detritus and snow in Antarctica (Sinclair and Stokes, 1965; Di Menna, 1966).

V. Specific Influence of Some Environmental Factors on Vegetation

A. HUMIDITY

The influence of climate on Antarctic plants is fully reviewed by Greene and Longton (1970: this symposium) and the adaptations of lichens to this climatic region by Ahmadjian (1970: this symposium). In this section, em-phasis will be placed on topics not fully discussed by these authors.

1. *Snow Cover*

A winter snow cover is advantageous to most types of terrestrial vegetation by the protection which it affords against the abrasive action of violent winds laden with ice crystals and dust particles, and by the conservation of more favourable levels of temperature (see Greene and Longton 1970: this sym-posium, for details). Some species, including lichens and bryophytes, are well adapted to deep winter snow cover; the ecology of these so-called chiono-phile organisms has been described in a general way by Du Rietz (1930) and Gjaerevoll (1956). More detailed studies on chionophile lichens have been made by Du Rietz (1931) and Riehmer (1935). The latter showed that in alpine localities of central Europe the formation of reproductive structures (apothecia) was actually favoured by a winter snow cover of five to six months' duration. The writer observed that the crustose lichen *Huea cerussata* (Caloplacaceae) grew abundantly in deep gullies on Goudier Island, off the west coast of the Antarctic Peninsula, where it was buried under up to 3 m of snow in the winter and exposed for less than two months during the summer; the thallus was nevertheless thickly covered with apothecia producing abun-dant spores, and a sample taken at midwinter, by digging down through the snow cover, showed that the symbiotic algae (*Trebouxia*) were bright green and of healthy appearance. Ahmadjian *et al.*, (1967) have shown that reduc-tion of light intensity by a snow cover operates favourably for the photo-synthesis and metabolism of the symbiotic algae in rock lichens under 38 cm of snow at Hallett Station. In the site investigated, which was 4 m from the melting edge of the snow patch, the temperature of the buried rocks was often above freezing, apparently due to lateral conduction of heat from the exposed rocks at the margin.

B. Supply of Organic Nutrients by Birds and Mammals

A pronounced feature of the coastal lichen vegetation, especially in the Peninsula sector, is the nitrophilic character of many of the species, mainly of the crustose type. The fruticose genera, such as *Usnea* (*Neuropogon*), *Himantormia*, *Alectoria*, etc., seem for the most part to be indifferent to organic nutrients, as far as the writer's observations go. Among the most nitrophilous components of the lichen vegetation are the orange-yellow species of *Caloplaca* and *Xanthoria*, which grow on the sides of rocks frequented by gulls and skuas, and on stones near penguin colonies. Certain species of *Buellia*, e.g. *B. augusta* and *Rinodina Petermannii*, also favour similar well-manured habitats. Even more nitrophilous is the green alga *Prasiola*, which thrives in direct contact with bird excrement, and was once observed by the writer on Deception Island, South Shetland Islands, growing in lush profusion over a mass of decaying whale-baleen, which presumably provided a similar source of nitrogenous and phosphatic compounds. The lichenized condition of this alga, called *Mastodia*, is somewhat less markedly nitrophilous (Lamb, 1948).

The ornithocoprophilous terrestrial vegetation of Antarctic coastal regions forms an ecological *facies* strongly resembling that described from the Lofoten Islands in northern Norway by Grønlie (1948) and on the coasts of E. Sweden by Du Rietz (1932), although the component species are mostly different. Some physiological experiments with ornithocoprophilous lichens were made in Finland by Hakulinen (1962). Bird guano in the vicinity of coastal colonies in Antarctica is undoubtedly the most important source of nitrogen for the terrestrial vegetation and also supplies mineral elements derived from the ocean in which the birds feed. Massé (1966) has shown that bird excreta, when freshly deposited, have a nitrogen content amounting to over 7% of the dry weight; subsequently it falls to lower levels due to volatilization as ammonia and washing out by rain or snow-melt water. This downwash is, of course, effective in the distribution of the nutrients, as has been demonstrated by the analyses made by Allen and Northover (1967) of soils in the vicinity of colonies on Signy Island, South Orkney Islands.

VI. Present and Past Geographical Distribution Patterns

The general Antarctic distribution of selected species of lichens, mosses, freshwater algae, flowering plants, and fungi has been mapped in the Antarctic Folio series (Greene *et al.*, 1967) by Rudolph, Greene, Koob, Greene, and Singer respectively. Rudolph, in this study, has tentatively distinguished the following Antarctic distribution patterns in the lichens:

1. Antarctic Peninsula.
2. Coastal (Peninsula to Victoria Land).
3. Coastal (Ross Sea to Princess Martha Coast).
4. Coastal (circumpolar).
5. Interior mountains.
6. Interior mountains + Ross Sea sector.
7. Ubiquitous Antarctic.

Bipolar species (those common to both the Arctic and Antarctic regions) are well represented in most groups, and may actually constitute quite a high percentage of the Antarctic flora, although the computation of the exact figures must await critical taxonomic revision in most groups. Figures compiled from existing reports are mostly quite misleading, as there has been a regrettable tendency to describe new species from the Antarctic regions without sufficient knowledge, or at least without adequate consideration, of the Arctic and boreal taxa. Bartram (1957) has stated that out of twenty-five species of mosses identified by him from the Antarctic Peninsula sector, no less than 15 (60%) were either identical with, or closely related to, Arctic species. The origin of bipolar distribution patterns is a problem of too great a scope to be entered into in any detail here; it has been discussed at length by Du Rietz (1940), who considers that contemporary distribution across the equatorial regions by airborne spores is unlikely; the lichens, for instance, showing distinct distribution patterns analagous to those of higher plants and apparently governed by the same general rules. Stebbins (1950) is also of the opinion that the gradual "stepping-stone" type of long-distance dispersal is the most likely one to account for bipolar distribution. Du Rietz (op. cit.) comes to the conclusion that the transtropical (and, in some instances, trans-Antarctic) migration must have taken place considerably earlier than Pleistocene times, for some of the bipolar elements are rain-forest or only moderately alpine species which could not have withstood extreme glaciation; examples given are the mosses *Sphagnum magellanicum* and *Drepanocladus uncinatus* and the lichens *Thamnolia vermicularis* and *Cetraria islandica*. He suggests that the period during which bipolar and trans-Antarctic migrations took place must date back to the Alpine Orogen in Tertiary times, probably during the Miocene or Pliocene.

This brings us to the consideration of the extent to which the present-day Antarctic biota may have been able to persist on the continent throughout the period of maximal Pleistocene glaciation, and of the evidence for such persistence. The question hinges largely on the presence of endemic Antarctic genera and species, which are represented in most of the lower plant groups (Llano, 1965), and the length of time necessary for their evolution.

The studies of Emiliani (1954) on oxygen isotope ratios in fossil foraminifera led him to the conclusion that the Antarctic continent had become covered with ice approximately one million years ago. Holdgate (1967a) has adduced evidence that Signy Island in the South Orkneys was completely overridden by an ice sheet at the time of maximal glaciation, and that substantial retreat has occurred during the past few thousand years only. The available evidence indicates that the present habitats for terrestrial vegetation have probably been in existence for the past 10,000 years or so (Holdgate, 1967b). Lamb (1949) expressed the opinion that from the genetic standpoint it is impossible to conceive that the present Antarctic endemic species could have evolved in such a relatively short space of time, especially in the case of such slow-breeding (bradytelic) organisms as the lichens. Such considerations have led other authors also (Llano, 1965; Rudolph, 1965) to the conclusion that the endemics most probably survived the maximal glaciation on ice-free coastal refugia or nunataks. In the opinion of Dunbar (1968), the present-day glaciation of Antarctica is probably not very much less extensive than it was at its Pleistocene maximum. Indeed, it has even been suggested (Mortensen, 1952) that the climate of Antarctica may have been warmer during the Pleistocene than it is today. Studies in the European Alps and the Himalayas by Merxmüller and Poelt (1954) and Poelt (1963) also point strongly to the probability of survival of lichens there in ice-free refugia of limited extent during the period of maximal glaciation, and Gelting (1941) claims to have established conclusively the existence of plant refugia in Greenland during the same period.

Conditions prevailing at the present day in the close vicinity of ice fields and glaciers are certainly not so hostile to plant life as has been commonly supposed. The studies of Lindroth (1965) at the edge of the Skaftafell Glacier in Iceland have shown that vegetation of a subarctic character, corresponding to that of the birch zone of Scandinavia, grows up to the edge of the ice, the climatic and biological influence of which upon its immediate surroundings is slight. Dahl (1946) has demonstrated, on the grounds of theoretical geomorphology and glaciology, that where high mountains are situated near the margin of oceans the ice sheet, even during its greatest possible thickness and extent, will not cover them completely, and not only will nunataks remain exposed, but unglaciated areas will occur almost down to sea-level on the side sheltered by the mountain complex from the flow of the ice.

It would be a mistake, however, to assume that all forms of plant life now existing in Antarctica have been there since pre-Pleistocene times. Some of the non-endemic elements are no doubt postglacial immigrants from the Subantarctic zones, brought over by wind or bird dispersal, as Skottsberg

(1954) considered to be the case with the two flowering plants *Deschampsia* and *Colobanthus*.

One of the most pressing and important tasks, as mentioned previously, necessary to the elucidation of past and present phytogeographical relationships is the critical systematic revision of the taxa of the lower land plants of Antarctica, together with field studies in the most closely adjacent Subantarctic areas to determine the exact degree of endemism. In the writer's recent survey (Lamb, 1968) of the species of the crustose lichen genera *Buellia* and *Rinodina* on the Antarctic Peninsula and adjacent islands, some attempt was made to do this. Careful search was made in several coastal localities with somewhat comparable ornithocoprophilous conditions around Ushuaia (Tierra del Fuego) for species which are exceedingly common on the west side of the Antarctic Peninsula and in the South Shetland and Orkney Islands, such as *Buellia russa* (Hue) Darb., but without success, and it was concluded that this observed fact was a rather strong argument against the efficacy of wind-borne dispersal of spores. Strictly controlled transplantation experiments between the Antarctic Peninsula sector and southermost South America would be desirable to demonstrate the possibility or otherwise of colonization if successful transmigration ever took place. The two genera in question (*Buellia* and *Rinodina*) show a very high proportion of Antarctic endemic species; other, not very dissimilar genera, such as *Rhizocarpon*, show little or no Antarctic endemism, and are largely bipolar; this fact is obviously one of great significance, the implications of which yet remain to be fully elucidated.

Another interesting problem, which appears to have hitherto escaped notice, is the historical background of the numerous endemic Antarctic lichen species which are strongly adapted to very nitrogen-rich conditions (ornithocoprophilous). Can this adaptation have arisen in the relatively short space of time subsequent to the maximal glaciation? In our opinion this is unlikely. The only alternative would seem to be the postulation of abundant bird life along the ice-bound coasts of Antarctica throughout the entire Pleistocene period, a hypothesis which, on the face of it, seems almost equally improbable.

Human activities in Antarctica have now increased to such an extent that there is danger of their interfering with the natural biological balance of plant and animal life and it is well that our attention should now be focused acutely on this problem. An interesting illustration of this point is the recent isolation by Wicklow (1968) mentioned above, of the mould *Aspergillus fumigatus* from ornithogenic soil at Hallett Station, East Antarctica, but not in other Adélie penguin colonies sampled. If its presence at Hallett is indeed due to contamination by human agencies, the case should impress us forcibly with the urgent necessity of regulating the introduction of potentially

748

harmful and disruptive organisms into the comparatively defenceless terrestrial biosystem of Antarctica.

References

Ahmadjian, V. (1958). Antarctic Lichen algae. *Carolina Tips* (Publ. Carolina Biological Supply Co., Elon College, N. Carolina), XXI, No. 5, 17–18.

Ahmadjian, V. (1970). Adaptations of Antarctic terrestrial plants. This symposium, 801–11.

Ahmadjian, V., Gannutz, T. P., and Frisham, S. (1967). Photosynthesis and Respiration of Antarctic Lichens. *Antarct. J. U.S.* 2, No. 4, 100–1.

Allen, S. E. and Northover, M. J. (1967). Soil types and nutrients on Signy Island. *In* "A Discussion on the Terrestrial Antarctic Ecosystem" Smith, J. E., ed.), pp 179–85. *Phil. Trans. R. Soc.* B 252, No. 777, 167–392.

Bartram, E. B. (1967). Mosses from the United States Antarctic Service Expedition, 1940–41. *Bryologist*, 40, 139.

Beschel, R. E. (1961). Dating rock surfaces by lichen growth and its application to glaciology and physiography (lichenometry). *In* "Geology of the Arctic," Univ. of Toronto Press. pp. 1044–1062.

Braun-Blanquet, J. (1932). *Plant Sociology, the Study of Plant Communities.* (Translated, revised and edited by G. D. Fuller and H. S. Conrad.) New York and London.

Cooke, W. B. and Fournelle, H. T. (1960). Some soil fungi from an Alaskan tundra area. *Arctic.* B, No. 4, 266–9.

Corte, A. (1961). La primera fanerógama adventicia hallada en el continente antártico. *Contr. Inst. Antártico Argentino*, 62.

Dahl., E. (1946). On different types of unglaciated areas during the Ice Ages and their significance to Phytogeography. *New Phytol.* 45, 225–42.

Di Menna, M. E. (1966). Three new yeasts from Antarctic soils: *Candida nivalis, Candida gelida*, and *Candida frigida* spp. n. *Antonie van Leetwehnoek*, 32, 25–28.

Dunbar, M. J. (1968). "Ecological Development in Polar Regions. A Study in Evolution." Concepts of Modern Biology Series, Prentice-Hall Inc., Englewood Cliffs, N. J.

Du Rietz, G. E. (1930). The fundamental units of biological taxonomy. *Svensk bot. Tidskr.* 24, 333–428.

Du Rietz, G. E. (1931). Studier över vinddriften på snöfält i de skandinaviska fjällen. Ett bidrag till de nordiska fjäll-lavarnas spridningsbiologi. *Bot. Notiser*, 1931, 31–44.

Du Rietz, G. E. (1932). Zur Vegetationsökologie der ostschwedischen Küstenfelsen. *Beih. bot. zbl.* 49, Ergänzungsband, 61–112.

Du Rietz, G. E. (1940). Problems of Bipolar Plant Distribution. *Acta phytogeogr. suec*, 13, 215–82.

Eardley, A. J. (1964). Polar rise and equatorial fall of sea level. *Am. Scient.* 32, 488–97.

Emiliani, C. (1954). Temperatures of Pacific bottom waters and polar superficial waters during the Tertiary. *Science, N.Y.* 119, No. 3103, 853–5.

Fogg, G. E. (1967). Observations on the snow algae of the South Orkney Islands. *In* "A Discussion on the Terrestrial Antarctic Ecosystem" (Smith, J. E. ed.), pp. 279–87. *Phil. Trans. R. Soc.* B 252, No. 777, 167–392.

Follmann, G. (1964). Das Pflanzenleben der Antarktis. *Die Umschau in Wissenschaft und Technik*, Jahrg. 64, 100–3.

Follmann, G. (1965). Una asociación nitrófila de líquenes epipétricos de la Antártica occidental con *Ramalina terebrata* Tayl. et Hook. como especie caracterizante. *Inst. Antárt. Chileno*, Publ. No. 4, 3–18.

Follmann, G. (1967). Vegetationsanalytische Untersuchungen an Flechtengesellschaften zwischen Atacamawüste und Grahamland. *Ber. dt. bot. Ges.* 60, 199–205.

Gelting, P. (1941). Uber pleistozäne Pflanzenrefugien in Grønland. *Mitt. naturf. Ges. Schaffhausen*, 17, 74–96.

Gimingham, C. H. (1967). Quantitative community analysis and bryophyte ecology on Signy Island. *In* "A Discussion on the Terrestrial Antarctic Ecosystem" (Smith, J. E., ed.) pp. 251–9. *Phil. Trans. R. Soc.* B 252, No. 777, 167–392.

Gjaerevoll, O. (1956). The plant communities of the Scandinavian alpine snowbeds. *K. norske Vidensk. Selsk. Skr.* I, 1–405.

Godwin, H. and Switsur, V. R. (1966). Cambridge University natural radio carbon measurements. VIII. *Radiocarbon* 8, 390–400.

Greene, S. W. (1964*a*). Plants of the Land. *In* "Antarctic Research" (Adie, R. J., Priestley, R., and Robin, G. de Q. eds.), London, p. 240–53.

Greene, S. W. (1964*b*). The Vascular Flora of South Georgia. *Br. Antarct. Surv. Sci. Repts.* 45, 1–58.

Greene, S. W. (1964*c*). Problems and progress in Antarctic bryology. *In* "Biologie Antarctique; Antarctic Biology". (Carrick, R., Holdgate, M. and Prévost, J. eds.) Hermann, Paris. pp. 173–9.

Greene, S. W., Longton, R. E. (1970). The effects of climate on Antarctic plants. This symposium, 786–800.

Greene, S. W., Gressitt, J. L., Koob, D., Llano, G. A., Rudolph, E. D., Singer, R., Steere, W. C. and Ugolini, F. C. (1967). Terrestrial Life on Antarctica. Antarctic Map Folio Series, Publ. Amer. Geogr. Soc., Folio 5.

Gronlie, A. M. (1948). The ornithocoprophilous vegetation of the bird-cliffs of Røst in the Lofoten Islands, Northern Norway. *Nyt Mag. Naturvid.* 66, 117–243.

Hakulinen, R. (1962). Okologische Beobachtungen uber die Flechtenflora der Vogelsteine in Süd—und Mittelfinnland. *Arch. Soc. Zool. Bot. Fenn. "Vqanamo"* 17, No. 1, 12–15.

Heal, O. W., Bailey, A. D. and Latter, P. M. (1967). Bacteria, Fungi and Protozoa in Signy Island soils compared with those from a temperate moorland. *In* "A Discussion on the Terrestrial Antarctic Ecosystem" (Smith, J. E., ed.), pp. 191–7. *Phil. Trans. R. Soc.* B 252, No. 777, 167–392.

Heywood, R. B. (1967). The freshwater lakes of Signy Island and the fauna. *In* "A Discussion on the Terrestrial Antarctic Ecosystem (Smith, J. E., ed.), pp. 347–62. *Phil. Trans. R. Soc.* B 252, No. 777, 167–392.

Holdgate, M. W. (1964). Terrestrial ecology in the maritime Antarctic. *In* "Biologie Antarctique: Antarctic Biology" (Carrick, R., Holdgate, M. and Prévost, J. eds.), Hermann, Paris. pp. 181–93.

Holdgate, M. W., (1967*a*). Signy Island. *In* "A Discussion on the Terrestrial Antarctic Ecosystem (Smith, J. E., ed.), pp. 173–7. *Phil. Trans. R. Soc.* B 252, No. 777, 167–392.

Holdgate, M. W. (1967*b*). The Antarctic ecosystem. *In* "A Discussion on the Terrestrial Antarctic Ecosystem" (Smith, J. E. ed.), pp. 363–83. *Phil. Trans. R. Soc.* B 252, No. 777, 167–392.

Holm-Hansen, O. (1963). Algae: nitrogen fixation by Antarctic species. *Science, N.Y.* 139, 1059–60.

Holtom, A. and Greene, S. W. (1967). The growth and reproduction of Antarctic flowering plants. *In* "A Discussion on the Terrestrial Antarctic Ecosystem". (Smith, J. E., ed.), pp. 323–37. *Phil. Trans. R. Soc.* B 252, No. 777, 167–392.

Janetschek, H. (1963). On the terrestrial fauna of the Ross Sea area, Antarctica. *Pacif. Insects* 5, 305–11.

Lamb, I. M. (1948). Antarctic Pyrenocarp Lichens. *"Discovery" Rep.* 25, 1–30.

Lamb, I. M. (1949). La importancia de los líquenes como indicadores fitogeográficos en el Hemisferio Austral. *Lilloa* 20, 65–68.

Lamb, I. M. (1954). Studies in frutescent Lecideaceae (lichenized Discomycetes). *Rhodora* 36, 105–29, 137–53.

Lamb, I. M. (1964). Antarctic Lichens I. The genera *Usnea, Ramalina, Himantormia, Alectoria, Cornicularia. Br. Antarct. Surv. Sci. Repts.* 38, 1–34.

Lamb, I. M. (1968). Antarctic Lichens II. The genera *Buella* and *Rinodina. Br. Antarct. Surv. Sci. Repts.* 61, 1–129.

Lange, O. L. (1962). Die Photosynthese der Flechten bei tiefen Temperaturen und nach Frostperioden. *Ber. bot. Ges.* 55, 351–2.

Lindroth, C. H. (1965). Skaftafell, Iceland; a living glacial refugium. *Oikos, Acta Oecologica Scand.* 6, 142 pp. Copenhagen.

Llano, G. A. (1965). The flora of Antarctica. *In* "Antarctica, A New Zealand Antarctic Society Survey" (Hatherton, T., ed), 331–50. Methuen, London.

Longton, R. E. (1965). Additions to the alien flora of South Georgia. *Br. Antarct. Surv. Bull.* 5, 47–49.

Longton, R. E. (1966). Alien vascular plants on Deception Island, South Shetland Islands. *Br. Antarct. Surv. Bull.* 9, 55–60.

Longton, R. E. (1967). Vegetation in the Maritime Antarctic. *In* "A Discussion on the Terrestrial Antarctic Ecosystem" (Smith, J. E., ed.), pp. 213–35. *Phil. Trans. R. Soc.* B 252, No. 777, 167–392.

Longton, R. E. and Holdgate, M. W. (1967). Temperature relationships of Antarctic vegetation. *In* "A Discussion on the Terrestrial Antarctic Ecosystem" (Smith, J.E., ed.), pp. 237–50. *Phil. Trans. R. Soc.* B 252, No. 777, 167–392.

Masse, L. (1966). Etude comparée des teneurs en azote total des Lichens et de leur substat: les espèces "ornithocoprophiles". *C. r. hebd. Seasc. Acad. Sci. Paris* 262, 1721–4.

Matsuda, T. (1964). Microclimate in the community of mosses near Syowa Base at East Ongul Island, Antarctica. *Antarctic Rec.* 21, 12–24.

Merxmüller, H. and Poelt, J. (1954). Beiträge zur Florengeschichte der Alpen. *Ber. bayer. Bot. Ges.* 30, 91–101.

Mortensen, H. (1952). Heutiger Firnrückgang und Eiszeitklima. *Erdkunde* 6, 145–60.

Phillpot, H. R. (1964). The climate of the Antarctic. *In* "Biologie Antarctique: Antarctic Biology" (Carrick, R., Holdgate, M. and Prévost, J., eds.), Hermann, Paris. pp. 73–80.

Poelt, J. (1963). Flechtenflora und Eiszeit in Europa. *Phyton* 10, 206–15.

Poelt, J. and Oberwinkler, F. (1964). Zur Kenntnis der flechtenbildenden Blätterpilze der Gattung *Omphalina. Öster. Bot. Zeitschr.* 41, 393–401.

Riehmer, E. (1935). Die Flechtenflora des Auersberges im säshsischen Erzgebirge. *Sber. Abh. Naturw. Ges. Isis, Dresd.* Jahrg. 1933–4 (1935), 52–76.

Rubin, M. J. and Weyant, W. S. (1965). Antarctic Meteorology. *In* "Antarctica, A New Zealand Antarctic Society Survey" (Hatherton, T., ed.), pp. 375–401. Methuen, London.

Rudolph, E. D. (1964). Germination and growth of bluegrass seeds near Hallett Station, Antarctica, as related to microclimatic conditions. *Bull. ecol. Soc. Am.* 5, 151, (abstract).

Rudolph, E. D. (1965). Antarctic lichens and vascular plants: their significance. *Bio Science* 15, 285–7.

Rudolph, E. D. (1966a). Terrestrial vegetation of Antarctica: past and present studies. *In* "Antarctic Soils and Soil Forming Processes" (Tedrow, J. C. F., ed.). *Antarct. Res. Ser.* VIII, 109–24. Publ. Amer. Geophys. Union.

Rudolph, E. D. (1966b). Lichen ecology and microclimate studies at Cape Hallett, Antarctica. *In* "Biometeorology II", Proc. Third Internat. Biometeorol. Congress, pp 900–10. Oxford.

Sabbagh, M. E. (1962). A preliminary regional dynamic climatology of the Antarctic continent. *Erdkunde* 16, 94–111.

Scott, G. D. (1967). Studies of the lichen symbiosis: 3. the water relations of lichens on granite kopjes in central Africa. *The Lichenologist* III, pp. 368–85.

Sinclair, N. A. and Stokes, J. L. (1965). Obligately psychrophilic yeast from the polar regions. *Can. J. Microbiol.* 11, 259–69.

Singer, R. (1957). A fungus collected in the Antarctic. *Sydowia*, Beiheft I (Franz Petrak Festschrift), pp. 16–23.

Skottsberg, C. (1954). Antarctic flowering plants. *Bot. Tidsskr.* 2, 330–8.

Skottsberg, C. (1960). Remarks on the plant geography of the southern cold temperate zone. *Proc. R. Soc. Ser.* B 132, 447–57.

Stanley, S. O. and Rose, A. H. (1967). Bacteria and yeasts from lakes on Deception Island. *In* "A Discussion on the Terrestrial Antarctic Ecosystem" (Smith, J. E., ed.), pp. 199–207. *Phil. Trans. R. Soc.* B 252, No. 777, 167–392.

Stebbins, G. Ledyard. (1950). "Variation and Evolution in Plants". Columbia Univ. Press, New York.

Steere, W. C. (1961). A preliminary review of the bryophytes of Antarctica. *In* "Science in Antarctica. Part I. The Life Sciences in Antarctica." Nat. Research Council, Washington, Publ. No. 839, pp. 20–33.

Stokes, J. L. (1963). General biology and nomenclature of psychrophilic microorganisms. *In* "Recent Progress in Microbiology," vol. VIII, pp. 187–92. Univ. of Toronto Press.

Ugolini, F. C. (1965). Ornithogenic soils of Antarctica. *Agronomy Abstracts*, 1965 Annual Meeting, Columbus, Ohio, p. 109.

Weber, W. A. (1962). Environmental modification and the taxonomy of the crustose lichens. *Svensk bot. Tidskr.* 36, 293–333.

Wicklow, D. T. *Aspergillus fumigatus* Fresenius isolated from ornithogenic soil collected at Hallett Station, Antarctica. *Can. J. Microbiol.* 14, 717–19.

Zahlbruckner, Z. (1926). Lichenes (Flechten). *In* "Die Natürlichen Pflanzenfamilien", (Engler, A. and Prantl, K, eds.), 2, VIII, Leipzig.

Bryophyte and Lichen Communities in the Maritime Antarctic

C. H. GIMINGHAM
Department of Botany, University of Aberdeen
and
R. I. LEWIS SMITH
British Antarctic Survey

I. Introduction

During the Swedish South Polar Expedition of 1901–3, Skottsberg (1912) recorded lists of species for a range of habitat types in the South Shetland Islands and a number of islands off the northern region of the Antarctic Peninsula. He recognized several categories of moss and lichen tundra vegetation and provided the earliest comprehensive account of the flora of the maritime Antarctic. However, it was not until about 1960 that straightforward descriptions began to give place to a more analytical and quantitative approach, as shown in the classification of community types prepared by Holdgate (1964). The three intergrading assemblages of bryophytes and lichens which he recognized on Signy Island (*Andreaea-Usnea, Polytrichum-Dicranum* and *Drepanocladus-Acrocladium-Brachythecium* "formations") laid the foundations for further ecological surveys and experimental research. This classification has been considerably extended by Holdgate (unpublished), Longton (1967), Gimingham (1967) and Smith (1968), while a different approach to classification of certain lichen communities has been described by Follmann (1965).

Climatic, topographic and edaphic variations are responsible for a wide range of different habitats and consequently of cryptogamic community types, in the maritime Antarctic. The factors determining the distribution of vegetation as a whole and of individual community types have been described by Holdgate (1964), Longton (1967) and Smith (1968). These and other accounts emphasize that under the severe climatic conditions prevailing, maximum development of vegetational cover is usually consequent upon a degree of shelter, a northerly aspect, adequate water supply in the growing season, direct solar radiation and a stable substratum. Throughout the maritime

Antarctic, vegetation is best developed in habitats with a northerly aspect, to which it may be exclusively confined in the southern parts of the region where oceanic influences decline and conditions become increasingly continental. Here, as pointed out by Longton (1967), the vegetation becomes more sparse and open, with fewer species and community types.

Several long-term studies of certain environmental factors have been undertaken in relation to the vegetation, particularly on Signy Island. Temperature regimes at plant level have been investigated by Holdgate (1964), Longton and Holdgate (1967), Smith (1968), Longton (in preparation), while useful comparisons may be made with similar studies on the Subantarctic island of South Georgia (Longton and Greene, 1967) and on East Ongul Island in eastern continental Antarctica (Matsuda, 1964). The influence of soil types, topography, erosional processes, patterned ground, nutrient availability and seasonal trends, etc., on certain plant communities have been discussed by Chambers (1966), Holdgate et al. (1967), Allen and Northover (1967), Northover and Allen (1967), Northover and Grimshaw (1967) and Allen et al. (1967). The relationship between bryophyte growth-form and moisture supply in the habitat has been stressed by Longton (1967), while experimental studies on the water balance of a number of moss species of different growth-forms from a range of habitats have been described by Gimingham (1967), Smith (1968) and Gimingham and Smith (in press).

II. Classification of Communities

As data accumulate on the composition and structure of Antarctic plant communities, it becomes increasingly important to develop an acceptable framework of reference. This is essential, first, to allow the correlation of results from different studies and surveys and, second, to provide a uniform treatment of vegetation useful to workers in other sciences, e.g. zoology, pedology, micro-climatology.

Two approaches are available in attempting to reduce a complex of vegetational variation to a system of categories. One, which is essentially subjective, involves the selection of certain criteria on which distinctions are to be based (e.g. physiognomy, floristic composition, dominance), and the grouping of stands according to their resemblance in respect of these criteria. The other, which aims to be objective, demands the analysis of a large number of sample stands, arranged so as to eliminate selective bias. Subsequently, stands are classified by statistical techniques. Despite the theoretical advantages of the second approach, the achievement of a sufficient intensity of sampling and the subsequent computation make great demands on time and labour. Hence, only small study areas have been tackled from the latter standpoint (Gimingham, 1967) and more extensive surveys have relied on the former.

This task, of preparing a scheme of vegetation classification applicable throughout an extensive region and acceptable to a variety of workers, is beset with difficulties. Some phytosociologists, following the code of procedure laid down by the school of Braun-Blanquet, prefer to use floristic composition as the sole guide in grouping stands into community types. In the Antarctic, Follmann (1965) has adopted this system in describing certain communities composed mainly of lichens, particularly the *Ramalinetum terebratae* association and its two ecological variants, *Polycaulionetosum regalis* and *Thamno-lecanietosum gerlachei*. This association, he suggests, can be classified along with certain epipetric lichen communities of central Europe, in the hierarchy proposed by Klement (1955). Other workers, less ready to accede to all the principles underlying this scheme, have found that since dominance is well developed in the floristically simple Antarctic communities, it offers a convenient means of distinguishing community types (Holdgate, 1964; Longton, 1967).

Not only is it desirable to avoid too great a diversity of treatment at this level, but there is also a need to investigate the relationships between the community types recognized and to fit them into broader vegetational categories on the basis of physiognomy and community structure (Longton, 1967; Gimingham, 1967; Smith, 1968).

As a contribution to this aim, the vegetation of Signy Island in the South Orkney Islands was investigated in detail during the period 1964–7, following the preliminary survey carried out by M. W. Holdgate between 1961 and 1964 (Holdgate, 1964). In addition to Signy Island, a number of other localities in the South Orkney Islands and from the South Shetland Islands to Neny Island in Marguerite Bay have been studied in some detail. However, the classification of assemblages from the more southerly stations is incomplete and many of the predominantly lichen communities are understudied.

A large number of stands was examined, first by inspection and subsequently by detailed quadrat analysis. Quadrats of 20 cm × 20 cm proved to be quite adequate for the purpose. On the basis of the qualitative and quantitative data obtained on species composition, structure and habitat, the system of vegetational classification proposed in this paper was developed.

III. Formations

Following most systems of vegetational classification, physiognomic criteria are here used as a basis for the broadest categories in the hierarchy. Two Formations (Antarctic Non-vascular Cryptogam Tundra and Antarctic Herb Tundra) are recognized on the basis of a major physiognomic distinction between communities composed largely of non-vascular cryptogams and those constructed around the two angiosperm species. Although Antarctic examples are lacking from the two most recent world-wide systems of vege-tion classification (Ellenberg and Mueller-Dombois, 1966, and Fosberg, 1967), the formations of these authors are parallel in rank with those here pro-posed. In the former scheme, the appropriate broader category embracing both formations would be the Formation Subclass "Moss, lichen and dwarf-shrub tundras".

IV. Subformations

However, the formations still comprise considerable diversity in com-munity structure. In bryophytes and lichens, this diversity is shown by varia-tion in the occurrence and representation of growth-form types, irrespective of floristic composition. Although growth-form is only one of many aspects of the structural and physiological organization of a species which determine its ecological amplitude, it is one which often clearly affects performance in different habitats (Gimingham and Birse, 1957). Hence, where similar envi-ronmental complexes occur, communities of similar structure may be ex-pected, although the species concerned may differ. This reflection of habitat by community structure is valuable in the simple ecosystems of the Antarctic, and advantage is taken of it by the creation of a series of "Subformations" (again in agreement with the procedure of Ellenberg and Mueller-Dombois, 1966, and Fosberg, 1967).

A few of these may be selected for comment, to indicate the relationships between community structure and characteristics of the habitat. As far as the mosses are concerned, a striking feature throughout is the preponderance of dense types of colony (e.g. cushions and turfs). It has been demonstrated that these play a part in restricting evaporation during periods of exposure (Gimingham, 1967; Smith, 1968). Many species are dependent upon a water reserve held externally between the leaves and stems; conservation of this against evaporation may be significant in the more exposed habitats. Hence species possessing a cushion form, most effective in this respect, are pre-dominant, and, along with lichens, are used to designate the "Fruticose lichen and Moss Cushion subformation".

Of entirely different structure, the "Moss Turf subformation" is a peat-forming community of plants producing dense stands of erect shoots usually held together by intertwined rhizoids from a tomentum on their stems. Such stands are again effective in conserving moisture and can readily absorb it from rain or melting snow on the surface. Further, when in summer the peat banks thaw to depths of around 25 cm, the tomentum may act as a wick supply-ing water to the growing apices from a source just above the permafrost.

A third prominent subformation is that of the "Moss Carpets". Although most bryophytes in this category are typically pleurocarpous, some acrocarpous species tend to modify their colony structure under certain environmental conditions and develop a similar growth-form. Such species share a distinctive type of growth-form in which the distal portions of the shoots are parallel and erect or ascending, derived from an intertwined matrix below. This produces a deep carpet, with the pleurocarpous taxa occurring chiefly in swampy habitats where melt water accumulates or along the margins of runnels and pools; the modified acrocarps are more typical of drier volcanic ash. The swamp species have a shoot structure and colony-form which offers little resistance to evaporation and in which there is little internal water conduction. Their growth-form appears to be associated with habitats in which, during the active season, some part of the shoot system is always in contact with water, permitting passage externally along the stem to the growing regions.

The three subformations discussed are the most widespread in the maritime Antarctic; others are associated with more specialized types of habitats.

V. Associations and Sociations

Within subformations, according to phytosociological practice, community types are differentiated on floristic grounds. In the Antarctic the restricted number of species seems to result in most of them displaying wide habitat ranges, as well as some degree of variation in growth-form. Consequently, few if any show high degrees of fidelity to particular communities, although their quantities or constancy may be diagnostic. Hence the method of Poore (1962) was followed to group communities in "Associations", which are based on the general floristic similarity of component stands and differentiated according to the high constancy of a small group of species.

A typical feature of these community types is the uniformity of the assemblages, which show little variation in species composition and habitat requirements. However, the role of dominant in different stands may be played by any one of a series of the chief species of one Association; this has been attributed to minor habitat variations and provides some evidence of succession and continua within these groups of communities. It is catered for by listing "Sociations", based on dominance, within Associations.

The classification of the vegetation of the maritime Antarctic is presented in Table 1.

VI. Outline of Bryophyte and Lichen Subformations and Associations in the Maritime Antarctic

A. FRUTICOSE LICHEN AND MOSS CUSHION SUBFORMATION

This subformation embraces the largest number of community types and the widest range of habitats. Generally speaking, the sociations occupy the

TABLE 1

Classification of the Terrestrial Vegetation of the maritime Antarctic

---

A. ANTARCTIC NON-VASCULAR CRYPTOGAM TUNDRA FORMATION

(i) Fruticose Lichen and Moss Cushion Subformation

   (a) *Andreaea spp.–Usnea spp.* association
     1. *Andreaea spp.*–Lichen sociation
     2. *Andreaea spp.* sociation
     3. *Andreaea spp.*–Foliose hepatic sociation (South Orkney Is.)
     4. *Andreaea spp.*–*Rhacomitrium crispulum* sociation
     5. *Andreaea spp.*–*Dicranoweisia subinclinata* sociation (South Orkney Is.)
     6. *Andreaea spp.*–*Dicranoweisia subinclinata*–*Usnea spp.*–*Omphalodiscus spp.* sociation
     7. *Andreaea spp.*–*Grimmia spp.*–*Usnea spp.*–*Omphalodiscus spp.* sociation (Argentine Is.)
     8. *Andreaea spp.*–*Himantormia lugubris* sociation (South Orkney Is.)
     9. *Usnea spp.*–*Himantormia lugubris* sociation
     10. *Usnea spp.*–*Omphalodiscus spp.*–*Himantormia lugubris* sociation
     11. *Usnea antarctica*–*Omphalodiscus decussatus*–*Alectoria spp.* sociation (Blaiklock and Horseshoe Is.)
     12. *Usnea antarctica* sociation
     13. *Usnea fasciata* sociation
     14. *Usnea sulphurea* sociation (esp. E. coast Antarctic Peninsula)

   (b) Bryophyte and Lichen assemblages of rock micro-habitats
     1. Assemblages in siliceous rock crevices
     2. Assemblages in calcareous and base-rich rock crevices

   (c) *Tortula spp.–Grimmia spp.* association
     1. *Tortula spp.* sociation
     2. *Grimmia spp.* sociation
     3. *Tortula* spp.–*Grimmia* spp. sociation
     4. *Tortula spp.*–*Grimmia spp.*–*Bryum spp.*–*Usnea antarctica* sociation (Deception Is.)
     5. *Tortula conferta*–*Bryum spp.* sociation

   (d) *Pottia austrogeorgica* association

(ii) Crustose Lichen Subformation

   (a) *Caloplaca spp.* association
     1. *Verrucaria spp.* sociation
     2. *Caloplaca spp.* sociation
     3. *Caloplaca elegans* sociation
     4. *Caloplaca elegans*–*Ramalina terebrata* sociation
     5. *Caloplaca regalis* sociation
     6. *Caloplaca spp. Pertusaria spp.* sociation (Signy I).

   (b) *Placopsis contortuplicata* association (esp. South Shetland Is.)

   (c) *Buellia spp.–Lecanora spp.–Lecidea spp.* association

(iii) Moss Turf Subformation

  (a) *Polytrichum alpestre–Dicranum aciphyllum* association

    1. *Polytrichum alpestre* sociation
    2. *Polytrichum aplestre*–Lichen sociation
    3. *Dicranum aciphyllum* sociation (South Orkney Is.)
    4. *Dicranum aciphyllum*–Lichen sociation (South Orkney Is.)
    5. *Polytrichum alpestre–Dicranum aciphyllum* sociation
    6. *Polytrichum alpestre–Dicranum aciphyllum*–Lichen sociation
    7. *Polytrichum–Dicranum* banks heavily colonised by epiphytic lichens

  (b) *Polytrichum alpinum* association

    1. *Polytrichum alpinum* sociation
    2. *Polytrichum alpinum–Drepanocladus uncinatus* sociation
    3. *Polytrichum alpinum–Pohlia nutans* sociation (Candlemas Is.)
    4. *Polytrichum spp.* sociation (excluding South Orkney Is.)

(iv) Encrusted Moss Subformation

  (a) Lichen encrusted *Bryum spp.–Ceratodon spp.– Pohlia nutans* association

    1. *Pohlia nutans–Lepraria spp.* sociation (Candlemas Is.)
    2. *Ceratodon sp.–Lepraria spp.* sociation (Candlemas Is.)
    3. *Bryum spp.–Ceratodon sp.–Cephaloziella sp.–Psoroma sp.* sociation (South Shetland Is.)

(v) Moss Carpet Subformation

  (a) *Brachythecium antarcticum–Calliergon spp.–Drepanocladus uncinatus* association

    1. *Brachythecium antarcticum* sociation
    2. *Calliergon spp.* sociation
    3. *Drepanocladus uncinatus* sociation
    4. *Brachythecium antarcticum–Calliergon spp.* sociation
    5. *Calliergon spp.–Drepanocladus uncinatus* sociation
    6. *Brachythecium antarcticum–Calliergon spp.–Drepanocladus uncinatus* sociation

(vi) Moss Hummock Subformation

  (a) *Bryum algens–Drepanocladus uncinatus* association

    1. *Bryum algens–Drepanocladus uncinatus* sociation
    2. *Bryum algens–Drepanocladus uncinatus–Tortula excelsa* sociation

  (b) *Brachythecium cf. subplicatum* association

(vii) Alga Subformation

  (a) *Prasiola crispa* association
  (b) *Nostoc sp.* association
  (c) Snow algae association

(viii) Miscellaneous Cryptogam Community Types

    (a) *Marchantia berteroana* community

    (b) Short turf communities associated with fumaroles (South Sandwich Is.)

B. ANTARCTIC HERB TUNDRA FORMATION

  (i) Grass and Cushion Chamaephyte Subformation

    (a) *Deschampsia antarctica–Colobanthus quitensis* association
      1. *Deschampsia antarctica* sociation
      2. *Colobanthus quitensis* sociation
      3. *Deschampsia antarctica–Colobanthus quitensis* sociation

---

Note: Names in brackets indicate known localities of sociations with a restricted range

rockier and more exposed situations, such as windswept screes, plateaux, knolls and rock faces, from near sea-level to the highest areas where vegetation exists. The structure of the different associations is similar with respect to the growth-form of the species, i.e. principally short cushion mosses, tall fruticose lichens and a large number of less prominent crustose lichens, while those habitats with pockets of soil frequently have small quantities of various short turf-forming mosses and associated hepatics. Bryophytes usually predominate where soil has become stable and particularly where the substratum holds moisture. Such conditions are to be found in hollows, deposits of glacial detritus and on sheltered, gently sloping hillsides. A number of the community types have specialized habitat requirements; many lichen species predominate in exceptionally exposed situations which are rarely protected by snow in winter, while the sociations of the *Tortula–Grimmia* association are restricted to basic rocks and soils.

1. Andreaea *spp.* -Usnea *spp. association*

The sociations which comprise this association are physiognomically similar, often differing only in the varying predominance of members of a small group of species common to each community type, particularly species of *Andreaea* and *Usnea*. This is the most common and widespread association in the maritime Antarctic, since the habitats occupied cover the greater part of the snow-free ground, especially at higher altitudes. However, it is not represented on base-rich substrata and most sociations also tend to avoid volcanic rocks and soils.

A number of the principal sociations are dominated by species of *Andreaea*, and occupy the more sheltered and moister habitats, where the cushions may coalesce to form a closed, almost turf-like mat or carpet. The remainder of the communities are dominated by species of *Usnea* and, in northern regions, by

Himantormia lugubris in the more exposed, arid situations, rock faces, boulder fields and screes are commonly colonized by these lichens, together with species of *Alectoria* and *Omphalodiscus*, numerous crustose and occasional foliose species, scattered cushions of *Andreaea, Dicranoweisia, Grimmia* and *Rhacomitrium*, and a variety of hepatics. The bryophytes are typical of sheltered faces moistened by trickling melt water, where they locally form mixed stands giving complete cover.

In the more arid, southerly regions, bryophytes become rare and the number of species diminishes rapidly south of the Antarctic circle. *Himantormia* and several other lichens, common farther north, are absent, while species of *Alectoria, Omphalodiscus* and *Usnea* which are infrequent or unknown in the north, become increasingly important as the maritime Antarctic merges with continental Antarctica.

2. *Bryophyte and lichen assemblages of rock micro-habitats*

The micro-habitats of crevices, fissures, overhangs and narrow ledges possess a varied flora, which at low altitudes may be exceedingly rich in species, particularly in the more northerly regions of the maritime Antarctic. Depending upon the nature of these micro-habitats, most bryophyte species are to be found in varying abundance, while some occur almost exclusively in the damp and shaded crevices.

It is impossible to divide these assemblages into distinct sociations because of the large variation within the habitats and the consequent diversity and heterogeneity of the vegetation. However, two widely differing groups, one comprising calcifuge and the other calcicole species, may be recognized according to the type of rock being colonized. The assemblage occupying micro-habitats in siliceous rock bears a close resemblance to certain sociations within the *Andreaea-Usnea* association, while those species found in similar situations in calcareous and volcanic rock represent a depauperate type of *Tortula-Grimmia* community.

3. Tortula *spp.* -Grimmia *spp. association*

This association is structurally similar to the *Andreaea-Usnea* association but is confined to base-rich soils derived from outcrops and knolls of marble, amphibolite and less commonly of volcanic scoria. Such soils have a pH ranging from 7·0 to 8·5, occasionally exceeding 9·0, although those containing the highest concentrations of mineral ions tend to be devoid of vegetation. The communities are rich in bryophytes; cushions of *Bryum spp., Grimmia spp., Tortula spp.*, and numerous short acrocarpous calcicoles provide most of the cover. These, together with several foliose lichens and a few hepatics, produce some of the most complex stands of vegetation in the Antarctic. In *Tortula-Grimmia* communities on Signy Island, more than twenty species have been recorded in an area of only 10 cm × 10 cm. Fruticose lichens appear to be rare, except on isolated non-calcareous stones.

Volcanic rocks on certain of the South Shetland Islands bear communities containing species of *Bryum*, *Grimmia* and *Tortula*, usually accompanied by *Usnea antarctica*. On coastal rock ledges used as bird perches, or where gulls (*Larus dominicanus*) nest or deposit large quantities of limpet shells (*Patinigera polaris*), particularly in the more southerly regions, this association is represented by small stands of *Bryum spp.*, *Tortula conferta* and occasionally *T. grossiretis*.

4. Pottia austrogeorgica *association*

In low-lying coastal areas where the ground is locally unstable due to frost heaving and solifluction, or disturbed by itinerant and wallowing elephant seals (*Mirounga leonina*), temporary colonization by various short acrocarpous mosses may take place. However, small cushions of *Pottia austrogeorgica*, one of the most prolifically fruiting mosses in the maritime Antarctic, may form small, permanent stands affording up to 25% cover. Few other species contribute much cover, although *Ceratodon cf. grossiretis* and *Marchantia berteroana* may be frequent associates, while the presence of several other mildly calcicolous species suggests a close affinity to the *Tortula–Grimmia* association.

B. CRUSTOSE LICHEN SUBFORMATION

Several lichen communities, mainly on rock surfaces, have been recognized in which bryophytes are totally lacking or at the most very sparsely distributed. Communities in which *Usnea spp.*, *Omphalodiscus spp.*, *Himantormia lugubris* and various crustose lichens predominate, have been included in the Fruticose Lichen and Moss Cushion subformation because of the local occurrence of small cushion mosses, especially of *Andreaea* and *Dicranoweisia*.

In the maritime Antarctic the communities within this subformation appear to be largely restricted to coastal rocks, indicating tolerance or requirement of high concentrations of marine salts as well as nitrogen and phosphate from bird dunging. The species are principally crustose in habit and several genera are well represented, in particular *Acarospora*, *Biatorella*, *Buellia*, *Caloplaca*, *Lecanora*, *Lecidea*, *Rinodina* and *Verrucaria*, while the folio crustose *Caloplaca elegans* and frutico-crustose *Caloplaca regalis* may also be plentiful. A few fruticose lichens are locally frequent, e.g. *Mastodia tesselata*, *Ramalina terebrata* and *Usnea antarctica*. Foliose genera are represented chiefly by species of *Parmelia* and *Physcia*. However, in inland montane areas of oceanic and continental Antarctica, the flora consists predominantly of crustose lichens, particularly of the genera *Buellia*, *Lecanora*, *Lecidea* and *Rhizocarpon*. In these stiuations, the richest plant cover occurs in the vicinity of bird colonies and trickles of melt water (Siple, 1938; Perkins, 1945). Too few data are available to the authors to recognize and classify communities of this second category.

1. Caloplaca *spp. association*

This association is characteristic of most coastal rocks and seldom extends far inland, although *Caloplaca* communities are known in the Tottanfjella, some 300 km from the sea (Longton, 1967). The species lists for most of the sociations are similar, with various species prominent throughout but with a different lichen attaining dominance in each case. Communities dominated by species of *Verrucaria*, *Caloplaca*, *Ramalina terebrata* and to a lesser extent *Haematomma sp.*, *Catillaria corymbosa* and *Mastodia tesselata* commonly form distinct zones in relation to the height above the high-water mark (see p. 772). In some northern coastal areas, the blackish cushion moss *Orthotrichum crassifolium* may be locally present in *Caloplaca* dominated sociations.

Communities of ornithocoprophilous taxa (*Biatorella*, *Haematomma*, *Caloplaca regalis*, *C. elegans* etc.), are best developed below nesting ledges and on rocks used as bird perches, forming elongated, colourful strips of vegetation on the rock-faces.

2. Placopsis contoruplicata *association*

Pinkish thalli of *Placopsis contortuplicata* occasionally form small, open stands on stones and gravel on gently sloping stone 'rivers' and the margins of stone stripes in exposed situations. In these habitats the central colony of the lichen is often disrupted by solifluction, dispersing the thalli downhill in a radiating pattern. This creates a very open stand of dispersed individual thalli covering a square metre or more. On dry, sheltered faces of metamorphic and volcanic rocks, *P. contortuplicata* forms large, almost circular colonies which may merge with each other. The associated species are chiefly crustose lichens of the genera *Buellia*, *Lecanora* and *Lecidea*, with *Rhizocarpon* occasionally present on non-volcanic rock.

3. Buellia *spp.*-Lecanora *spp.*-Lecidea *spp. association*

Small stands of grey and white species of *Buellia*, *Lecanora* and *Lecidea* frequently occur above or sometimes amongst sociations of the *Caloplaca* association of coastal rocks. In some instances these lichens constitute a fairly well defined zone comprising numerous circular colonies of thalli, but in general *Caloplaca spp.* are not associated.

Species of these genera, together with other crustose lichens (species of *Ochrolechia*, *Pertusaria*, *Rhizocarpon*, *Rinodina*, etc.), commonly form an understorey in certain lichen-dominated communities of the Fruticose Lichen and Moss Cushion sub formation, and hence may represent an intergraduation with these sociations.

C. Moss Turf Subformation

The taxa which constitute this subformation have an erect growth-form which typically builds up deposits of peat formed from the accumulation of dead shoots. In stands dominated by *Dicranum aciphyllum* and *Polytrichum alpestre* the tall, densely packed shoots are held tightly together by rhizoids. Continued vertical growth year after year results in peat banks of over a metre in depth. However, other *Polytrichum* species are generally of a shorter habit, but retain the turf growth-form typical of the genus. They, and other turf-forming mosses, e.g. *Campylopus introflexus* and *Psilopilum antarcticum* in the South Sandwich Islands build peat only a few centimetres deep.

The associations are usually restricted to well-drained slopes or gravelly, porous ground, although once a peat is developed a permanent reservoir of water is maintained and, in the case of the deeper peat banks, a perma-frost layer forms about 20–30 cm below the surface.

1. Polytrichum alpestre-Dicranum aciphyllum *association*

The banks formed by *P. alpestre* and *D. aciphyllum* constitute one of the most prominent floristic features of the South Orkney Islands and certain other localities as far south as the Argentine Islands, with less extensive, shallower banks being reported from islands in the north of Marguerite Bay (Bertram, 1938; Bryant, 1945; Longton, 1967). Mixed or pure stands of these mosses are best developed on steep, boulder-strewn, north-facing slopes and also gently sloping or level ground. The altitudinal range is from near sea-level to about 165 m, with small patches to about 250 m. On well-drained, north-facing slopes overlying a stony substratum, *Polytrichum* is usually dominant, producing a hard compact peat, up to a metre deep. In some of the more southerly localities, *Dicranum* may be absent as an associate and the banks often become stepped and heavily encrusted with lichens.

As the gradient lessens and the substratum becomes moister, *Dicranum* tends to assume dominance and some deep banks may have no *Polytrichum*. In the South Orkney Islands, these mosses locally form isolated, dome-shaped banks with vertical, eroding faces of 1–2 m in height. Such banks are permanently frozen below about 25 cm. The surface of most peat banks is colonized, particularly on their most exposed parts, by a wide variety of epiphytic crustose and fruticose lichens. An extremely slender form of *Cephaloziella varians* is almost always present among the stems of *Dicranum* or forms small dark mats on the surface of the *Polytrichum*. The successive stages in the development and degeneration of these peat banks is outlined on p. 773.

2. Polytrichum alpinum *association*

Polytrichum alpestre-Dicranum aciphyllum banks are largely replaced in some areas, particularly on volcanic substrata, by stands of *Polytrichum alpinum*. Some of the largest occur on Deception Island, where coalesced mounds up to 30 cm deep, form almost pure closed turf, while smaller mounds of *P. alpinum* have been reported from Candlemas Island, with *Pohlia nutans* as a frequent associate (Longton, 1967). On both these islands a different type of community occurs on level or gently sloping volcanic ash, where *Polytrichum alpinum*, *P. juniperinum*, *P. piliferum* and rarely *Psilopilum antarcticum* form almost pure, short, more or less open, turfs. On Robert Island, South Shetland Islands, mixed, closed stands of *P. alpinum*, *P. piliferum*, *Drepanocladus uncinatus* and various lichens develop a peat of up to 30 cm deep on moist ash slopes.

On non-volcanic substrata, stands of *P. alpinum*, usually in association with *Drepanocladus uncinatus*, are developed near sea-level on sheltered, damp slopes commonly influenced by colonies of seabirds or near seal wallows. On certain islands off the north-west coast of the Antarctic Peninsula, *P. juniperinum* or *P. piliferum* may occasionally be associated with *P. alpinum*.

D. MOSS CARPET SUBFORMATION

The most extensive closed bryophyte communities in the maritime Antarctic occur in wet areas in depressions and around freshwater melt pools and melt streams in lowland coastal regions. These large stands are composed of carpet-forming pleurocarpous mosses of the genera *Brachythecium*, *Calliergon* and *Drepanocladus*. Both *C. sarmentosum* and *D. uncinatus* posses a wide range of growth forms which are probably correlated with their wide ecological amplitude. Similarly, *Pohlia nutans*, which is more typically a short cushion or turf-forming species, occasionally develops a mat or carpet growth-form according to the habitat occupied. A feature of these wet habitat communities is the scarcity of associated species and almost total absence of lichens. Scattered stems of *Cephaloziella* are commonly present among the mosses, however, and the hepatic occasionally forms small mats on the surface of the carpet.

1. Brachythecium antarcticum-Calliergon *spp*.-Drepanocladus uncinatus *association*

Although some small stands of *C. sarmentosum* and *D. uncinatus* occur to over 250 m in the South Orkney Islands, all the extensive communities of this association are restricted to coastal areas with a permanent supply of water. *Calliergon spp.* and *B. antarcticum* become increasingly rare as the environment becomes drier, as in more southerly latitudes and on porous volcanic ash soils. The distribution of these principal species is fairly closely related to the wetness of the habitat, and the communities may be arranged in a simple zonation (see p. 772). Any combination of the four chief mosses may occur, while local pure stands of each are equally common. An interesting development of pure *Drepanocladus* stands occurs at Coppermine Cove, Robert Island. Here, the moss has locally built up peat banks to a depth of up to 85 cm on steep, moist slopes. The lack of associated species may be attributed to the permanently wet nature of the habitat, which in winter is generally covered by thick ice for up to eight months.

E. Moss Hummock Subformation

Moist or permanently wet habitats influenced by basic rocks and soils support several bryophyte species of a large cushion growth-form, giving a hummocky appearance to the community. On Signy Island, for example, such situations occur below marble outcrops or on soils with a fairly high base status, on wet rock surfaces and along the margins of swiftly flowing runnels. The growth-forms of the principal species vary from the tall, compact cushion (*Bryum spp.*), and tall, loose cushion (*Brachythecium cf. subplicatum*, *Tortula excelsa*), to the deep, undulating carpet (*Drepanocladus uncinatus*).

1. Bryum spp.-Drepanocladus *spp. association*

In low-lying areas, species of *Bryum*, *Drepanocladus* and *Tortula* form stands of deep, coalesced hummocks, but these are seldom extensive. In more southerly localities, *T. excelsa* is absent, and communities of *B. algens* and *D. uncinatus* form one of the most widespread bryophyte-dominated assemblages. On Neny Island, at approximately 68°S, *Bryum* and *Drepanocladus* form stands of up to 10 sq. m in area. Like other wet habitat communities, lichens are scarce, with a mildly calcicolous species of *Leptogium* being the most prominent associate, at least in northern areas.

2. Brachythecium cf. subplicatum *association*

Where enriched melt water trickles over rock faces, or along the margins of fast-moving runnels where there is some degree of flushing *Brachythecium cf. subplicatum* typically forms golden-green, coalesced hummocks. Although this moss sometimes forms pure stands, other hummock-forming species are usually associated, such as *Bryum*, *Tortula* and *Drepanocladus*. Moist rock ledges, especially those used as bird nesting sites, also commonly support large cushions of *Brachythecium*.

F. Encrusted Moss Subformation

Longton (1967) describes this subformation as comprising "a thin crust of small turf and cushion-forming mosses, largely moribund, and so heavily colonized by crustose lichens that the vegetation as a whole assumes the colour of the most abundant lichen". Although largely restricted to the plains and gentle slopes of volcanic ash at low altitudes in the South Shetland and South Sandwich Islands, small stands of similar assemblages occur in damp coastal areas in the South Orkney Islands.

The heavily encrusted surface of many *Polytrichum-Dicranum* banks has not been included in this subformation as these are considered merely as a stage in a simple succession (see p. 773).

1. *Lichen encrusted* Bryum *spp.*-Ceratodon *spp.*-Pohlia nutans *association*

On Candlemas Island, Longton (1967), reports that *Pohlia nutans* is the principal bryophyte component of this association, while species of *Polytrichum*, *Ceratodon* and *Bryum argenteum* may also be present. These mosses are heavily encrusted by lichens, with a greenish-white species of *Lepraria* giving up to 80% cover.

On Deception, Robert and King George Islands, in the South Shetland Islands, the association is represented by basically similar communities, although the typically elongated cushions of species of *Bryum* and *Ceratodon* are impregnated with ash and hollow in the centre (Longton, 1967). Associated bryophytes may include species of *Brachythecium* and *Tortula*, *Drepanocladus uncinatus*, *Polytrichum alpinum* and *Cephaloziella varians*. A reddish-brown species of *Psoroma* and various crustose lichens are often abundant epiphytes on the surface of the short bryophytes.

In the South Orkney Islands a diminutive assemblage resembling this association occurs in or adjacent to *Polytrichum alpinum-Drepanocladus uncinatus* communities. These two species, together with *Ceratodon*, *Pohlia* and *Cephaloziella* are frequently encrusted with white, grey and yellowish sterile crustose lichens, *Psoroma cf. hypnorum* and grey and yellow fruticocrustose species of *Cladonia*. The dead central areas of circular colonies of *Polytrichum alpinum* are typically colonized by these lichens.

G. MISCELLANEOUS BRYOPHYTE AND LICHEN COMMUNITY TYPES

The majority of the bryophyte-lichen communities occurring in the maritime Antarctic can be conveniently fitted into sociations belonging to one of the subformations described above. However, there are occasional assemblages which are extremely local in distribution, small in area or comprise a variety of species of different growth-forms. Certain bryophytes and lichens may form small, pure or mixed stands, but as the species concerned are normally subordinate associates in other community types, these minor stands may be considered as variants of communities already described. On the other hand, those assemblages which differ physiognomically from the subformations so far recognized, have for the present been accommodated under the heading of "Miscellaneous Community Types".

1. Marchantia berteroana *community*

Small mats formed by this thallose hepatic have been reported from Signy Island and around fumaroles on the South Sandwich Islands (Longton, 1967). In the latter locality *Marchantia* occasionally forms one of the outer zones of the fumarole vegetation typical of these volcanic islands, colonising both bare ash and the surface of other plants. On Signy Island, however, the scattered associated bryophytes suggest that this is probably an extreme variant of one of the *Tortula-Grimmia* sociations in which *Marchantia* is regularly present in small quantities.

2. *Short turf communities associated with fumaroles*

On certain of the South Sandwich Islands, there exists a unique type of habitat which supports plant communities not seen elsewhere in the Antarctic. Such communities occur around fumarole vents and are particularly characteristic of the vegetation of Candlemas Island (Longton, 1967). The zoned distribution of these communities around the vents is related to gradients in soil temperature and moisture maintained by fumarolic activity, and several of the species occur exclusively in this environment. A full account of these communities is being prepared by M. W. Holdgate and R. E. Longton. Although some of these communities structurally resemble other community types already described, they have been treated separately on account of the unusual environment and the consequent modification of the growth-form of several of the principal species.

The cruptogamic assemblages associated with fumaroles have not yet been classified according to the present system, but most may be considered as modified short turf communities. Different stands form various intermediates between turfs and carpets (Longton, *personal communication*). The predominant bryophytes are *Campylopus introflexus*, *Pohlia nutans*, *Polytrichum spp.*, a dicranoid moss and several species of hepatics, including *Cephaloziella varians*, *Lophozia propagulifera* and *Jamesoniella grandiflora*. A gelatinous species of *Mesotaenium*, and occasional other algae and crustose lichens may be regular associates. The vegetation is up to 10 cm tall comprising living shoots overlying more or less undecayed peat.

On Candlemas Island, many fumarole vents are occupied by shallow mats of *Cephaloziella sp.* and a slender form of *Pohlia nutans*, together with an abundance of *Mesotaenium* and other gelatinous algae. These communities are seldom extensive, but they are none the less a very distinctive feature.

The main stands of vegetation around the vents comprise a series of three intergrading communities dominated by *Pohlia nutans*, *Jamesoniella grandiflora* or by the two as co-dominants.

In certain non-volcanic localities, notably Avian Island in Marguerite Bay, small stands of *Pohlia nutans* with a short turf growth-form occur in moist depressions, usually in association with *Drepanocladus uncinatus*.

A group of communities comprising more typical turf-forming species sometimes occurs around fumaroles. These include mixed or pure stands of species of *Polytrichum*, *Psilopilum antarcticum*, *Campylopus introflexus* and one or more species of dicranoid moss. *Campylopus*, which is unknown elsewhere in the Antarctic, forms turfs up to 10 cm deep and affords 30–100% cover around vents among lava boulders. *Pohlia* and several hepatics are occasional associates.

VII. Vegetation Patterns

The pattern of dispersion of plants in bryophyte-lichen communities is often striking and may be more easily accounted for than in complex stands of flowering plants. Because of their short habit and lack of underground stem systems (except in *Polytrichaceae*), the causal factors of the patterns seen in the maritime Antarctic are environmental rather than morphological. Several workers have described similar community distributions and pattern systems in predominantly cryptogamic vegetation in northern tundra regions (Watson, 1925; Burges, 1951; Wilson, 1952; Mårtesson, 1956; Sheard, 1968).

Within the more extensively vegetated areas, minor variations in the environment (e.g. exposure, degree of snow accumulation, availability of moisture, soil pH and base status, aspect, stability and texture of the substratum, etc.), produce distinct differences in the vegetation. This results in a small-scale, colourful mosaic of different community types, many only a few metres square. Most assemblages are extremely homogeneous within themselves and uniform with regard to species composition and abundance within each community type. The pattern produced by micro-environmental gradients is usually relatively simple and takes the form of a series of intergrading sociations. The transition from one community type to another along an environmental gradient is often particularly clear. Occasionally this change is gradual, with a decrease in abundance of one dominant species and increase of another; generally, however, it is rather abrupt so that the two adjacent sociations are separated only by a narrow heterogeneous belt containing species characteristic of both. Because of the similarity in species composition between groups of sociations, and less commonly between associations or even subformations, there is evidence of several simple, small-scale continua of variation. In some instances, notably communities of coastal rocks and swamps, the pattern takes the form of a distinct zonation of floristically similar sociations with different dominants. As with other aspects of pattern, this is related to minor variations in one or more environmental factors, providing further evidence of a continuum of variation.

The patterns found within the principal associations and their causal factors will be reported more fully elsewhere, but a few examples may be outlined here.

A. PATTERNS RESULTING FROM ENVIRONMENTAL HETEROGENIETY

One of the most common forms of pattern is seen in the *Andreaea-Usnea* association in dry, stony, windswept situations. Although the vegetation in such areas may be continuous, but open, a number of distinct sociations may be represented according to the microtopography and consequent degree of exposure, soil accumulation and moisture. Thus, the most exposed rock crests may be dominated by *Himantormia lugubris*, giving way to *Usnea antarctica* and *U. fasciata* below this level or on boulder fields; *U. antarctica* predominates on windswept gravel-covered cols and wind gaps, while *Andreaea spp.* and occasional associated bryophytes and lichens occupy the more sheltered, soil-filled depressions and level, stony ground. Measurements of snow depths in winter, or after summer falls, provide an indication of the degree of exposure to which each community type is subjected (Fig. 1.). The most windswept sociations may receive no protection against low winter temperatures and desiccation, or at the most have a thin coating of ice over the surface of the plants, whereas wherever some shelter is afforded, a metre or more of snow may accumulate and remain until summer. The moisture content of these habitats is also correlated with the duration of snow lie, as well as with the porosity of the substratum and depth of fine soil. A similar series of intergrading communities, but with fewer lichens, occurs within the *Tortula-Grimmia* association on base-rich soils, and as with the previous association the continuity of the vegetation is frequently disrupted by frost heaves and solifluction.

Cryoturbic action creates small patterns in various communities of the Fruticose Lichen and Moss Cushion subformation. Polygons, frost boils, clay puddles, stone stripes, etc. are dynamic phenomena and their superficial instability rarely permits any colonization by plants. Generally the larger stones are sorted to the periphery with finer material grading towards the centre, although smaller stones may be arranged in the form of small polygons throughout the fine clay, while in some cases there may be no obvious sorting at all (Chambers, 1966, 1967). On level ground, the pattern of vegetation may be regular with the unstable soil being devoid of plants, a band of *Usnea spp.* on the slightly raised fringe of peripheral stones, species of *Usnea* and *Himantormia* on scattered boulders, and *Andreaea spp.* with occasional other mosses, hepatics and fruticose lichens on the fine, but relatively stable, debris and pockets of soil between the frost heaves. A similar pattern system occurs in areas of solifluction where stone stripes and mobile clay "streams" are often frequent. According to the degree of stability, the margins of these areas may support a large number of bryophytes and crustose lichens, forming long, heterogeneous stands, often only 10–20 cm wide. Various cushion

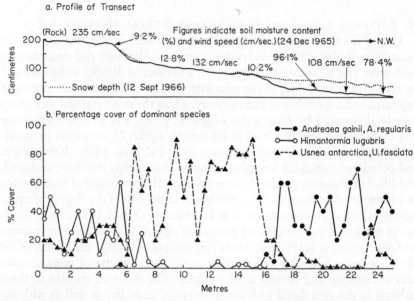

FIG. 1 Distribution of dominant species in relation to microtopography and consequent exposure, as indicated by wind-speed and snow-depth measurements, and soil moisture content. The 25 m transect traverses three sociations (*Usnea–Himantormia, Usnea antarctica, Andreaea*) of the *Andreaea–Usnea* association, and the percentage cover of species was recorded in 20 cm × 20 cm quadrats at intervals of 0·5 m. The erratic distribution of the plants is due to the open nature of the stands. Site: Between Observation Bluff and Rusty Bluff, Signy Island, South Orkney Islands. Altitude: *c.* 100 m; aspect: 315°.

mosses, prostrate forms of carpet species and numerous foliose hepatics are typical of the damp, stabilized marginal ramp of soil and gravel at the edge of the stripes. Fruticose lichens and occasional cushions of *Andreaea, Dicrano-weisia* and other mosses colonize the larger stones.

Marked differences in the vegetation exist where soils of different origins are juxtaposed. On Signy Island, soils derived from local outcrops of marble or amphibolite support communities of the *Tortula-Grimmia* association. There is generally a sharp transition from these soil types to others with a considerably lower base status, usually overlying quartz-mica-schist, and colonized by sociations of the *Andreaea-Usnea* association (Fig. 2). A difference of four pH units has been recorded over a distance of less than half a metre on either side of such a boundary. Small, isolated marble erratics sometimes occur at considerable distances from the parent outcrops. Although the natural vegetation of the area is largely dominated by species of *Andreaea* or *Usnea*, several calcicolous bryophytes and lichens may be found on the alien boulder or weathered debris immediately around it. Alternatively, schist pebbles are quite frequently scattered amongst marble-derived soil and support occasional calcifuge species in an otherwise calcicole community.

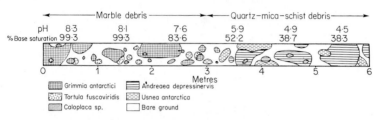

FIG. 2. Distribution of principal calcicole species (*Grimmia, Tortula, Caloplaca*) and calcifuge species (*Andreaea, Usnea*) along a belt transect (6 m × 0·4 m) crossing the boundary between marble and quartz-mica-schist debris (see Plate 9). The abrupt change occurs midway along the transect. Site: Gourlay Peninsula, Signy Island, South Orkney Islands. Altitude: *c*. 40 m; level ground.

Sudden changes in the flora in relation to increased base status are seen where melt runnels traverse base-rich rock types. Such areas characteristically support tall hummocks of *Bryum algens, Brachythecium* cf. *subplicatum* and *Tortula excelsa*, while beyond the flushed zone, carpets of *Brachythecium antarcticum, Calliergon* spp. and *Drepanocladus uncinatus* predominate in various combinations and proportions.

The distribution of certain lichen communities in which ornithocoprophilous species are abundant has been described by Follmann (1965). Such communities are clearly related to rocks subjected to the influence of birds, and often occur below ledges used as perches and nesting sites, forming dark or colourful streaks on the rock faces. Many plants occupying coastal rock habitats must tolerate high concentrations of marine salts as well as nitrogen and phosphorus. Follmann describes one of these communities, in which *Ramalina terebrata* is the principal species, as being "halophytic, phototolerant, subneutrophilic, ornithocoprophilic and hygrophilic". In penguin colonies and elephant seal wallows, where the effects of trampling and excavating are added to those of extremely high concentrations of marine and organic salts, often the only macroscopic plant capable of colonising the mud is the thallose alga *Prasiola crispa*.

B. ZONATIONS

The principal species of swamp habitats appear to have slightly different preferences with regard to wetness of substratum and may be distributed in a simple zonation. *Brachythecium antarcticum* usually predominates in the wettest situations or along the courses of slow-moving melt streams, although *B. cf. subplicatum* may replace it where the runnels are stonier and swifter. The *Brachythecium* intergrades with a zone dominated by a species of *Calliergon* which in turn gives place to stands of *C. sarmentosum* or *Drepanocladus uncinatus* at the margins of the swamp. However, mixed stands comprising any combination of these species are frequently encountered.

On certain volcanic islands in the South Shetland Islands, the dry, porous and unstable nature of the ash slopes and knolls, although limited in vegetation cover, may support a simple series of communities. The level, relatively stable ground at the base of slopes, where moisture collects as a result of run- -off and snow accumulation, supports locally extensive stands of *Drepanocladus* with other damp habitat species associated. Immediately above this, towards the foot of the slope, *Polytrichum alpinum* and sometimes other species of *Polytrichum* typically form a narrow belt, while the dry, loose ash over the rest of the slopes is generally barren. However, outcrops of crumbling volcanic rock, particularly on the knoll crests, may be colonized by *Usnea antarctica* and more calcicolous taxa such as *Grimmia* and *Tortula*.

In the South Sandwich Islands there occurs a unique type of zonation around the vents of fumaroles (Longton and Holdgate, 1967; Longton, 1967). A number of concentric communities frequently occur around the vents, corresponding to the gradient in temperature, which in turn produces gradients in soil moisture and humidity, as a result of the condensation of water droplets. The pattern of zonation is not constant but typically the area in and around the vent supports an open community dominated by foliose hepatics with *Pohlia nutans* associated, although *Mesotaenium* and other genera of gelatinous algae may be abundant. Outside this zone, on the ash slopes, the usual sequence of zones is as follows: *Pohlia* with hepatics; *Polytrichum alpinum* or other *Polytrichum* species; *Pohlia* encrusted with *Lepraria*; however, the former may be replaced by extensive turfs of *Campylopus introflexus* where the vents are situated among lava boulders.

Some of the best examples of zoned communities are seen on coastal cliffs and rocks. Here a number of sociations in the *Caloplaca* association form distinct bands from the high-water mark, or just below, to over 100 m above sea-level. The distribution of each zone is correlated with the degree of salt deposition by spray and with exposure to rough sea and strong wind. In this series of hygrohaline lichen communities that nearest the high-water mark, if the rock is not too severely scoured by loose pack ice, is dominated by one or several brown and black species of *Verrucaria*. A metre or more above this zone is one dominated by orange species of *Caloplaca*. At higher levels one or more of a number of lichens predominate, e.g. *Haematomma sp.*, *Mastodia tesselata*, *Caloplaca regalis*, *C. elegans*, *Ramalina terebrata*, while at the upper limits of marine influence the increase of *Usnea antarctica* and certain cushion mosses indicates a transition to *Andreaea-Usnea* communities.

C. Patterns Resulting from Dynamic Interactions Between Species

A number of pattern systems occur within the *Polytrichum-Dicranum* association, being largely correlated with exposure. Individual peat banks may frequently exhibit a sequence of floristic phases, commencing with pure *Dicranum aciphyllum* and/or *Polytrichum alpestre* where the bank is afforded most shelter, snow accumulation and moisture. At higher, more exposed levels on the slope, or towards the crest of isolated, dome-shaped peat "islands", epiphytic fruticose lichens and ultimately crustose species give increasing cover over the moss. Once the moss is entirely killed and encrusted, the surface becomes loose and irregularly hummocky. This stage in the simple succession is susceptible to wind and frost erosion, and indeed the most exposed areas may be completely denuded and devoid of living vegetation. In winter these expanses of eroded, puckered peat receive no snow cover, thus exposing the surface to extremely low temperatures and desiccating winds. Recolonization of such areas does not appear to take place, except for occasional regeneration of the original mosses and the establishment of small cushions of other species. On more level banks of pure *Dicranum*, the surface may be moulded into a system of ridges and depressions about 10–15 cm high and 15 cm or more apart, by wind or frost action. These ripple systems lie at right angles to the local prevailing wind. Generally the depressions and windward slopes of the ridges comprise healthy, living *Dicranum*, while the eroded, leeward sides are encrusted by black *Buellia punctata* and the more exposed ridge crests with white *Ochrolechia frigida*. The moist hollows may also possess *Drepanocladus uncinatus*, *Pohlia nutans* and scattered shoots of foliose hepatics.

Shallow peat banks, usually on well-drained, stony ground, often intergrade with adjacent swamp communities or stands of *Andreaea* and associated lichens. Although the boundary of each community type is clearly defined, there is usually some degree of marginal invasion, particularly by small cushion shaped turfs of *Dicranum*, into the neighbouring communities. To a lesser extent *Drepanocladus uncinatus*, *Calliergon sarmentosum* and *Andreaea depressinervis* may encroach into the marginal ramp formed by the mixed *Polytrichum* and *Dicranum* turf. This is one of the few examples of community displacement by the invasion of a species or group of species. In fact, the cryptogamic assemblages of the maritime Antarctic very rarely exhibit

evidence of competition either by individual taxa or by well developed sociations, and there is little or no sign of serious displacement of one community
type by another. It would appear that when a habitat becomes available for
plant colonization, those species which constitute the sociation typical of the
prevailing environmental conditions become established and retain their
status virtually uninfluenced by surrounding communities.

D. Patterns Resulting from Morphological Development of
Species

Patterns arising from the vegetative development of certain species are
restricted to members of the Polytrichaceae, which produce radiating underground stem systems from which aerial shoots arise. Thus, colonies of these
mosses tend to develop circular stands, particularly on fairly dry, porous,
gravelly soils, being most typical of the ash slopes and plains in certain of the
South Sandwich and South Shetland Islands. However, they are not un-
common in other regions, near the shore where there is usually some biotic
influence. On Deception Island, a single, small colony of *Polytrichum alpinum*
with a diameter of 27 cm produced a total of eighty leafy aerial shoots and at
least fifty six immature shoots still below the surface of the ash; all belonged
to one subterranean stem system.

Circles of *Polytrichum alpinum*, and to a lesser extent, *P. juniperinum*, *P.
piliferum* and *Psilopilum antarcticum* sometimes undergo modified cyclical
changes. As the colony expands, the moss in the central, oldest portion becomes brownish and gradually dies. The dead moss turns blackish before
disappearing and leaving the central area bare. By this stage, however, as the
moss becomes moribund, other species begin to colonize the peaty soil
amongst the *Polytrichum* shoots. *Ceratodon cf. grossiretis, Drepanocladus
uncinatus, Pohlia nutans* and *Cephaloziella varians* are frequent associates. As
the stand becomes more open and more soil is revealed, various yellowish,
grey and white sterile crustose lichens recolonize the decaying *Polytrichum*
turf and debris. *P. alpinum* may eventually regenerate in the central area, but
many of the larger, older circles remain static once this part is dead, leaving
only a ring of tall, living moss with shorter, dead or dying moss immediately
inside.

VIII. Discussion

The relative richness and variety of the flora of the maritime Antarctic in
relation to that of continental Antarctica may be attributed to the modified
Antarctic climate. Because of the oceanicity of this region, considerable areas
of low-lying ground may become free of snow in summer, a large number of
habitats are available for cryptogam colonization and water is locally plentiful

during the short growing season. Thus a combination of climatic, edaphic and topographic factors is responsible for the wide range of community types and locally extensive stands of vegetation. However, the paucity of species and life-forms in the Antarctic botanical zone is very pronounced when compared with corresponding latitudes in the Arctic, and this has been the subject of much discussion (Brown, 1906; Siple, 1938; Longton and Holdgate 1967; Greene and Longton, 1970: this symposium). The chief reasons for these differences are that southern polar regions have a short growing season with air temperatures only occasionally above freezing-point, while geographical isolation acts as a barrier to the dispersal of propagules. As Longton and Holdgate (1967) point out, the impoverished Antarctic flora results from biogeographical as well as ecological factors. They stress that "this isolation is intensified by the additional barrier of the west wind belt, whose strong circum-polar airstreams and associated ocean currents must reduce the chance of airborne or waterborne propagules being carried south to the Antarctic. Even if the problems of dispersal are overcome, however, the environmental conditions within Antarctic regions are unfavourable for the establishment of many land plants, due to the low temperatures, the shortage of available water in many areas, and, locally to intense competition from large and densely packed sea-bird colonies".

Dissemination and subsequent establishment of Antarctic cryptogams is largely by vegetative propagules (Steere, 1965). Both Brown (1906) and Cardot (1908) commented on the scarcity of sporophytes in Antarctic mosses. Barely 25% of the mosses are known to produce fruit, whereas in lichens, apothecia are common in many genera. Sexual reproduction in Antarctic hepatics is unknown. Longton and Greene (1967) believe that one of the main reasons for this scarcity is the irregular sex distribution in bryophyte populations, although unfavourable climatic conditions also play an important role. In fact, several species common to both the South Orkney Islands and to the Argentine Islands have been seen in fruit only in the latter locality (Longton, 1966), where there is a higher sunshine record and less strong wind. It is not fully known how viable the moss and lichen spores are and to what extent the spread of fertile species depends upon them. Of the moss genera which fruit most profusely in the maritime Antarctic, i.e. *Andreaea*, *Bryum*, *Dicranoweisia*, *Encalypta*, *Grimmia* and *Pottia*, only *Encalypta* and *Pottia* readily colonize bare ground near the parent plants after the spring thaw.

Thus, in the majority of species dispersal and the ability to take part in community formation in suitable habitats is dependent upon vegetative propagules. These include simple fragments of shoot apices (e.g. *Bryum spp.*, *Dicranum aciphyllum*, *Pohlia nutans*, *Polytrichum spp.*, etc.), leaf apices (*Sarconeurum glaciale*), deciduous buds (*Bryum argenteum*), axillary bulbils

(*Barbula spp.*,), leaf filaments (in a small moss resembling *Brachythecium antarcticum*) and gemmae (*Barbilophozia hatcheri, Marchantia berteroana*) (Smith, 1968).

Little is known at present as to the origin of the Antarctic flora; some theories hold that it is largely due to postglacial immigration (e.g. Cardot, 1908), while others support glacial survival on account of the high degree of endemism, particularly in the lichen flora (Rudolph, 1965). Whichever may be correct, the earliest stable habitats to become available for plant colonization as glaciers, ice caps, etc., are usually exposed cliff-faces, screes and rock micro-habitats. In many instances unstable soils, whether resulting from freeze-thaw cycles or biotic influences, may be colonized by transient populations of short, cushion-forming bryophytes capable of rapid establishment either by spores or vegetatively (e.g. species of *Andreaea, Bryum, Ceratodon, Pohlia, Pottia*). Even well-established and extensive communities may be regularly disrupted by various forms of frost action.

The more stable substrata are often extensively vegetated by a wide variety of community types, depending on the nature of the habitats and the degree of exposure. Where optimum conditions prevail, the establishment of mixed stands probably proceeds fairly rapidly, with bryophytes predominating in the moister, more sheltered, north-facing situations, and lichens in the more arid, exposed rocky habitats. These communities form a characteristic patchwork of marginally intergrading stands, uniform within themselves and frequently linked to each other by certain species with a wide ecological amplitude, which are common to several community types but vary considerably in their abundance from one to another. Unlike the vegetation of the less stable, stonier and more exposed habitats, such communities may form extensive, closed units comprising many species or even pure stands of a single bryophyte species.

The plant communities of the maritime Antarctic, once established, appear to be "climax" units of vegetation and only rarely is there some evidence of successional or cyclical stages. There does not appear to be effective competition for available habitats and, generally speaking, each habitat type is occupied by a specific group of bryophytes and lichens which constitutes a distinct and easily recognizable community type. The Antarctic tundra vegetation is basically a single, simple continuum of variation which can be reduced to a number of well-defined categories (subformations) according to the growth-form of the principal components; within each of these can be recognized a range of community types (associations and sociations) depending upon constancy and dominance of certain species. When a particular habitat becomes available for plant establishment it is colonized only by the species typical of a sociation favouring the conditions provided by that habitat. In most cases, one or a few species are more successful than the rest and will form the basis of the community, usually as the dominant or co-dominant members. Various sociations which lie adjacent to one another show little evidence of serious competition or the displacing of one by the other, but merely form a heterogeneous band where the stands merge.

Without necessarily applying objective and statistical techniques to the larger categories of vegetation, the relatively homogeneous and uniform sub-units can be subjectively and quantitatively analysed. Commencing with studies on Signy Island, numerous communities have been described, analysed quantitatively and arranged in a hierarchical classification (Smith, 1968). Further work in other localities in the maritime Antarctic by Longton (1967) and Smith (unpublished) has revealed that many of the community types are virtually identical to those found on Signy Island. Several assemblages not occurring in the South Orkney Islands, however, have been treated in the same manner and have been incorporated in this classification without major alteration.

Now that botanical research in the Antarctic is entering a more sophisticated experimental phase, it is important that an acceptable framework of reference to the vegetation is available. It is hoped that the classification of terrestrial vegetation of the maritime Antarctic presented in this paper may serve this purpose and that the proposed scheme may be extended to include other regions in the Antarctic, so that eventually a complete classification of the Antarctic terrestrial vegetation can be compiled.

Acknowledgements

Grateful acknowledgement is made to the British Antarctic Survey for providing the opportunity and facilities to carry out the work described in this paper.

The authors also wish to thank Drs S. W. Greene, M. W. Holdgate and R. E. Longton for their invaluable discussion and advice in the preparation of this paper. We are indebted to Dr Longton for providing data on the vegetation of the South Sandwich Islands, to Dr Greene for certain bryophyte determinations, and to Mr D. C. Lindsay for identifying most of the lichens.

PLATE 1. *Andreaea*–Lichen sociation, disrupted by frost heave. The dominant black moss is *Andreaea depressinervis*; the principal lichens include *Himantormia lugubris* (top right), *Stereocaulon alpinum* (bottom left) and *Usnea antarctica* (around frost heave). The scale object is 8 cm in length. Rusty bluff, Signy Island. (British Antarctic Survey Photo)

PLATE 2. *Usnea–Himantormia* sociation. The whitish fruticose lichens are *U. antarctica* and *U. fasciata*; black fruticose lichen is *H. lugubris* and black cushions of moss *Andreaea spp.* The scale object is 8 cm in length. Observation Bluff, Signy Island (British Antarctic Survey Photo)

PLATE 3. *Usnea–Himantormia–Omphalodiscus* sociation. The greyish fruticose lichen is *U. antarctica*, the thalli are of *O. antarcticus* (smooth) and *O. decussatus* (crinkly). Crustose species of *Lecanora* and *Rhizocarpon* occur at the bottom right. The scale object is 5 cm in diameter. Observation Bluff, Signy Island. (British Antarctic Survey Photo)

PLATE 4. *Tortula–Grimmia* sociation. The tall cushions are of *T. fuscoviridis* and *T. grossiretis*; shorter cushions are of *Bryum algens* (dark) and *Grimmia antarctici* (light); the whitish shoot tips are *Brachythecium sp*. The scale object is 5 cm in diameter. Near Waterpipe Beach, Signy Island. (British Antarctic Survey Photo)

PLATE 5. *Dicranum*–Lichen sociation. The deep peat bank in the foreground reaches 140 cm, and is built up solely by *D. aciphyllum* with numerous fruticose and crustose lichens on the more exposed parts of the surface. Near N.W. coast, Signy Island. (British Antarctic Survey Photo)

PLATE 6. *Brachythecium–Calliergon–Drepanocladus* sociation. The lighter coloured moss along the margins of the melt stream (filled with snow) is *B. antarcticum*; *Calliergon spp.* and *D. uncinatus* predominate on the slightly less wet ground which is flanked by shallow banks of *Polytrichum–Dicranum* stands (right and bottom left). The ski stick is approximately 130 cm in length. Near Gourley Peninsula, Signy Island. (British Antarctic Survey Photo)

PLATE 7. *Drepanocladus–Bryum–Tortula* sociation. The deep, light hummocks along the course of the melt stream are mainly of *B. algens* and some *T. excelsa* and *Brachythecium cf. subplicatum*. The dark moss on the less wet ground is *D. uncinatus*. Near Mirounga Cove, Signy Island. (British Antarctic Survey Photo)

PLATE 8. Colonization of a moss carpet community (mainly *Calliergon spp.* and *Drepano-cladus uncinatus*) by small cushions of the tall turf moss *Dicranum aciphyllum* spreading from a shallow peat bank at the left. Such invasion and ultimate displacement of one community type by another is rare in Antarctic vegetation. Near Gourlay Peninsula, Signy Island. (British Antarctic Survey Photo)

PLATE 9. Boundary between marble (white, on left) and quartz-mica-schist (grey, on right). Black moss cushions on marble are of *Grimmia antarctici* and *Tortula fuscoviridis*, those on the schist are of *Andreaea depressinervis*. The grey fruticose lichen covering most of the schist is *Usnea antarctica*. The ski stick is approximately 130 cm long. Gourlay Peninsula, Signy Island, South Orkney Islands. Altitude: *c.* 40 m. (British Antarctic Survey Photo)
PLATE 10. Distribution of communities on volcanic ash. The closed vegetation in the middle-ground is predominantly *Drepanocladus uncinatus* (grey) and *Brachythecium sp.*

Bibliography

Allen, S. E., Grimshaw, H. M. and Holdgate, M. W. (1967). Factors affecting the availability of plant nutrients on an Antarctic island. *J. Ecol.* 55, 381–96.

Allen, S. E. and Northover, M. J. (1967). Soil types and nutrients on Signy Island. *Phil. Trans. R. Soc.* B 252, 179–85.

Bertram, G. C. L. (1938). Plants and seals. *In* "Notes on the scientific work of the British Graham Land Expedition, 1934–37," Fleming, W. L. S., Stephenson, A., Roberts, B. B. and Bertram, G. C. L. *Geogrl. J.* 91, 508–28.

Brown, R. N. Rudmose (1906). Antarctic botany: its present state and future problems. *Scott. geor. Mag.* 22, 473–84.

Bryant, H. M. (1945). Biology at East Base, Palmer Peninsula. *Proc. Am. phil. Soc.* 89, No. 1, 256–69.

Burges, A. (1951). The ecology of the Cairngorms. III. The *Empetrum-Vaccinium zone. J. Ecol.* 39, 271–84.

Cardot, J. (1908). La Flora bryologique de l'Antarctide. *Wiss. Ergebn. shcwed. Südpolarexped.* 1901–03 4, 8, 241–61.

Chambers, M. J. G. (1966). Investigations of patterned ground at Signy Island, South Orkney Islands: I. Interpretation of mechanical analyses. *Br. Antarct. Surv. Bull.* 9, 21–40.

Chambers, M. J. G. (1967). Investigations of patterned ground at Signy Island, South Orkney Islands: III. Miniature patterns, frost heaving and general conclusions. *Br. Antarct. Surv. Bull.* 12, 1–22.

Corte, A. (1961*a*). La primera fanerógama adventicia hallada en el Continente Antártico. *Contrnes Inst. antart. argent.* 62, 3–14.

Corte, A. (1961*b*). Fertilidad de las semillas en fanerogamas que crecen en Cabo Primavera (Costa de Danco), Peninsula Antartica. *Contrnes. Inst. antart. argent.* 65, 3–16.

Corte, A. (1962). Primera cita de la familia de Hepaticas "Marchantiaceae" para la Antartida. *Contrnes Inst. antart. argent.* 68, 3–12.

Ellenberg, H. and Mueller-Dombois, D. (1966). Tentative physiognomic-ecological classification of plant formations of the earth. *Ber. geobot. Inst. ETH, Stiftg. Rübel.* 37, 21–55.

Follmann, G. (1965). Una asociación nitrófila de líquenes epipétricos de la Antártica Occidental con *Ramalina terebrata* Tayl. et Hook. como especie caracterizante. *Instituto Antartico Chileno.* Publ. No. 4, pp. 3–18.

Fosberg, F. R. (1967). A classification of vegetation for general purposes. *In* "Guide to the Check-sheet for I.B.P. Areas". (Peterken, G. F., ed.), I.B.P. Handbook No. 4, 73–120. Oxford and Edinburgh.

Gimingham, C. H. (1967). Quantitative community analysis and bryophyte ecology on Signy Island. *Phil. Trans. R. Soc.* B 252, 251–9.

Gimingham, C. H. and Birse, E. M. (1957). Ecological studies on growth-form in bryophytes. I. Correlations between growth-form and habitat. *J. Ecol.* 45, 533–45.

(white), occupying a wet depression. The moss in the foreground is also *Drepanocladus*, on drier ground locally disrupted by frost heaving. The blackish fringe on either side of the depression is chiefly *Polytrichum alpinum* and *P. piliferum*, while the more extensive black patches in the background are of *Nostoc sp.*, on wet mud. The prorous, loose slope of the knoll is barren, except for the rockier parts which support *Grimmia sp.*, *Tortula spp.* and *Usnea antarctica*. Coppermine Cove, Robert Island, South Shetland Islands. Altitude: *c.* 50 m. (British Antarctic Survey Photo)

Gimingham, C. H. and Smith, R. I. L. (in press). Growth form and water relations of mosses in the maritime Antarctic. *Br. Antarct. Surv. Bull.*

Greene, S. W. (1964). Problems and Progress in Antarctic Bryology. *In* "Biologie Antarctique: Antarctic Biology" (Carrick, R., Holdgate, M. W. and Prévost, J., eds.), Hermann, Paris. pp. 173–9.

Greene, S. W. (1967). The Changing Pattern of Antarctic Botanical Studies. *JARE Sci. Rep.* Special Issue No. 1. Proceedings of the Symposium on Pacific-Antarctic Sciences, 236–44.

Greene, S. W., Greene, D. M., Brown, P. D. and Pacey, J. M. (in press). Antarctic Moss Flora. I. The genera *Andreaea, Pohlia, Polytrichum, Psilopilum* and *Sarconeurum. Br. Antarct. Surv. Sci. Rep.* **64**·

Greene, S. W. and Longton, R. E. (1970). The effects of climate on Antarctic plants. This symposium, 786–800.

Holdgate, M. W. (1964). Terrestrial Ecology in the Maritime Antarctic. *In* "Biologie Antarctique: Antarctic Biology" (Carrick, R., Holdgate, M. W. and Prévost, J., eds.). Hermann, Paris. 181–194.

Holdgate, M. W., Allen, S. E. and Chambers, M. J. G. (1967). A preliminary investigation of the soils of Signy Island, South Orkney Islands. *Br. Antarct. Surv. Bull.* **12**, 53–71.

Klement, O. (1955). Prodromus der mitteleoropaeischen Flechtengesellschaften. *Rep. spce. nov. Beih.*, Vol. 135, p. 5.

Lamb, I. M. (1948). Antarctic pyrenocarp lichens. *"Discovery" Rep.* **25**, 1–30.

Lamb, I. M. (1964). Antarctic lichens. I. The genera *Usnea, Ramalina, Himantormia, Alectoria, Cornicularia. Br. Antarct. Surv. Sci. Rep.* **38**, 1–34.

Lamb, I. M. (1968). Antarctic lichens. II. The genera *Buellia* and *Rinodina. Br. Antarct. Surv. Sci. Rep.* **61**.

Longton, R. E. (1966). Botanical studies in the Antarctic during the 1963–64 and 1964–65 seasons. *Br. Antarct. Surv. Bull.* **10**, 85–95.

Longton, R. E. (1967). Vegetation in the maritime Antarctic. *Phil. Trans. R. Soc.* B **252**, 213–35.

Longton, R. E. and Greene, S. W. (1967). The growth and reproduction of *Polytrichum alpestre* Hoppe on South Georgia. *Phil. Trans. R. Soc.* B **252**, 295–322.

Longton, R. E. and Holdgate, M. W. (1967). Temperature relationships in Antarctic vegetation. *Phil. Trans. R. Soc.* B **252**, 237–50.

Mårtesson, O. (1956). Bryophytes of the Torneträsk Area, Northern Swedish Lapland. III. General Part. *K. Svenska VetenskAkad. Avh. Naturskydd.* **15**, 7–48.

Matsuda, P. (1964). Microclimate in the community of mosses near Syowa Base at East Ongul Island, Antarctica. *Antarctic Rec.* **21**, 12–24.

Northover, M. J. and Allen, S. E. (1967). Seasonal availability of chemical nutrients on Signy Island. *Phil. Trans. R. Soc.* B **252**, 187–9.

Northover, M. J. and Grimshaw, H. M. (1967). Some seasonal trends in nutrient content of the soils of Signy Island, South Orkney Islands. *Br. Antarct. Surv. Bull.* **14**, 83–88.

Perkins, J. E. (1945). Biology at Little America. Botany. *Proc. Am. phil. Soc.* **89**, No. 1, 282–4.

Poore, M. E. D. (1962). The method of successive approximation in descriptive ecology. *In* "Advances in Ecological Research", Vol. 1 (Cragg, J. B., ed.), pp. 35–66. Academic Press. London and New York.

Rudolph, E. D. (1965). Antarctic lichens and vascular plants: their significance. *Bioscience* **15**, No. 4, 285–7.

Sheard, J. W. (1968). Vegetation Pattern in a moss-lichen heath associated with primary topographic features on Jan Mayen. *Bryologist*, 71, No. 1, 21–28.
Siple, P. A. (1938). The second Byrd Antarctic Expedition—Botany. I. Ecology and geographical distribution. *Ann. Mo. bot. Gdn.* 25, 476–514.
Skottsberg, C. J. F. (1912). Einige Bemerkungen über die Vegetationsverhältnisse des Graham Landes. *Wiss. Ergebn. schwed. Südpolarexped.* 1901–03 4, 13, 1–16.
Smith, R. I. L. (1968). Ecology of the Vegetation of Signy Island, South Orkney Islands, British Antarctic Territory. Ph.D. thesis, University of Aberdeen. 228 pp. (Unpublished).
Steere, W. C. (1965). Antarctic Bryophyta. *Bioscience* 15, No. 4, 283–5.
Watson, W. (1925). The bryophytes and lichens of Arctic-Alpine vegetation. *J. Ecol.* 13, 1–26.
Wilson, J. W. (1952). Vegetation patterns associated with soil movement on Jan Mayen Island. *J. Ecol.* 40, 249–64.

The Effects of Climate on Antarctic Plants

S. W. GREENE AND R. E. LONGTON
Department of Botany, University of Birmingham, England, and British Antarctic Survey.

I. Flora and Vegetation

The flora of the Antarctic regions, the floristic composition of which is reviewed by Lamb (1970: this symposium), contains a number of distinct phytogeographical elements which can be recognized in each plant group. Thus, endemic, austral, southern circumpolar, bipolar and cosmopolitan species have been reported, while attempts have been made at defining regional elements such as Magellanic, Novae Zealandic, Insular and Continental (Skottsberg, 1960; Wace, 1965). In spite of this diversity the range of growth forms is small, and it is striking that, as in the Arctic, perennial forms dominate the spectrum throughout both botanical zones, annuals being virtually unknown. Moreover, a physiognomic depauperation is evident in response to a latitudinal climatic gradient, selection being towards plants of low stature and compact growth form; that is to say, precisely those forms which are best adapted to retain heat and moisture under the environmental extremes of Antarctic regions.

In the Subantarctic zone low-growing herbaceous hemicryptophytes are dominant, although chamaeophytes and geophytes are well represented, but phanerophytes are unknown. Acrocarpous growth forms predominate in the bryophytes, the most abundant type being turfs, especially tall turfs, but cushions and pleurocarpous mats and carpets may be important locally. Open growth forms, such as wefts, are rare but numerous small, thread-like forms occur among some of the more important species. All three lichen growth forms are well represented, but their relative importance is unknown.

Non-vascular cryptogams predominate in the Antarctic zone, where the surface of the vegetation is from 0–10 cm above the level of the substrate. However, extensive areas may lack plant cover, even where the ground is normally snow free in summer. In the maritime region bryophytes are limited mainly to compact growth forms such as cushions, turfs and carpets (Gimingham, 1967). Mosses are more important than liverworts both in terms of their abundance and number of species, while crustose and fruticose lichens are more abundant than foliose forms. The native phanerogams are a small, tufted hemicryptophyte and a low cushion-forming chamaeophyte.

Much of the scattered vegetation in continental regions comprises lichens, and Rudolph (1967) has noted that "the predominant form in Antarctica is crustose; there are three times as many crustose (species) present as either of the other forms". The few mosses occurring in continental areas are again restricted to compact growth forms and are normally short turfs or cushions. Quite large cushions may occur locally, but in many areas the mosses grow as short turfs barely projecting above soil level. Only one hepatic has been recorded and that appears to be rare at its two known sites (Greene, 1967b). Algae are locally abundant in both maritime and continental areas, the most abundant species forming extensive, thallose mats.

II. Reproductive Success

The existence of large peat banks on Signy Island and the Argentine Islands bears witness to the capacity for extensive and prolonged vegetative growth in some species (Longton, 1970: this symposium). However, the measure of a species' adaptation must also be judged by its capacity to produce successive new generations. In these terms it is apparent that most bryophytes within the Antarctic botanical zone are incompletely adapted to the conditions, as, in general, sporophytes are seldom formed, although a few species fruit regularly (Longton, 1966a).

The inability to develop gametangia of one or both sexes is known to contribute to the low bryophyte fertility, as is either failure of fertilization or postzygotic development in species of *Polytrichum* (Longton, unpublished). Failure in later stages of sporophyte development is an additional factor, as demonstrated by the aborted capsules of *Bryum antarcticum* in South Victoria Land (Greene, 1967b); abnormal capsules have also been noted in a few other species.

Bryophyte fertility appears to be high on some Subantarctic islands, where it has been shown that several species regularly develop sporophytes, for example *Polytrichum alpinum* and *P. alpestre* on South Georgia, although their reproductive success declines sharply further south (Longton, 1966a). It has also been established that gametangial and sporophyte development in the Polytricha show a well-marked seasonal pattern and thus appear to be under environmental control (Longton and Greene, 1967), but the climatic factors involved have not been identified.

In contrast to the bryophytes, the two native flowering plants in the Antarctic zone are thought to reproduce successfully in most seasons, although local failure may occur at times (Holtom and Greene, 1967). Both appear to be entirely cleistogamous and to flower and set seed regularly on South Georgia and from the Argentine Islands southwards to Marguerite Bay. The seed in some of these areas is viable and will germinate under natural conditions (Corte, 1961a; Holtom and Greene, 1967). However, seed production may be achieved only infrequently on the South Shetland Islands, while on the South Orkney Islands it appears that viable seed is produced only in "good years".

In the Subantarctic zone some vascular species, such as *Acaena magellanica* (= *A. adscendens*) on South Georgia, produce viable seed which germinates under field conditions, probably in most seasons. Reproductive success may occur less frequently in other cases, however, as shown by the extreme rarity of *Poa foliosa* seedlings on Macquarie Island noted by Ashton (1965).

Field observations on South Georgia suggest that all the native species produce inflorescences annually, but at different times throughout the season, i.e. a sharply circumscribed phase during which all the species are in flower or fruit, as occurs in many Arctic areas, is absent. For example *Poa flabellata* reaches anthesis early in the season, towards the end of November and, as withered heads are present during February, this species appears to be one of the first to mature seeds. *Phleum alpinum*, on the other hand, has not been observed in anthesis before the end of January or early February and there is some doubt if its seeds are normally mature before winter. A further species, *Galium antarcticum*, has an extended flowering period from December to March, with capsules appearing towards the end of this period.

Some aliens appear to be less successful. *Ranunculus repens* flowers regularly at all sites on South Georgia, but seems to fail to set seed, presumably due to the absence of suitable insect pollinators. *Carex aquatilis* is also interesting in that it is vegetatively well established at Husvik, but it has never been seen in flower there, although South Georgian plants produce inflorescences under cultivation in Birmingham. Along the Antarctic Peninsula, *Poa annua* produces viable seed at Deception Island (Longton, 1966b), while *P. pratensis* forms inflorescences at Almirante Brown, but apparently fails to develop viable seed before winter (Corte, 1961b).

III. The Climate

Many components of the environment affect plant growth and development. Temperature is one of the most obvious in the context of Antarctic studies, and the one which has so far received most detailed attention; other factors such as water availability, snow cover, photoperiod and the quantity of incident radiation are also of major importance.

The need to study many climatic factors at plant level rather than relying on standard meteorological observations has been stressed repeatedly, yet this type of data has been collected from only a few scattered localities.

Records at plant level, some covering periods of over a year, have been obtained on the Subantarctic island of South Georgia (Longton and Greene, 1967; Lewis and Greene, 1970: this symposium), on Signy Island (Holdgate, 1964a) and the Argentine Islands in the maritime Antarctic (Longton, 1970: this symposium) and in continental Antarctica at East Ongul Island (Matsuda, 1964) and Cape Hallett (Rudolph, 1966a). Extensive measurements of soil temperatures in Victoria Land have been reported by Pryor (1962), Wise and Spain (1967) and other workers, while new data have been obtained from McKelvey Valley, South Victoria Land (Benoit and Hall, 1970: this symposium) and the South Shetland Islands (Sáiz et al., 1970: this symposium). It is clear that these limited results can only indicate the more obvious features of the environment at plant level due to the circumpolar distribution of Antarctic vegetation and its extension through 40° of latitude, and because small differences in aspect, topography, etc., can bring about marked changes in microclimate within short distances. Nevertheless, the available results suggest gradients between the Subantarctic and continental Antarctica which undoubtedly influence plant distribution and performance.

A. RADIATION

Radiation receipt is one of the overriding factors controlling plant growth, acting both directly through the provision of energy for photosynthesis and indirectly through its effect on temperature and therefore on the rates of metabolic processes. On theoretical grounds the total amount of solar radiation reaching the Earth's atmosphere in polar regions, during high summer, can be shown to equal or exceed the comparable figures for the tropics (since the longer polar days compensate for the lower daily maxima) (Gates, 1965; Rubin and Weyant, 1965). The amount of energy reaching the land will vary greatly from place to place due to such factors as absorption by atmospheric gases, scattering by the atmosphere and reflection from clouds. It may also be noted that in polar regions the diurnal variation in light intensity is relatively small, and it has been suggested that this may increase the efficiency of light utilization by plants (Warren Wilson, 1966). So although no measurements at plant level are yet available from Antarctic regions, it is reasonable to assume that the amount of radiant energy is not limiting for assimilation and plant growth in these regions during summer.

B. PHOTOPERIOD

Diurnal variation in light intensity during summer also influences growth and development through photoperiodic responses. As the areas under consideration extend through a wide range of latitudes, there are considerable differences in the photoperiodic regime, day length during December varying from approximately seventeen hours on South Georgia to twenty-four hours south of the Antarctic Circle. A chart giving maximum values for day length at any latitude in the southern polar region has been provided by Rubin and Weyant (1965). Thus, it is clear that different populations of some species can tolerate a range of photoperiodic regimes as they are widely dispersed in Antarctic regions and even extend into temperate areas in lower latitudes. For example, *Colobanthus quitensis* (=*C. crassifolius*) and *Deschampsia antarctica* grow and flower from approximately 68°S in Marguerite Bay, northwards along the Antarctic Peninsula and the Scotia Ridge to at least 34°S in South America, while *C. quitensis* extends further north into Peru and even crosses the Equator into Mexico. Experimental studies on South Georgian material of *C. quitensis* indicate that both vegetative growth and reproductive development are largely independent of photoperiod (Holtom and Greene, 1967). Similar results were obtained for vegetative growth in *Deschampsia antarctica*, but in this species flower and seed development are under long day control.

C. TEMPERATURE

Much of the solar radiation reaching polar regions is reflected from snow and ice surfaces. Air temperatures are therefore low, even in summer, while the winters are extremely cold, especially in areas receiving no direct radiation for several months of the year. Mean monthly air temperatures on Subantarctic islands are within a few degrees of 0°C during the coldest months each year. There is a progressive decrease in winter temperatures with increasing latitude and in continental Antarctica mean winter air temperature may fall below −40°C.

Much of the Antarctic vegetation is covered by an insulating blanket of snow for up to nine months each year and so, during winter, deep snow may maintain temperatures around the plants at a level higher than the air above. In places, however, strong winds remove all but a thin layer of snow, thereby allowing plant temperatures to fluctuate slowly with changes in air temperature, so reducing the difference between aerial and plant-level conditions. Vegetation on exposed rock surfaces may be clear of snow throughout the year, for example lichen colonies on the Argentine Islands (R. W. M. Corner, *personal communication*), and in these cases the temperature at plant level may be expected to differ very little from air temperature.

The winter temperature experienced by a stand of vegetation therefore results from the interaction of at least two factors, air temperature and the depth of snow. For example, in a South Georgian colony of *Polytrichum alpestre* temperatures under 30 to 100 cm of snow remained steady at around, or slightly above, freezing throughout the winter of 1961, despite diurnal fluctuations in air temperature which fell to a mean of −4°C during a two-week period in August. Indeed, the lowest temperatures at plant level were recorded in autumn and spring when the site was clear of snow, but even then mean daily minima seldom fell below $-2°C$. In contrast, temperatures near the surface of a *Bryum argenteum* cushion on East Ongul Island were as low as $-17°C$, despite a 50 cm covering of snow, while temperatures down to $-29°C$ were recorded for exposed mosses in the same region. Results currently being analysed for the maritime Antarctic are, in general, intermediate between those from Subantarctic and continental Antarctic sites, and provide further evidence that differences in winter plant-level temperatures are associated with local variation in snow cover.

It is clear that Antarctic plants must be able to survive long periods at temperatures well below $0°C$, a capacity which has been demonstrated experimentally for both lichens (Ahmadjian, 1970: this symposium) and mosses (Longton and Holdgate, 1967 Horikawa and Ando, 1967). Even young sporophytes of *Polytrichum alpestre*, collected on South Georgia in the over-wintering *Calyptra in Perichaetium* stage, developed normally at $10°C$ after being kept at $-10°C$ for fourteen months and then slowly thawed (Longton, unpublished).

As Ahamdjian has pointed out, in terms of survival the actual temperatures in winter are probably of less importance than the rates at which freezing and thawing take place. The available results, from moss colonies in the maritime Antarctic show that these processes occurred at rates unlikely to cause severe frost damage (Longton, 1970: this symposium).

During summer, heating from insolation by day and cooling from re-radiation at night give rise to wide and rapid diurnal fluctuations in temperature at plant level, the daily range, at times, exceeding $30°C$. At sites receiving less than twenty-four hours' sunshine, temperatures during clear nights may sometimes be slightly lower near the ground than in the air above. However, mean temperatures at plant level normally exceed mean air temperatures throughout the summer, due to the reduction of wind velocity near the ground and the effects of absorption of solar radiation by day.

Like air temperatures mean summer temperatures at plant level, in general, appear to decrease with increasing latitude. Thus, mean daily summer temperatures at the surface of bryophyte colonies, averaged over fourteen-day periods, reached $10·8°C$ on South Georgia compared with $7·1°C$ on the Argentine Islands and approximately $4·0°C$ on East Ongul Island.

The highest summer temperatures in moss turfs are normally recorded during early afternoon in bright sunlight: temperatures exceeding $30°C$ have been recorded near the surface of *Polytrichum alpestre* colonies both on South Georgia and in the maritime Antarctic. Similar results were obtained for lichen-covered rocks at Cape Hallett, while on East Ongul Island readings in the surface of a moss cushion reached $19°C$. These figures are maxima, but it is clear that differences of $10°$ to $20°C$ commonly exist between plant level and air temperatures.

Even in overcast conditions plant level and air temperatures may still show substantial differences. For example, no sunshine was recorded on Signy Island on 10 January 1966, but the maximum temperature at plant level reached 9·0°C, exceeding the maximum air temperature by 6·5°C. Similarly, figures of 9·1°C and 3·1°C were recorded for mean daily maximum plant level and air temperatures respectively at Signy Island during a fourteen-day period in January when sunshine averaged only 0·7 hours per day. This effect may be influenced by the type and thickness of cloud cover, as during other periods of overcast weather there was little difference between air and plant-level temperatures.

Aspect also has a pronounced effect on temperature, particularly during the day. There appear to have been few quantitative investigations of its influence in Antarctic regions, so far, but a difference of 11·2°C was recorded between "spot" readings of moss-surface temperatures in north- and south-facing situations on Deception Island (Longton and Holdgate, 1967).

At night temperatures at plant level normally remained above 0°C during high summer in a colony of *Polytrichum alpestre* on South Georgia, but fell rapidly to around or below 0°C at sites in the maritime Antarctic. Minimum temperatures in these areas were seldom below −2·75°C, however, and frequent ice formation within the plant tissues during summer was considered unlikely (Longton, 1970: this symposium). In contrast, daily minimum plant-level temperatures at East Ongul Island and Cape Hallett fell considerably below 0°C, and Rudolph (1966b) considered that plants at the latter site regularly withstand being frozen at least once a day.

It is thus interesting that the work of Gannutz and Lange, reviewed by Ahmadjian (1970: this symposium), has shown that some Antarctic lichens can resume photosynthesis very rapidly on thawing. In addition, Gannutz showed that the optimum temperature for photosynthesis in some species may be between −10°C and +10°C compared with a range of 7° to 27°C for material of *Prasiola crispa* and a species of *Bryum*. Photosynthesis was not recorded in *Deschampsia antarctica* at temperatures below 0°C, but Holtom and Greene (1967) have shown that South Georgian material of both *D. antarctica* and *Colobanthus quitensis* grow well at a constant temperature of only 5°C. The best vegetative growth in *D. antarctica* occurred in fluctuating temperatures of 20°C by day and 5°C at night, conditions comparable with those obtaining in the field during summer. This regime also proved optimal for several stages in flower production as well as seed development and germination in both species, but a continuous temperature around 20°C proved lethal. It was demonstrated that a cold pretreatment was necessary for panicle formation in *D. antarctica* and the number of seeds germinating in both species was also increased by cold pretreatment.

D. HUMIDITY AND PRECIPITATION

The availability of water for plant growth is another factor which varies greatly within the region under consideration. Precipitation averages approximately 160 cm per year on South Georgia, falling largely as rain in summer. Frequent heavy rain also occurs on other oceanic Subantarctic islands. Precipitation is lighter in the maritime Antarctic, but either rain or snow falls on over 200 days per year, with rain on over fifty days in summer. Further south at Marguerite Bay, precipitation is lower still, and it decreases further over much of continental Antarctica, where it falls exclusively as snow. Moreover, with increasing latitude the lower air temperatures reduce the period during which melt water is available.

Few data have been obtained for relative humidity at plant level, but records were kept for a colony of *Polytrichum alpestre* on South Georgia from January to March 1961 (Longton and Greene, 1967). Almost 50% of the records, based on readings every three hours, were above 80%, the mean daily values over two-week periods ranging from 72% to 80%. There was considerable diurnal fluctuation with mean daily minimum values of 53% to 67% occurring in the afternoon, while at night the maxima averaged as high as 92%. Similar mean values were obtained in a Stevenson screen, approximately 300 m from the study site, and since mean annual relative humidities at screen level at sites in the maritime Antarctic normally exceed 80%, comparable conditions may exist at plant level. These results contrast strongly with data obtained by Rudolph (1966b) at Cape Hallett from November 1962 to January 1963. He noted that relative humidity just above the ground was normally less than 20% at midday and under 50% at night. The dew point was seldom reached, so that moisture was available to the plants only as melted snow.

It should be noted that the prevailing low air temperatures combined with the higher temperatures within the vegetation will give substantial vapour pressure gradients between plants and their environment. Nevertheless, it is considered unlikely that shortage of water is the most serious factor limiting the enrichment of vegetation on the Subantarctic islands or over much of the maritime Antarctic, as these areas provide a wide variety of habitats with adequate moisture ranging from permanently wet ground by snow banks and along melt-water pools and streams to well-irrigated rocky slopes and screes with local dry plains and slopes of volcanic ash. By contrast, conditions over much of continental Antarctica are extremely arid, a fact that impressed early observers such as Siple (1938) and Perkins (1945) as one of the most important factors restricting plant cover. Rudolph (1963) has shown that the distribution of mosses and algae at Cape Hallett is closely related to the configuration of melt-water channels, while a similar relationship between bryophyte distribution and ground water supply has been noted by Longton

(1967) in Marguerite Bay. Rudolph (1966a) later found that some species of lichens on dry rock surfaces can survive long periods of drought in a semi-dehydrated state, but rehydrate rapidly when water becomes available. Gimingham (1967), from experimental results obtained on Signy Island, suggested that the distribution of bryophytes in the maritime region is closely linked to a species' capacity for water retention. He found that plants which dry out slowly and rehydrate quickly occupy drier habitats than those with little or no ability to retain water even if they can rehydrate rapidly. Thus it appears that the growth form of cryptogams, by exercising a control on their water-holding capacity, is of importance in determining the habitats they can colonize.

E. WIND AND SNOW

No detailed studies have yet been made on the influence of wind and snow on Antarctic vegetation, but by analogy with the Arctic and elsewhere some effects seem obvious. For example, the shortage of water experienced by much Antarctic vegetation may be accentuated by high winds causing an increase in transpiration rates and in the rate of evaporation from the surface of the colony. Increased rates of evaporation may cause reduction in plant temperatures, while further cooling will result from the removal of the layer of air that has exchanged heat with plant and soil surfaces. Warren Wilson (1959), when considering the effects of wind on Arctic vegetation, reported substantial reductions in net assimilation rates and relative growth rates of vascular plants in windy, compared with sheltered, situations on Jan Mayen Island. He also showed that a reduction in wind speed had the effect of increasing leaf surface temperatures in *Salix arctica* by up to $7 \cdot 1°C$ and he suggested that, in the Arctic, wind may be more important in limiting growth by depression of plant temperatures than by its influence on the rates of water loss.

Snow, as an ecological factor, has been little studied, but it plays two important roles, firstly as insulation in winter and secondly as a source of melt water during summer. The effects of snow cover on winter temperatures have already been referred to, but this cover also affords protection from strong winter winds and from abrasion by the ice crystals and dust they carry. The provision of water as the snow melts is a further vital effect, since, as noted earlier, this may be the only source of moisture on soil and rock surfaces in much of continental Antarctica. In some circumstances, snow cover appears to provide optimal conditions for the growth of some lichens (Ahmadjian, 1970: this symposium), but by persisting into the summer season it may restrict the growth of many other plants. The snow-free period in summer at experimental sites at South Georgia, Signy Island and East Ongul Island was limited to five, four and three months respectively, but the duration of snow-free conditions varies from place to place and from season to season within any given area. Snow may at times persist over plants for one or more complete years, but the effects of such prolonged cover are unknown.

IV. Discussion

In this review an attempt has been made to summarize existing knowledge of the more important characteristics of Antarctic plants and their aerial environment. The Antarctic regions, as understood here, extend over some 40° of latitude, and the data so far available indicate the presence of a latitudinal gradient of increasing climatic severity extending from the Sub-antarctic islands towards the centre of the Continent. The present results are too few and come from too widely scattered areas to give an accurate picture of the range of microclimates associated with local variations in general weather conditions, aspect, slope, snow cover, etc. Moreover, it is known that at a given site some years are "good" while others are "bad" for plant growth and reproduction, but again there is insufficient knowledge to define the climatic factors involved. In general, however, it may be noted that summer conditions over much of the Antarctic are coooler than at comparable latitudes in the Arctic, where many of the most northerly lands experience short periods of frost-free conditions at least in the lowlands. In contrast, winter conditions on the Subantarctic islands and in the maritime Antarctic are warmer than in areas in the Arctic which support heaths dominated by dwarf shrubs or even forests.

Before an immigrant species can be regarded as fully adapted to Antarctic conditions it must first overcome considerable dispersal barriers, secondly become established vegetatively and thirdly demonstrate the ability to re-produce sexually and give rise to new generations. Although the origin of the present Antarctic flora is as yet obscure, some species may have survived the period of maximum glaciation, but it seems likely that many, if not the majority, are postglacial immigrants. If this is so, then the relict species might be supposed to be those best adapted to the prevailing conditions, but the immigrants may well have superior powers of dispersal.

Evidence is accumulating that additional species are already capable of, or could rapidly adapt to, survival under the climatic severity of Antarctic regions were they able to overcome the dispersal problems of the ocean barrier. It is known, for example, that as a result of human activities, several species of alien phanerogams have become established on Subantarctic islands (Greene and Greene, 1963), while *Poa annua* and *Poa pratensis* have survived for several years at sites near the Antarctic Peninsula (Corte, 1961b; Longton 1966b). Moreover, successful germination and seedling growth in *Poa pratensis* has been reported from Cape Hallett (Rudolph, 1966b). On the other hand, many aliens which have been accidentally or experimentally introduced into Subantarctic or Antarctic areas have died within one or two years (Holdgate, 1964b; Longton and Holdgate, 1967). Taken together these observations suggest that, in the absence of dispersal barriers, some additional species would become established in the Antarctic, but that others would fail to survive.

Considering the second prerequisite for successful adaptation, it would appear that aridity and the short cool summers are the most likely causes limiting the vegetative growth of Antarctic plants, radiation receipt being almost certainly more than adequate throughout high summer. It has already been suggested that aridity is less important as a limiting factor on South Georgia, or near the west coast of the Antarctic Peninsula, than it is in continental areas. Temperature becomes more important in the former areas, as evidenced by the increased abundance, greater vegetative vigour and superior reproductive success of many species on north-facing slopes, in sheltered hollows and around fumaroles.

Low temperatures have been held responsible for the lower growth and assimilation rates which have been demonstrated for indigenous species and temperate test plants in the Arctic compared with temperate sites (Warren Wilson, 1966) while Lewis and Greene (1970: this symposium) have produced evidence of a comparable reduction between South Georgia and northern sites. Warren Wilson (1966) has suggested that under low-temperature conditions the rate at which assimilates are used in respiration and incorporated into new plant parts is suppressed, sugars tending to accumulate, which in turn depress the assimilation rate. However, as Pearsall (1950) has pointed out, high sugar concentrations may benefit plants by increasing their frost resistance.

Due to the depressing effects of low summer temperatures on plant growth it seems clear that the duration and amplitude of the daily periods above freezing are of the utmost importance in determining the growth of many Antarctic plants. Although these periods are warmest under bright sunny conditions, the less dramatic heating of plant colonies under overcast conditions, as demonstrated for bryophyte turfs on Signy Island, may also be significant, especially in areas of high cloud cover for, as pointed out by Warren Wilson (1957), a small rise in temperature near the lower cardinal point for metabolic processes may greatly increase the metabolic rate.

The growth form of a species is another feature influencing the extent to which temperatures increase and the period over which warm conditions may be sustained. For example, low growing species with a dense, compact growth form will incorporate a body of moist air in the interstices between the overlapping leaves and stems, a feature which will be absent in more robust plants with a laxer habit and widely spaced leaves. Thus, it is not surprising that the greatest differences between plant and ambient temperatures in polar regions have been recorded in moss turfs, plants with more open habit such as *Salix arctica* giving lower values (Warren Wilson, 1957).

Species may also become adapted to growth in cold climates by adjustments in the temperature requirements of their metabolic processes. Thus, for some plants e.g. *Oxyria digyna*, Mooney and Billings (1961) have shown that photosynthetic and respiratory rates are greater in Arctic races at lower temperatures than in alpine races of the same species from lower latitudes. Few metabolic studies have yet been carried out on Antarctic plants, but the work reviewed by Ahmadjian (1970: this symposium) has demonstrated that many Antarctic lichens have remarkable physiological adaptations, e.g. the ability to photosynthesise at or below O°C.

It appears, then, that in each group of plants, there exists a variety of adaptations which enables them to make sufficient growth to survive vegetatively from season to season under the diverse summer regimes within the Antarctic regions. Sexual reproduction, however, poses great problems, as each stage may be under precise control by one or more environmental factors. Thus, if the initation of flower buds or gametangia requires the stimulus of a certain combination of temperature and photoperiod, the process may fail if the photoperiodic requirement is fulfilled but the temperature is too low. Even if the right conditions to initiate the reproductive process are provided, failure will occur unless they are received early enough in the season to allow a sufficient period for development.

Thus an ability to complete the reproductive cycle rapidly, or to enter winter at a stage able to withstand its severity yet sufficiently advanced to allow maturation in the following season, are obvious advantages. These features are shared by the two flowering plants, both of which have relatively short developmental times for flowering and seed production while there is evidence that where seed has failed to mature by the beginning of winter it may continue to develop under snow cover and reach full size by the following spring. In most Antarctic bryophytes it is normal for the reproductive cycle, lasting from the initiation of gametangia to the liberation of spores from the ripe capsules, to take at least two growing seasons, with overwintering occurring at some intermediate stage. While a few species complete this process successfully, it is clear that most bryophyte species in the Antarctic zone are maintained largely by vegetative propagation.

In conclusion, then, it may be said that Antarctic vegetation is composed of species, the majority of which have demonstrated an ability to overcome substantial dispersal problems. They are frost resistant and have the capacity to grow and sometimes reproduce in short, cool summers characterized by rapid, diurnal fluctuations in temperature and relative humidity; in areas of low precipitation many can endure periods of prolonged dehydration. They survive the winter, a period of often intense cold, either blanketed by snow or less commonly exposed to the low temperatures. They have overcome the problem of strong winds causing physical damage, dehydration or too great a depression of temperature throughout the year. The predominance of low, compact, perennial growth forms is, therefore, not surprising, as these forms appear to offer most advantages to survival under such inhospitable conditions.

Bibliography

Ahmadjian, V. (1970). Adaptation in Terrestrial polar plants. This symposium, 801–11.

Ashton, D. H. (1965). Regeneration pattern of *Poa foliosa* Hook. f. on Macquarie Island. *Proc. R. Soc. Vict.* 79, Part 1, 215–33.

Benoit, R. E. and Hall, C. L. (1970). The microbiology of some dry valley soils of Victoria Land, Antarctica. This symposium, 697–701.

Corte, A. (1961a). Fertilidad de las semillas en fanerógams que crecen en Cabo, Primavera (Costa de Danco), Peninsula Antarctica. *Contrnes. Inst. Antart. Argent.* 65, 1–16.

Corte, A. (1961b). La Primera fanerógama adventicia hallada en el continente Antártico. *Contrnes. Inst. Antart. Argent.* 62, 3–14.

Gates, D. H. (1965). "Energy Exchange in the Biosphere." Harper Reprint Series in Plant Physiology. Vol. III. Harper and Row, New York.

Gimingham, C. H. (1967). Quantitative community analysis and bryophyte ecology on Signy Island. *Phil. Trans. R. Soc.* B 252, No. 777, 251–9.

Godley, E. J. (1960). The botany of southern Chile in relation to New Zealand and the Subantarctic. *Proc. R. Soc.* B 152, No. 949, 457–75.

Greene, S. W. (1964). Plants of the land. *In* "Antarctic Research" (Priestley, R., Adie, R. J., and Robin, G. de Q, eds). Butterworths, London, 240–53.

Greene, S. W. (1967a) The changing pattern of Antarctic botanical studies. Proceedings of the Symposium on Pacific-Antarctic Sciences. *J. A. R. E. Sci. Repts.*, Special Issue. No. 1. National Science Museum, Tokyo, 236–244.

Greene, S. W. (1967b). Bryophyte distribution. *In* "Terrestrial Life in Antarctica", *Antarctic Map Folio Series*. American Geographical Society, New York. 11–13.

Greene, S. W. and Greene, D. M. (1963). Check list of the sub-Antarctic and Antarctic vascular flora. *Polar Rec.* 11, No. 73, 11–18.

Holdgate, M. W. (1964a). Terrestrial ecology in the Maritime Antarctic. *In* "Biologie Antarctique: Antarctic Biology", (Carrick, R., Holdgate, M. W. and Prévost, J. eds.). Hermann, Paris. 181–94.

Holdgate, M. W. (1964b). An experimental introduction of plants into the Antarctic. *Br. Antarct. Surv. Bull.* 3, 13–16.

Holtom, Anne and Greene, S. W. (1967). The growth and reproduction of Antarctic flowering plants. *Phil. Trans. R. Soc.* B 252, No. 777, 323–37.

Horikawa, Y. and Ando, H. (1967). The mosses of the Ongul Islands and adjoining coastal areas of the Antarctic Continent. Proceedings of the Symposium on Pacific-Antarctic Sciences, *J.A.R.E.Sci. Repts.*, Special Issue, No. 1, National Science Museum, Tokyo, (1970). 245–52.

Lamb, I. M. (1970) Antarctic Terrestrial vegetation and its ecology. This symposium, 733–51.

Lewis, M. C. and Greene, S. W. (1970) A comparison of plant growth at an Arctic and Antarctic station. This symposium, 838–50.

Longton, R. E. (1966a). Botanical studies in the Antarctic during the 1963–64 and 1964–65 seasons. *Br. Antarct. Surv. Bull.* **10**, 85–95.

Longton, R. E. (1966b). Alien vascular plants on Deception Island, South Shetland Islands. *Br. Antarct. Surv. Bull.* **9**, 55–60.

Longton, R. E. (1967). Vegetation in the maritime Antarctic. *Phil. Trans. R. Soc.* B **252**, No. 777, 213–35.

Longton, R. E. (1970) The growth and reproduction of the moss *Polytrichum alpestre* Hoppe in Antarctic regions. This symposium, 818–37.

Longton, R. E. and Greene, S. W. (1967). The growth and reproduction of *Polytrichum alpestre* Hoppe on South Georgia. *Phil. Trans. R. Soc.* B **252**, No. 777, 295–322.

Longton, R. E. and Holdgate, M. W. (1967). Temperature relationships of Antarctic vegetation. *Phil. Trans. R. Soc.* B **252**, No. 777, 237–50.

Matsuda, T. (1964). Microclimate in the community of mosses near Syowa Base at East Ongul Island, Antarctica. *Antarctic Rec.* **21**, 12–24.

Mooney, H. A. and Billings, W. D. (1961). Comparative physiological ecology of Arctic and Alpine populations of *Oxyria digyna*. *Ecol. Monogr.* **31**, No. 1, 1–29.

Pearsall, W. H. (1950). "Mountains and Moorlands". New Naturalist Series. Collins, London.

Perkins, J. E. (1945). Biology at Little America III. The west base of the United States Antarctic Service expedition 1939–1941. *Proc. Am. Phil. Soc.* **89**, No. 1, 270–84.

Pryor, M. (1962). Some environmental features of Hallett Station, Antarctica, with special reference to soil arthropods. *Pacif. Insects.* **4**, 681–728.

Rubin, M. J. and Weyant, W. S. (1965). Antarctic Meteorology. *In* "Antarctica", (T. Hatherton, ed.). Methuen, London. 375–401.

Rudolph, E. D. (1963). Vegetation of Hallett Station area, Victoria Land, Antarctica. *Ecology* **44**, 585–6.

Rudolph, E. D. (1966a). Lichen ecology and microclimate studies at Cape Hallett, Antarctica. *Biometeorology* II. *Proceedings of the Third International Biometeorological Congress held at Pau, S. France, 1–7 September, 1963*, 900–10.

Rudolph, E. D. (1966b). Terrestrial vegetation in Antarctica: Past and present studies. "Antarctic Soils and Soil forming Processes", *Antarctic Research Series*, Vol. 8, The American Geophysical Union, New York. 109–24.

Rudolph, E. D. (1967). Lichen distribution. *In* "Terrestrial Life in Antarctica", *Antarctic Map Folio Series*. American Geographical Society, New York. 9–11.

Sáiz, F., Hajek, E. R. and Hermosilla, W. (1970). Colonization of introduced litter by subantarctic moss and soil arthropods. This symposium, 897–907.

Siple, P. A. (1938). The second Byrd Antarctic Expedition, Botany I. Ecology and Geographical distribution. *Ann. Mo. bot. Gdn.* **25**, No. 2, 467–514.

Skottsberg, C. (1960). Remarks on the plant geography of the southern cold temperate zone. *Proc. R. Soc.* B **152**, No. 949, 447–57.

Ugolini, F. C. (1970). Antarctic soils and their ecology. This symposium, 673–92.

Wace, N. M. (1960). The botany of the southern oceanic islands. *Proc. R. Soc.* B **152**, No. 949, 475–90.

Wace, N. M. (1965). Vascular Plants. *In* "Biogeography and Ecology in Antarctica", (Miegham, Van J., Oye, Van P. and Schell, J. eds.). *In Monographiae biol.* **15**. 201–66.

Warren Wilson, J. (1957). Observations on the temperature of Arctic plants and their environment. *J. Ecol.* **45**, 499–531.

Warren Wilson, J. (1959). Notes on wind and its effect in Arctic-Alpine vegetation. *J. Ecol.* **47**, 415–27.

Warren Wilson, J. (1966). An analysis of plant growth and its control in Arctic environments. *An. Bot.* **30**, 383–402.

Wise, K. A. J. and Spain, A. V. (1967). Entomological investigations in Antarctica, 1963–64 season. *Pacif. Insects* **9** ,No. 2, 271–93.

Adaptations of Antarctic Terrestrial Plants

VERNON AHMADJIAN
*Department of Biology, Clark University, Worcester,
Massachusetts, U.S.A.*

I. Introduction

The existence of life in polar areas has always intrigued explorers, for to the casual observer it seems paradoxical that land with conditions so inhospitable to life could support a flora and fauna. Surely, these life forms must have evolved remarkable adaptive mechanisms which allow them to survive and to colonize such rigorous environments. This paper is concerned with the nature of such adaptations, concentrating mainly on Antarctic species and relating their adaptations to those of organisms from other extreme environments.

One question which must precede our discussion is whether adaptation in Antarctica is a real phenomenon. Have organisms evolved adaptations in specific response to the Antarctic conditions or did they arrive at the continent already adapted for life under the existing conditions? This then raises the question as to the origin of terrestrial life in Antarctica—relict or immigrant? Several theories purport to explain the colonization of this continent. One interesting theory proposed by Becquerel (1948) is that the lower life-forms such as insects and cryptogams, might survive for thousands of years under the polar ice and then resume growth once they are ice free. Such a theory, although attractive, is not likely. The frozen state might not be a problem, but the movement of ice and the pressures below and within the ice cap would preclude any survival of life. Observations in Antarctica and alpine areas have not revealed the presence of lichens on rocks exposed by receding ice covers (Swan, 1968; Gannutz, unpublished results).

Another theory is that life-forms survived the Ice Age on nunataks and then subsequently colonized ice-free areas. If so, then they were able to do this because of inherent characteristics rather than rapid adaptive changes. Terrestrial life on high mountains has adapted to conditions which are different from those of lower regions. During the more temperate periods of Antarctic history life on the mountains, which reach heights of more than 5000 m, was probably different, as it is now in temperate regions, from that of lower areas. Such life would survive the large environmental changes caused by the ice. Later, these survivors could colonize areas which became ice-free, since the environmental conditions of the lower exposed areas would be similar to those of their original habitats.

The other and possibly best alternative to explain the origin of terrestrial life in Antarctica is through postglacial invasion from outside the continent, either by land-bridge connections or better still through wind-dispersed propagules. The contamination of Antarctica by propagules carried through the atmosphere from other parts of the world has probably been underestimated, although there have been few direct studies of this long-distance dispersal. Gressitt (1967b) found that insects are blown on to the continent from elsewhere and Rudolph has studied lichen dissemination within Antarctica. It is reasonable to assume that plant propagules and fragments are continually seeding the Antarctic continent. The abundance and persistence of microbes and plant spores in the atmosphere is known (Gregory, 1961; Brown et al., 1964; Gregory and Monteith, 1967). Some of these microbial types and spores are resistant to the atmospheric conditions of desiccation and radiation, and these traits would not only enable them to endure long-distance dispersal but also to survive the Antarctic conditions. The argument which has been raised against this possibility is the presence of a high percentage of endemic forms, particularly lichens, in Antarctica. Many of the endemic lichens, however, are distinguished by small morphological and anatomical differences: there is a high degree of species endemism in Antarctic lichens, but few endemic genera have been described (Rudolph, 1966). Such small differences could be explained as responses to extreme environmental conditions, so that we might consider the so-called endemic lichens as ecotypes of forms which exist elsewhere. The difficulties in this sort of argument, particularly when applied to lichens, are difficult to resolve. At present, we are unable to culture lichens routinely in the laboratory or in the field and thus have no mechanism by which to test the morphological range of lichens and their responses to a variety of conditions. However, recognizing the plasticity of fungal structure and growth under different conditions, a fact seen also with isolated and cultured lichen fungi, one would expect significant variations in thallus structure dependent upon environmental conditions. Another argument against long-range dispersal of lichens might be that the lichens of Antarctica do not produce asexual propagules (Dodge and Baker, 1938; Dodge, 1965), the argument being that if the propagules established themselves in Antarctica then the individuals they formed should produce propagules. However, fragments of plants, if small enough, could also serve effectively in dissemination. Rudolph and Wetmore (Rudolph, 1966) found that the air in vegetated areas of Antarctica contained plant propagules in the form of both fragments and spores. Another point of consideration is that

Antarctic lichens belong to families with wide distribution around the world and most of the Antarctic lichens are crustose forms, a type which generally is highly polymorphic. The bipolar distribution of some of these lichens (Lamb, 1964) is also in favour of the long-distance dispersal theory.

In considering the origin of the Antarctic flora, attention must be paid not only to the mode of introduction of each plant to the continent via some propagule, but also to its establishment in an ecological niche favourable, or at least tolerant, to its development. The environmental conditions which terrestrial life in Antarctica must endure are formidable and include persistently low temperatures during the winter. In summer rapid fluctuations of temperature cause repeated freezing and thawing of organisms. High winds cause not only desiccation but also abrasion due to blowing snow and ice. The small amount of precipitation and the low water-vapour content of the atmosphere coupled with wind desiccation induce extreme desert-like conditions. Radiation is another problem along with short productive seasons due to long periods of darkness and nutrient-poor substrates. The two most critical conditions for life-forms appear to be desiccation and the shortness of the productive season. The adaptations of Antarctic organisms to these conditions can be grouped into three categories, i.e. ecological, morphological, and physiological.

II. Ecological Adaptations

The few ecological niches in Antarctica are limited to ice-free coastal areas and exposed nunataks. Availability of liquid water appears to be the overriding factor in determining the areas that are colonized by life. This fact has been observed by Rudolph (1966), Boyd et al., (1966), Gressitt (1967a), Schofield and Rudolph (1969), and Gannutz (1967). Rudolph, Schofield and Gannutz feel that water not only influences metabolism but also transports nitrogen and inorganic ions to the plants. Schofield (unpublished results) considers that the water also modifies the soil by removing large concentrations of toxic ions caused by weathering.

Recent field observations on vegetation have been made by Rudolph, Schofield and Gannutz. The main findings are that the vegetation is patchy (Rudolph, 1967) and microclimates which include water and protection from wind are favoured sites. In one interesting study, Gannutz recorded the density of lichens on rocks at varying distances from the melting edge of a snowfield, one large enough to persist through the summer. He found a greater number of lichens on rocks in the areas that were covered with snow for most of the summer. Microclimate measurements showed that areas beneath the snowfield, some distance from the edge, were favourable for growth in terms of available water, temperature and light intensity. The temperatures of the lichen-covered rocks beneath 36 cm of snow and from 2 to 3 m from the melting edge were above freezing for extended periods during extremely warm summer days. There appeared to be sufficient lateral conduction of the heat from exposed rocks near the edge of the snowfield to melt the snow over the rocks in the inner part of the snow cover.

Schofield and Rudolph in 1969, in ecological studies of macroscopic terrestrial cryptogams at Cape Royds and Cape Crozier, determined that wind, soil composition and moisture, substrate characteristics and atmospheric water vapour content were factors which appeared to interact to influence where plants will grow. Schofield found a distinct divergence between the distribution of soil and rock lichens in areas away from bird colonies. Soil lichens, along with mosses and blue-green algae, were confined to moist sheltered sites which faced eastward and northward, while rock lichens displayed no distributional pattern that could be related to either moisture or exposure. This seems to favour the idea that liquid water is important also as a means of making nitrogen available to nitrophilous lichens. These lichens are prevalent near penguin and other bird colonies where guano blown around the area by wind is dissolved in melting water and carried off. The accumulation of the nitrophilous lichens, therefore, around stream beds or any melting water in that area is understandable. A continuing study by Schofield and Rudolph on the distribution and availability of nitrogen in Antarctic substrates should give us further information on this matter.

III. Morphological Adaptations

Most of the information on this subject has been gathered from studies of the lichen flora (Siple, 1938; Dodge and Baker, 1938; Dodge, 1965).

The adaptive characteristics of lichens include the type, shape and size of thallus, pigmentation, anatomical details and reproduction. The majority of Antarctic lichens grow on rocks and have crustose thalli, which adhere closely to the rock surface. A few lichen species grow over mosses and soil. Antarctic lichen thalli are smaller than the same or similar species growing elsewhere. Many of the Antarctic lichens are pigmented with dark colours (Siple, 1938; Filson, 1966). The pigmentation may be less a reflection of a response to the light intensity than a natural selection of pigmented lichens; that is, only those lichens with a greater concentration of pigments or lichen acids in the outer layers of the thallus, above the light-sensitive algae, could survive the Antarctic light conditions. The dark-coloured thalli would also acquire higher temperatures than light-coloured forms (Lange, 1954). Thus, genera such as *Buellia*, *Caloplaca* and *Xanthoria* have many species represented in Antarctica. In addition to the protective pigmentation, which may be even more enhanced in normally pigmented forms, the lichens produce amorphous, protective layers either as part of the upper cortex or in addition to it. These layers reduce water evaporation and resist wind erosion.

In terms of reproduction, there has been little adaptation. Dodge (1965) mentions larger spermogonia in Antarctic species and suggests that this may be a compensation for more production of the male gametes or spermatia. Dodge believes that asexual multiplication is less common among Antarctic lichens. This, however, is due to the high proportion of crustose lichens which rarely have sorediate species. Many species form fruiting bodies which seem large, well developed and with numerous spores. Again, however, this seems to be no different from other areas.

The morphological adaptations of Antarctic lichens are similar to those of lichens of desert areas and indeed those of any fully exposed habitat. Galun (1963) found that in the Negev desert of Israel more than 80% of the lichens are crustose, a similar phenomenon being noted for the Algerian Sahara. Over 60% of the lichens have amorphous upper layers and a powdery superficial layer called a pruina. In lichens with no protective upper layer crystals of calcium oxalate were distributed throughout the upper cortex, another mechanism for preventing or retarding extreme evaporation from the thallus. About two-thirds of the Negev lichens have a white or greyish-white thallus and darker thalli, i.e. orange or brown, are covered with a whitish pruina. The explanation proposed for this is that the whitish-coloured thalli would absorb less heat rays than the darker ones—directly opposite to the situation found in Antarctica. Looman (1964) found that *Lecanora reptans*, described from Saskatchewan, had the thickest cortex in fully exposed thalli, the increase in thickness reaching 100% or more. Pigmentation and pruina were also evident among the lichens of fully exposed habitats. Galun (1963) described *Buellia canescens* as having a thick amorphous upper layer in Negev and no such layer in Sweden, where it also grows.

IV. Physiological Adaptations

The earliest physiological study of Antarctic lichens was begun by Schofield and Ahmadjian in 1963. These investigations, still in progress, are concerned with the temperature and nutritional preferences of the isolated symbionts of Antarctic lichens. Schofield found that the lichen fungus *Lecanora tephroeceta* assimilated nitrogen mostly as ammonium. This preference for ammonium nitrogen correlates well with the lichen's habitat, which was near a snow-petrel colony. Schofield also found that *Prasiola crispa* ssp. *antarctica* grew twice as well with uric acid as with other nitrogen compounds, another correlation with habitat, since this alga is very common in penguin colonies and uric acid is the principal form in which nitrogen is excreted by birds. The restrictive adaptations such as nitrophily which are exhibited by some Antarctic lichens and algae raises once again the problem of the colonization of Antarctica, that is, it is more logical to assume that these organisms arrived already pre-adapted for the nitrophilous habitats.

Studies on the photosynthesis and respiration of Antarctic lichens are being conducted by Prof. Lange at the University of Würzburg, Germany, and Dr. Gannutz from Clark University. Both have kindly made available to me their preliminary findings. Lange is studying Antarctic lichens as part of his overall research programme on the ecophysiology of lichens from xerophytic habitats, such as high mountains and desert areas. He served as a consultant to the Clark University research programme and spent several months at Hallett Station in 1966 during the first field season of the programme. The lichens which Lange collected at Hallett were transported to Germany in the dried state. Before testing, the specimens were soaked with water and transferred to temperature-controlled plant chambers. The CO_2 output and intake was measured with an infrared-recorder. Gannutz is studying lichen metabolism directly under field conditions using equipment designed by himself and Artisan Industries in Waltham, Massachusetts. The instrumentation is self-contained and mounted in heated, weatherproof, aluminium cases, with power supplied by gasoline generators. The equipment consists of an infrared-CO_2 analyser, and microclimate-recording devices which measure water vapour, temperature, light intensity and wind velocity (Gannutz, 1967). The instrumentation can record the relationship between microclimate and general weather conditions and correlate this information with the rates of carbon-dioxide turnover in lichens. The studies of Lange and Gannutz should provide an interesting and valuable comparison of field versus laboratory measurements.

Both Lange and Gannutz found that Antarctic lichens can maintain a positive metabolic balance at low temperatures. Lange found that *Neuropogon* showed a positive balance at $-18.5°C$ and other lichens bound considerable quantities of CO_2 at temperatures below zero. He has shown such CO_2 binding to be due without doubt to photosynthetic fixation. Both investigators found that respiration increased markedly with increased temperatures while photosynthesis decreased. Optimal photosynthetic CO_2 intake for *Neuropogon* at low light intensities (8757–20,000 lux) was in the region of $0°C$, while at the highest light intensity used (48,455 lux) the optimum was in the region of $+5°C$. At thallus temperatures higher than 20–22°C, under the greatest illumination, there was no positive balance because of the increased respiration. According to Lange, this strong respiration at high temperatures seems generally to be a typical phenomenon of lichens growing in cold climatic conditions. With *Xanthoria mawsoni* the optimal temperature was in the warmer regions and respiration did not rise as rapidly. The optimum photosynthetic peaks ranged from about 10°C at the lowest light intensity to about 20°C at the highest light level. Lange feels that *Xanthoria* is not strongly specialized for colder regions. However, its CO_2 fixation at low temperatures is quite high and allows it to grow in frigid areas.

Lange found that at a thallus temperature of $-8°C$ only about 500 lux are necessary for the light-compensation point. This small amount of light necessary for CO_2 intake under cold conditions indicates that the lichens can maintain a positive balance even under snow. As mentioned earlier, Gannutz in his ecological observations noted that snow cover provided optimal conditions for the growth of lichens.

Both Lange and Gannutz found that *Xanthoria* could absorb sufficient water vapour from the air to carry on measurable rates of photosynthesis. Lange passed air of high water pressure over dried lichen specimens and noted the first measurable CO_2 intake after about ten hours. Gannutz found that among the Hallett lichens only *Xanthoria* had this capacity of conducting some metabolism during periods when it was not saturated with liquid water. The rates, however, were much less than the maximum rates of photosynthesis and respiration. This ability to absorb water vapour helps to explain the abundance of this lichen in Antarctica, particularly along coastal areas where periods of high air humidity occur.

With respect to cold resistance of Antarctic lichens, Lange and his colleague Dr. Kappen tested five species. Each species survived a frost treatment at $-198°C$ if they were cooled by slow degrees and then warmed slowly. *Caloplaca elegans* and *Rinodina frigida* recovered most quickly, photosynthesis being normal within one day of the cold treatment. *Xanthoria mawsoni* took two days to recover full photosynthetic capacity and *Umbilicaria decussata* took seven to eight days. Respiration followed a similar pattern to photosynthesis. The lichens were more sensitive to a rapid cooling down to $-198°C$ (submersion in liquid N) and thawing at $+10°C$. Here the photosynthetic performance was at first greatly suppressed and returned to normal levels only after twenty-one to twenty-six days. *Buellia* attained only 30% of its capacity after twenty-one days. *Xanthoria* did not surpass the compensation point within this time, while *Umbilicaria* respired but showed no photosynthesis. This variable behaviour probably reflects the ecological distribution of these lichens.

Dehydration appears to increase the cold resistance of plants and animals (Scholander *et al.*, 1953). The formation of intracellular ice and not temperature *per se* is the major factor in cold damage. Intracellular ice can be prevented from forming by dehydration and increased sugar concentration, both of which increase the osmotic pressures. The extreme cold-resistance of lichens, for example, is undoubtedly due to their ability to undergo rapid dehydration. These investigators also showed that a lichen and an insect larva regularly have up to more than 90% of their total moisture frozen to ice during the coldest winter months.

Gannutz found that when lichens were wetted after the dry winter period high rates of photosynthesis began almost immediately. When *Umbilicaria* and *Neuropogon* were artificially darkened for a few hours during the day and then illuminated, they achieved maximum rates of photosynthesis after only nine minutes. This ability of Antarctic lichens to resume photosynthesis fully after a long freezing period is a fine adaptation to this habitat. They can thus utilize, without a long reactivation period, short periods of favourable conditions for nutrient gains. Lange (1966) first demonstrated this for the alpine lichen *Cladonia alcicornis*, which could still photosynthesize at near normal level after two years at −15°C. Reid (1960) showed that long-term drying had little effect on the photosynthesis and respiration of the arctic-alpine lichen *Rhizocarpon geographicum*, while in temperate lichens, drying caused an inhibition of photosynthesis and a stimulation of respiration rates after the lichens were wetted. Gannutz found that when the alga *Prasiola* and the moss *Bryum* were wetted after the winter period, they required from five to seven days in a wet condition to become photosynthetically active. Thus, these organisms are restricted to areas where they will be wet for extended periods of time, i.e. low areas where melt water from the mountain slopes accumulates. Their optimal temperatures for photosynthesis are between 7°C and 27°C, temperatures at which water is most available. Optimal conditions for Antarctic lichens to maintain a positive metabolic balance were between −10° to +10°C. Below −10°C respiration was not detected and photosynthesis was not quantitative. Gannutz further found that during a ten-day period at −17°C the lichens and mosses he studied at Palmer Station were damaged. He felt that complete recovery probably would not occur until spring. *Neuropogon* was the only plant not damaged during this period.

As temperature decreases the light compensation point for photosynthesis is lower. Respiration becomes inhibited at lower temperatures, while photosynthesis is little affected. Thus, lichens can maintain a positive metabolic balance more easily at low temperatures. At high temperatures, respiration increases markedly and the ratio is reversed. Thus, an extended period of high temperatures for these lichens is damaging.

Gannutz feels that lichen growth is not uniform for both partners, but a stepwise progression. His research indicates that the two lichen symbionts operate somewhat independently of each other, more so than previously suspected. The algae grow, divide, and build up reserves during periods of cold (as indicated by the photosynthetic activity at low temperatures) while the fungus is at rest. During warm periods, under heat and light conditions that may be damaging to the alga, the fungus is active (as indicated by measured respiration which from a lichen is largely that of the fungus). The fungus utilizes the algal reserves and the dead algal cells. Studies on the isolated *Trebouxia* phycobionts of Antarctic lichens (Ahmadjian, unpublished results) support this idea. These algae have optimal growth temperatures between 10°C and 15°C and low optimal light intensities (30–50 ft c). At higher temperatures and light intensities they are quickly damaged. Gannutz stresses that the long-term respiration versus photosynthesis ratio necessary for the sustenance of the lichen symbiosis is not known. The total yearly metabolic balance figures are necessary for determination of the true nature of the lichen symbiosis.

Mosses photosynthesize and respire at temperatures near −4°C, and below this photosynthesis ceases but respiration continues. *Deschampsia* does not photosynthesize below 0°C but respires at high rates down to −10°C. Adaptation to low temperatures is found also among the arthropods, most species still being active a few degrees below freezing (Gressitt, 1967a). The terrestrial fauna of Antarctica is similar to that of the summits of high mountains (Gressitt, 1967a). Like lichens, the arthropods are tolerant of extremely cold and windy habitats.

The recently discovered phenomenon of multiple temperature optima (Oppenheimer and Drost-Hansen, 1960) has been found to be quite common among Antarctic micro-organisms (Sieburth, 1965). This suggests that polar micro-organisms which are active at low temperatures may also be active in tropical environments and that an organism in its natural environment may have more than one optimal temperature for activity (Oppenheimer and Drost-Hansen, 1960). Schofield found two temperature optima for the Antarctic lichen fungus *Lecanora tephroeceta* in culture, one between 3°C and 7°C and the other near 19°C.

In general, the Antarctic terrestrial life-forms have not developed any unique adaptive mechanisms. The adaptations they exhibit, in terms of their ecology, morphology and physiology, are similar to those of organisms in high-latitude alpine, arctic and desert regions of the world. These adaptations reflect responses to three environmental conditions—availability of water, light intensity and extreme temperature. Lichens, however, may not be good indicators of adaptations to the Antarctic environment. Weber (1966), who found a low percentage of endemism among lichens of the Galapagos Islands, feels that lichens may have reached a point of genetic stability because they exhibit so little in terms of morphological-geographic races.

References

Becquerel, P. (1948). Reviviscence du *Xanthoria parietina* Desséché avec sa Faune, Six Ans dans le Vide et Deux Semaines à −189°C. Ses Conséquences Biologiques. *C. r. hebd. Searc. Acad. Sci. Paris.* **226**, 1413–15.

Boyd, W. L., Staley, J. T. and Boyd, J. W. (1966). Ecology of soil micro-organisms of Antarctica. *In* "Antarctic Soils and Soil Forming Processes", *Antarct. Res. Ser.* Vol. 8. American Geophysical Union, Washington, D.C. 125–59.

Brown, R. M., Larson, D. A. and Bold, H. C. (1964). Airborne Algae: Their Abundance and Heterogeneity. *Science* **143**, 583–5.

Dodge, C. W. and Baker, G. E. (1938). Lichens and lichen parasites. *In* "The Second Byrd Antarctic Expedition-Botany". *Ann. Mo. bot. Gdn.* **25**, No. 2,515–718.

Dodge, C. W. (1965). Lichens. *In* "Biogeography and Ecology in Antarctica". (Miegham, T. Van, and Oye, P. Van, eds), W. Junk, Den Haag. 194–200.

Filson, R. B. (1966). The Lichens and Mosses of MacRobertson Land. Antarctic Division, Department of External Affairs Australia, Publication No. 82. *ANARE Sci. Repts. Ser.* B (II) Botany 1–169.

Galun, M. (1963). Autecological and synecological observations on lichens of the Negev, Israel. *Israel J. Bot.* **12**, 179–87.

Gannutz, T. P. (1967). Effects of environmental extremes on lichens. *Soc. bot. Fr., Colloque sur les Lichens*, 169–79.

Gregory, P. H. (1961)."The Microbiology of the Atmosphere." Leonard Hill, London, 1–251.

Gregory, P. H. and Monteith, J. L. (eds.) (1967). "Airborne Microbes". *Symp. Soc. Gen., Microbiol.* **17**. 1–385.

Gressitt, J. L. (1967*a*). The Fauna. *In* "Terrestrial Life of Antarctica", *Antarctic Map Folio Series*. (Bushnell, V. C. ed.), American Geographical Society, N.Y. 17–21.

Gressitt, J. L. (1967*b*). Introduction. *In* "Entomology of Antarctica", (Gressitt, J. L. ed.). *Antart. Res. Ser.* **10**. American Geophysical Union, Washington, D.C. 1–33.

Lamb, I. M. (1964). Antarctic Lichens 1. The Genera *Usnea, Ramalina, Himantormia, Alectoria, Cornicularia. Brit. Antart. Surv. Sci. Repts* 38, 1–34.

Lange, O. L. (1954). Einige Messungen zum Wärmehaushalt poikilohyder Flechten und Moose. *Arch. Met. Geophys. Bioklim.* B 5, 182–90.

Lange, O. L. (1966). CO_2-Gaswechsel der Flechten *Cladonia alcicornis* nach langfristigem Aufenthalt bei tiefen Temperaturen. *Flora, Tena,* **156**, 500–2.

Looman, J. (1964). Ecology of lichen and bryophyte communities in Saskatchewan. *Ecology* **45**, 481–91.

Oppenheimer, C. H. and Drost-Hansen, W. (1960). A relationship between multiple temperature optima for biological systems and the properties of water. *J. Bact.* **80**, 21–24.

Reid, A. (1960). Nachwirkungen der Entquellung auf den Gaswechsel von Krustenflechten. *Biol. Zbl.* 79, 657–78.

Rudolph, E. D. (1966). Terrestrial vegetation of Antarctica: Past and present studies. *In* "Antarctic Soils and Soil Forming Processes", *Antarct. Res. Ser.* Vol. 8. American Geophysical Union, Washington, D.C. 109–24.

Rudolph, E. D. (1967). Lichen Distribution. *In* "Terrestrial Life of Antarctica", *Antarctic Map Folio Series* (Bushnell, V. C. ed). American Geophysical Society, N.Y. 9–11.

Schofield, E. and Rudolph, E. D. (1969). Factors influencing the distribution of Antarctic terrestrial plants. *Ant. J. U.S.*, 112–13.

Scholander, P. F., Flagg, W., Hock, R. J. and Irving, L. (1953). Studies on the physiology of frozen plants and animals in the Arctic. *J. Cell. Comp. Physiol.* **42**, (Suppl. 1), 1–56.

Sieburth, J. M. (1965). Microbiology of Antarctica. *In* "Biogeography and Ecology in Antarctica". (Miegham, J. Van and Oye, P. Van, eds), W. Junk, Den Haag, 267–95.
Siple, P. A. (1938). Ecology and Geographical Distribution. The Second Byrd Antarctic Expedition-Botany. *Ann. Mo. bot. Gdn.* **25**. 467–514.
Swan, L. W. (1968). Alpine and aeolian regions of the world. *In* "Arctic and Alpine Environments" (Wright, H. E., Jr. and Osburn, W. H. eds.). Indiana Univ. Press, 29–54.
Weber, W. A. (1966). Lichenology and Bryology in the Galapagos Island, with check lists of the lichens and bryophytes thus far reported. *In* "The Galapagos" (Bowman, R. I. ed.). Univ. of California Press, Berkeley and Los Angeles. 190–200.

Local Dissemination of Plant Propagules in Antarctica*

EMANUEL D. RUDOLPH
*College of Biological Sciences and
Institute of Polar Studies,
The Ohio State University, Columbus, Ohio, U.S.A.*

Long-distance dissemination of plant propagules is often cited as most pertinent to Antarctic plant colonization; however, little attention has been given
to the problem of local dissemination. Some data relating to the latter problem
were gathered at two sites in Antarctica: at the base of Cape Hallett in Victoria
Land 72°S 170°E, and in the vicinity of the Fosdick Mountains in Marie Byrd
Land 77°S 144°W. At ground level or a few inches above it, airborne propagules were trapped on continuously exposed slides made sticky with a
silicone coating and changed every twenty-four hours, or on petri plates containing Sabourand dextrose and malt extract agar and exposed daily for
thirty-minute periods. Using these methods, it was possible to count and
identify all of the trapped gravity-settling propagules with the exception of
bacteria.

At Cape Hallett macrovegetational propagules were found on the sticky
slides. They included algal thalli fragments and single cells, moss buds and
leaf fragments, and lichen soredia and spores (Fig. 1). The total numbers of
propagules isolated on the slides were 148 algae, nine mosses, and seventeen
lichens on 24 cm² of slide surface in the 1344 hours of continuous exposure.
Propagules were trapped at a rate of 0·74/m²hr (eliminating from the calculation those few sticky slides that were blown away). The macrovegetation in
the vicinity of the experiment was composed of green and blue-green algae with
a cover of 12·8% and an absolute frequency of 83%, mosses with a cover of
2·4% and a frequency of 16%, and lichens with a cover of 0·2% and a frequency
of 1% (Rudolph, 1963). The macrovegetational propagules were trapped with
the following frequencies: algae 85%, mosses 5%, lichens 10%. The frequency of moss propagules was lower and that of lichen propagules higher
than would have been anticipated from the parent plant frequencies in the

---

* This is Contribution No. 140 of the Institute of Polar Studies, The Ohio State University,
Columbus, Ohio 43210.

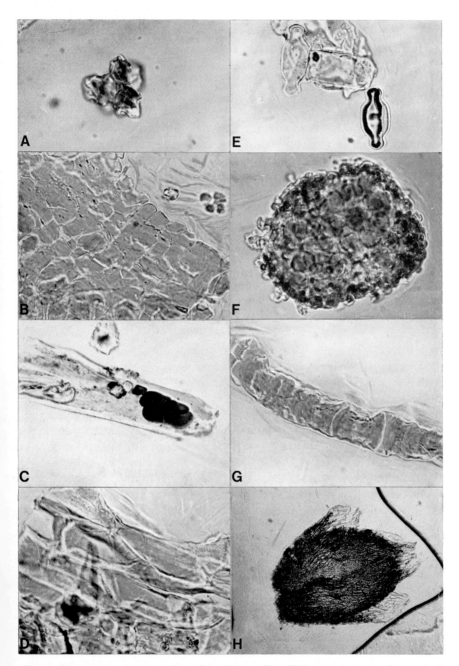

FIG. 1. Plant propagules trapped on sticky slides at Cape Hallett. A. A clump of green algal cells. B. A portion of a thallus fragment of the green alga, *Prasiola crispa*. C. Ascus with some ascospores of the lichen *Buellia* sp. D. A portion of a moss leaf fragment E. Two diatom cells. F. A lichen soredium. G. A portion of a green algal filament. H. A moss bud. (A-G ca 375X, H ca 180X.)

vicinity. Algal propagules were in frequencies close to that of their vegetational percentage. In addition, four genera of microfungi were isolated on the exposed petri plates. Over half the fungi isolated belong to the genus *Penicillium*. The other genera represented were *Phoma*, *Neurospora*, and the yeast genus *Rhodotorula*.

In Marie Byrd Land, where the nearest known vegetation was seven miles away, the sticky slides were devoid of propagules except for a few that appeared to be dried algal cells. The slides were exposed for a total of 456 hours. All of the fungi isolated on the petri plates belonged to the genus *Penicillium*.

Previous surveys reported in the literature have concentrated primarily on pollen and fungal spores due to their abundance in the temperate and tropical air "spora" and their allergenic importance. It is probable, as Brown *et al.*, (1964) have shown, that there are significant numbers of algal propagules in temperate air. Lichen and moss propagules are rarely reported. Pettersson (1940) summarizes much of the literature concerning these groups. Moss propagules are usually reported as being spores and only rarely as protonemal fragments. Lichen propagules are more frequently thallus fragments than soredia. Dispersal of lichen soredia has been induced in laboratory studies (Brodie and Gregory, 1953; Bailey, 1966). Bailey (1966) also reports that "extremely few soredia" were trapped in the field.

This study provides some significant data about mosses and lichens. The mosses whose propagules were in low frequencies were not producing sporophytes or spores; thus it is reasonable to find propagules that were either leaf fragments or buds, the latter common on the local *Bryum argenteum*. The mosses are in patches and one patch could represent growth from a single original propagule. Thus, the frequencies of moss propagules are consistent with the growth aspects of the local mosses. The lichen soredia were more common than spores and no thallus fragments were trapped. Apothecia were present on several local lichen species and most lichens had soredia. A possible explanation for the lack of thallus fragments might be that all the lichens were low-growing crustose or foliose types which would not be exposed to as strong winds as higher-growing lichens found in other regions of the world. In addition, in most regions animals cause fragmentation while walking over dry lichens. But in Antarctica there are no large land animals. The presence of algal thallus fragments could be explained by their very fragile nature when dry and by their presence near the penguin rookery where some penguins and skuas could have walked over them.

The predominance of *Penicillium* spores over other mould spores in the Antarctic air is at odds with findings from other parts of the world. Many surveys of Northern and Southern Hemisphere air (di Menna, 1955; van der Werff, 1958; Frey and Durie, 1960, 1962; Adams, 1964; Grose *et al.*, 1967), indicate that *Cladosporium* (*Hormodendron*) has the greatest frequency, generally composing over 50% of the spores trapped. The figures for *Penicillium* are usually between 6% and 13%. Some higher frequencies for *Penicillium* have been reported in the Netherlands and Switzerland (van der Werff, 1958) in the Northern Hemisphere and for New Zealand (di Menna, 1955) and Colombia (Grose *et al.*, 1967) in the Southern Hemisphere. *Cladosporium*, by its more seasonal variation than *Penicillium*, is perhaps more dependent upon large amounts of plant debris. In studies of soil organisms and air propagules, Heal (1967) states that many organisms reach Signy Island in the air. However, some of these, for example *Penicillium*, were not found in the soil. In soil studies at Cape Hallett (Table 1), *Cladosporium* was twice isolated from soil in association with mosses. Whereas Signy Island soils apparently lack *Penicillium* (Heal *et al.*, 1967), those in the McMurdo Sound area (Boyd and Boyd, 1963; Janetschek, 1967) at Ellsworth Station and Antarctic Peninsula sites (Corte and Daglio, 1963, 1964) and in the vicinity of Showa Base (Tubaki and Asano, 1965), contain this mould. *Penicillium* was present in soils at Cape Hallett (Table 1) and this fact could account for *Penicillium* spores in Cape Hallett air. Yeast taxa have been reported from Antarctic soils in recent years (di Menna, 1960, 1966a, 1966b; Sondeda, 1961; Corte and Daglio, 1963, 1964) and several were found at Cape Hallett (Table 1). One genus, *Rhodotorula*, was also found in the air. Skuas that had fed upon station garbage were nesting in the vicinity of the petri plates. This would help to explain the presence of *Saccharomyces cerevisiae* in the soil as yeasts were isolated from the bills and feet of the skuas. Human introduction of other fungal taxa is also a possibility.

TABLE 1

Fungi isolated

Organism	Victoria Land soil	Victoria Land air	Marie Byrd Land air
Cladosporium cladosporioides	+		
Mucor sp.	+		
Neurospora sitophila		+	
Paecilomyces sp.	+		
Penicillium charlesii	+	+	+
Penicillium chrysogenum ser.	+	+	+
Penicillium frequentans			+
Penicillium meleagrinum	+	+	+
Penicillium notatum	+		+
Phoma sp.		+	
Mycelia sterila	+		
Rhodotorula minuta		+	
Rhodotorula texensis	+		
Saccharomyces cerevisiae	+		

The hourly count of 0·74 propagules /m²hr of surface of sticky slide at Cape Hallett is low when compared with the hourly count of 16 fungal spores /m² on sticky slides exposed at Sydney, Australia (Frey and Durie, 1962). Where open petri plate sampling is reported in the literature, the number of spores as indicated by mould colonies average between 26 and 292/hr. At Cape Hallett the number was 1·6/hr and in the Fosdick Mountains 1·2/hr. It would appear that the concentration of local plant propagules in coastal Antarctic air is much lower than that found in other regions of the world where measurements have been made. Perhaps the only comparable low figures are those for the central Arctic Ocean basin (Barghoorn, 1957). Attempts to relate quantities of propagules to local Antarctic climatic conditions were inconclusive, but do indicate a slight positive correlation with strong winds and snowfall.

Plant propagules are present in low concentrations in Antarctic coastal air. These represent plants in the vicinity and may help to explain the invasion and establishment of vegetation in newly exposed areas. Further study of dissemination could help in the understanding of the spread of the Antarctic terrestrial vegetation.

Acknowledgements

The field studies upon which this paper is based were supported by grants GA-52 and GA-496 from the Office of Antarctic Programs, National Science Foundation; and the logistics were provided by the United States Navy.

I express my appreciation to Dr. Margaret di Menna, Department of Scientific and Industrial Research, Lower Hutt, New Zealand; Dr. Emory G. Simmons, United States Army Natick Laboratories, Natick, Massachusetts and Mr Donald T. Wicklow, Department of Botany, University of Wisconsin, Madison, Wisconsin for examining and identifying certain cultures. Dr. Clifford M. Wetmore, Wartburg College, Waverley, Iowa, isolated the fungi from the soil.

References

Adams, K. F. (1964). Year to year variation in the fungus spore content of the atmosphere. *Acta allerg.* 19, 11–50.
Bailey, R. H. (1966). Studies on the dispersal of lichen soredia. *J. Linn. Soc. (Bot.)* 59, 479–90.
Barghoorn, E. S. (1957). Palynological studies of organic sediments from Ice Island T-3 and of coated slides exposed on T-3 and Ellesmere Island. *Final Report Under Contract No. AF 19(604)-1371.* Cambridge, Massachusetts: Harvard University. 1–27.

Boyd, W. L. and Boyd, J. W. (1963). Soil organisms of the McMurdo Sound area, Antarctica. *Appl. Microbiol.* 2, No. 2, 116–21.

Brodie, H. J. and Gregory, P. H. (1953). The action of wind in the dispersal of spores from cup-shaped plant structures. *Can. J. Bot.* 31, 402–10.

Brown, R. M., Jr., Larson, D. A. and Bold, H. C. (1964). Airborne algae: Their abundance and heterogeneity. *Science*, 143, 583–5.

Corte, A. and Daglio, C. A. N. (1963). Micromicetes aislados en el Antártico. *Contrnes. Inst. Antart. Argent.* 74, 3–27.

Corte, A. and Daglio, C. A. N. (1964). A mycological study of the Antarctic air. *In* "Biologie Antarctique: Antarctic Biology" (Carrick, R., Holdgate, M. and Prévost, J. eds.) Hermann, Paris. 115–20.

di Menna, M. E. (1955). A quantitative study of air-borne fungus spores in Dunedin, New Zealand. *Trans. Br. mycol. Soc.* 38, No. 2, 119–29.

di Menna, M. E. (1960). Yeasts from Antarctica. *J. gen. Microbiol.* 23, 295–300.

di Menna, M. E. (1966a). Three new yeasts from Antarctic soils: *Candida nivalis*, *Candida gelida* and *Candida frigida* spp. n. *Antonie van Leeuwenhoek* 32, 25–28.

di Menna, M. E. (1966b). Yeasts in Antarctic soils. *Antonie van Leeuwenhoek* 32, 29–38.

Frey, D. and Durie, E. B. (1960). The incidence of air-borne fungus in Sydney. *Mycopath. Mycol. appl.* 13, 93–99.

Frey, D. and Durie, E. B. (1962). Estimation of air-borne fungus spores; a comparison of slide and culture methods. *Mycopath. Mycol. appl.* 16, 295–303.

Grose, E. S., Szekessy, M. and Muñoz, N. (1967). Airborne fungus spores in Bogota, Colombia: a five year study. *Sabouraudia* 6, No. 1, 42–50.

Heal, O. W. (1967). Discussion of papers. *Phil. Trans. R. Soc.* B 252, No. 777, 212.

Heal, O. W., Bailey, A. D. and Latter, P. M. (1967). Bacteria, fungi and protozoa in Signy Island soils compared with those from a temperate moorland. *Phil. Trans. R. Soc.* B 252, No. 777, 191–97.

Janetschek, H. (1967). Arthropod ecology of South Victoria Land. *Antarct. Res. Ser. Am. Geophysical Union.* 10, 205–93.

Pettersson, B. (1940). Experimentelle Untersuchungen über die euanemoche Verbreitung der Sporenpflanzen. *Acta bot. Fenn.* 25, 1–103.

Rudolph, E. D. (1963). Vegetation of Hallett Station area, Victoria Land, Antarctica. *Ecology* 44, No. 3, 585–86.

Sondeda, M. (1961). On some yeasts from the Antarctic region. *Special Publications from the Seto Marine Biological Laboratory, Sirahama, Japan. Biological Results of the Japanese Antarctic Research Expedition*, No. 15, 1–10.

Tubaki, K. and Asano. I. (1965). Additional species of fungi isolated from Antarctic materials. *J.A.R.E. Sci. Repts.* Ser. E. 27, 1–12.

van der Werff, P. J. (1958). "Mould Fungi and Bronchial Asthma. A Mycological and Clinical Study." Vol. 1. Charles C. Thomas, Springfield, Illinois.

Growth and Productivity of the Moss *Polytrichum alpestre* Hoppe in Antarctic Regions

R. E. LONGTON
British Antarctic Survey and Department of Botany
*University of Birmingham, England**

I. Introduction

Lewis and Greene (1969) have described a comparative study of growth in introduced crop plants at Arctic and Antarctic stations. A complementary study of relationships between the environment and growth and reproduction in bipolar mosses native to temperate as well as polar regions is in progress. The approach has been firstly to investigate the microclimate in different areas, secondly to compare plant performance in these field environments and thirdly to establish living collections from different populations for comparative experiments under controlled conditions (Longton, 1966). The growth and reproductive cycle of one species, *Polytrichum alpestre* Hoppe, on South Georgia has already been described (Longton and Greene, 1967), and the present paper compares vegetative growth in this species at different stations in the Scotia Ridge-Antarctic Peninsula sector (Fig. 1).

II. Temperatures at Plant Level

Temperature is regarded as one of the most important factors controlling plant growth in this region, and it has been recorded at intervals of three hours for twelve to fifteen-month periods in the surface layers of *P. alpestre* colonies on the Subantarctic island of South Georgia and on Signy Island and the Argentine Islands in the maritime Antarctic (Table 1). The study colonies were near meteorological stations, and the principal features of the macro-climate are described by Pepper (1954). The observations on South Georgia were made on the north-east coast, where conditions may be warmer than on the more exposed southern and western coasts.

The results demonstrate considerable differences in microclimate between the three stations, during both winter and summer (Fig. 2). The colony on South Georgia was covered by 30 to 100 cm of snow from mid-May to mid-

* Present address: Department of Botany, University of Manitoba, Canada.

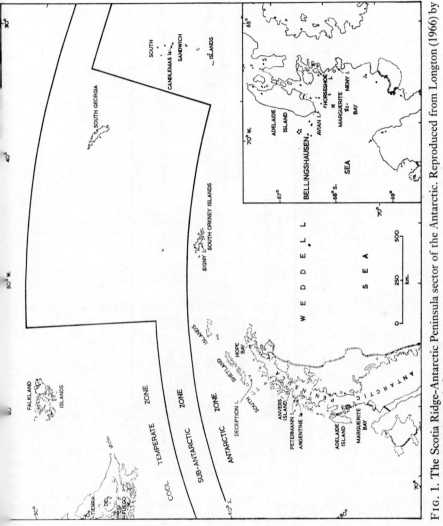

FIG. 1. The Scotia Ridge–Antarctic Peninsula sector of the Antarctic. Reproduced from Longton (1966) by courtesy of British Antarctic Survey.

TABLE 1

Study Colonies

Station	Latitude	Aspect	Slope	Altitude	Distance from meteorological station	Probe
King Edward Point, South Georgia	54°17'S	—	Level	5 m	400 m	Shiny-surfaced platinum resistance thermometer among moss leaves on surface of the turf
Factory Cove, Signy Island, South Orkney Islands	60°43'S	NE	20°	15 m	100 m	Thermistor placed 2–3 mm below surface of the turf
Marina Point, Galindez Island, Argentine Islands	65°15'S	NW	12°	15 m	85 m	Thermistor placed 2–3 mm below surface of the turf

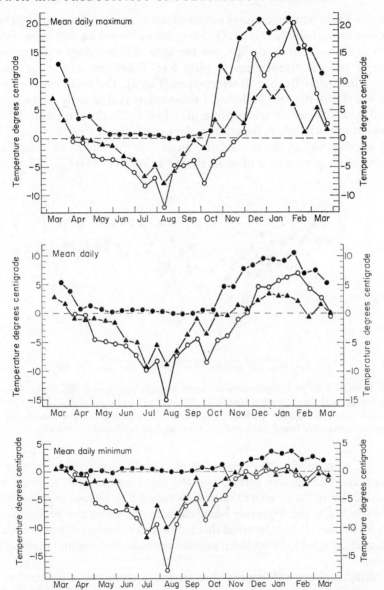

FIG. 2. Mean daily, mean daily maximum and mean daily minimum temperatures in the surface layers of *Polytrichum alpestre* colonies on South Georgia in 1961–62 (●), Signy Island in 1965–66 (▲) and the Argentine Islands in 1965–66 (○) based on eight readings per day averaged over fourteen-day periods. Mid-March 1966 data for Signy Island and the Argentine Islands are based on eleven and thirteen days respectively. Data for South Georgia are taken from Longton and Greene (1967).

October 1961 and temperatures remained steady at around, or slightly above, freezing throughout the winter. On Signy Island the colony was snow covered from April to October in 1965, but the snow was less deep than on South Georgia and the temperature at plant level fluctuated during the winter, though less markedly than air temperature (Fig. 3). The mean daily temperature fell slowly to $-8 \cdot 9°C$ during a two-week period in early August, compared with a mean air temperature of $-14 \cdot 0°C$. At the Argentine Islands, snow cover was largely removed from the study colony by gales in April 1965, and in early August the mean daily, mean daily maximum and mean daily minimum temperatures at plant level were as low as $-15 \cdot 0°C$, $-12 \cdot 1°C$ and

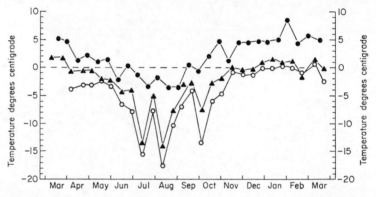

FIG. 3. Mean daily air temperatures on South Georgia in 1961–62 (●), Signy Island in 1965–66 (▲) and the Argentine Islands in 1965–66 (○), based on eight readings per day averaged over fourteen-day periods. Mid-March 1966 data for Signy Island and the Argentine Islands are based on eleven and thirteen days readings respectively.

$-17 \cdot 6°C$ respectively. An extreme low of $-22 \cdot 0°C$ was recorded among the moss leaves during this period, and the mean temperature at plant level exceeded that in the air above the snow by only $2 \cdot 5°C$. Deeper snow cover was re-established at the Argentine Islands later in the winter and persisted until early December. It may be noted that temperature changes during the winter were gradual at both the southern stations and rapid freezing and thawing was avoided.

During summer wide diurnal fluctuations in temperature occurred in all three colonies and mean temperatures at plant level exceeded mean air temperatures. Daily maxima of 10°C to 30°C were commonly recorded, but the temperature often fell rapidly at night to around or below 0°C. It can be seen from Table 2, however, that minimum temperatures during these short-term freeze-thaw cycles seldom fell below $-2 \cdot 75°C$, and were most frequently within $1 \cdot 75°C$ of zero. Moreover, most of the minima below $-3 \cdot 75°C$

TABLE 2

Number of Short-term Freeze-thaw Cycles in Colonies of *Polytrichum alpestre*

Minimum temperature (degrees C)	South Georgia 1961-62							Signy Island 1965-66							Argentine Islands 1965-66						
	> −0·75	> −1·75	> −2·75	> −3·75	> −4·75	> −4·75	Total	> −0·75	> −1·75	> −2·75	> −3·75	> −4·75	> −4·75	Total	> −0·75	> −1·75	> −2·75	> −3·75	> −4·75	> −4·75	Total
March	3	5	3	—	—	—	11	11	2	—	—	—	—	13	No data						
April	15	3	3	1	—	—	22	2	1	1	—	1	1†	6	—	—	—	—	—	—	0
May	7	3	1	—	—	—	11	—	—	—	—	—	—	0	—	—	—	—	—	—	0
June	2	—	—	—	—	—	2	—	—	—	—	—	—	0	—	—	—	—	—	—	0
July	1	—	—	—	—	—	1	—	—	—	—	—	—	0	—	—	—	—	—	—	0
August	3	—	—	—	—	—	3	—	—	—	—	—	—	0	—	—	—	—	—	—	0
September	—	—	—	—	—	—	0	—	1	—	—	—	—	1	—	—	—	—	—	—	0
October	5	—	—	—	—	—	5	11	2	1	—	—	1‡	15	5	—	—	—	—	—	5
November	6	6	2	2	1	—	17	15	2	1	1	1	—	20	17	4	2	1	—	—	24
December	5	—	—	—	—	—	5	18	2	1	—	—	—	21	12	2	—	—	—	—	14
January	3	—	—	—	—	—	3	12	2	2	1	1	—	18	10	6	6	1	1	1§	25
February	7	—	—	—	—	—	7	4	1	2	2	1	—	10	8	4	2	1	1	—	16
March*	1	1	—	—	—	—	2	15	2	1	1	—	—	19	4	2	1	1	—	—	...
Total	58	18	9	3	1	0	89	88	15	9	5	4	2	123	52	16	10	3	2	1	84

* Based on twenty-six days records from South Georgia, twenty-five days from Signy Island and twenty-seven days from the Argentine Islands.

† Minimum = −7·5°C. ‡ Minimum = −11·0°C. § Minimum = −5·5°C.

followed periods of several days with temperatures among the leaves continuously near 0°C.

The warmest summer conditions prevailed on South Georgia, where a mean daily temperature of 10·8°C was recorded in the colony between 18 and 31 January in 1962, with mean daily maxima and minima for this period of 21·2°C and 3·6°C respectively.

The delay in snow clearance at the Argentine Islands until December in 1965 resulted in a cooler microclimate there than on Signy Island during

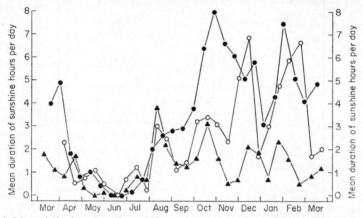

FIG. 4. Mean daily duration of sunshine on South Georgia in 1961–62 (●), Signy Island in 1965–66 (▲) and the Argentine Islands in 1965–66 (○), averaged over fourteen-day periods. Mid-March 1966 data for Signy Island and the Argentine Islands are based on eleven and thirteen days readings respectively.

October and November, and mean daily minimum temperatures remained close to freezing at both stations throughout the summer of 1965–66. However, from December to February a greater diurnal range was recorded on the Argentine Islands than on Signy Island, and mean daily and mean daily maximum temperatures were higher at the former station; mean daily temperatures at the two sites reached 7·1°C and 3·6°C respectively (Fig. 2). Similar differences between the stations were recorded during 1965–66 by thermistors in other colonies, although Signy Island lies some 500 km further north than the Argentine Islands and has marginally higher air temperatures (Fig. 3). This is undoubtedly due largely to the shorter duration of sunshine on Signy Island (Fig. 4), perhaps combined with the lower frequency of strong winds at the Argentine Islands. Signy Island regularly experiences slightly higher summer air temperatures but less sunshine and more frequent strong winds than the Argentine Islands (Pepper, 1954), and thus the difference in microclimate between the stations recorded in 1965–66 may be a regular feature.

III. Growing Season for *Polytrichum alpestre*

P. alpestre occurs in southern South America and the Falkland Islands (Podpěra, 1954), and extends southwards on islands of the Scotia Ridge and along the west coast of the Antarctic Peninsula as far as Jenny Island (lat. 68°S) in Marguerite Bay (Greene *et al.*, in press). It is also widespread in north temperate and Arctic regions.

It is a robust, turf-forming species and, in the Antarctic, it commonly forms extensive peat banks 1–2 m in depth, with *Dicranum aciphyllum* as a frequent associate. Smaller colonies also occur and on the Falkland Islands the stands

approx. 5 mm

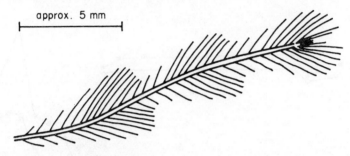

FIG. 5. Diagram of growth segments in *Polytrichum alpestre*. Reproduced from Longton and Greene (1967). By courtesy of the Royal Society.

seldom exceed 2 m wide. The individual shoots are erect, each maintaining terminal growth for several years, but there is continuous replacement of old shoots by young ones arising as erect growing branches up to several centimetres deep in the turf. The young shoot bases bear only tomentum and scattered juvenile leaves, but growth is at first rapid, and mature leaves develop after the shoot apices reach the surface of the turf.

It has been shown that there is regular fluctuation in the length of the fine, spreading limbs of successive mature leaves along each stem, thus giving the shoots a segmented appearance (Fig. 5), while leaf base dimensions show relatively little variation. Direct observations of marked plants on South Georgia confirmed that each shoot normally forms one segment per year, the shortest leaves developing at the beginning and end of the growing season, while the longest are formed in high summer (Longton and Greene, 1967). A similar pattern has since been shown for plants in the study colonies on Signy Island and the Argentine Islands.

The duration of the growing season in *P. alpestre* has been determined by comparing the size of the uppermost stem segments on ten plants per specimen in a series of samples collected from the three study colonies for periods of one to three years. Functionally sterile stems were scored, as the development of terminal inflorescences may affect growth. On South Georgia measurements were made on sterile stems from both male and female areas of turf, but only female turf was available further south.

It can be seen from Fig. 6, that little growth occurred in male turf in the South Georgian colony from March to mid-November in 1961, as the mean size of the two uppermost segments on each stem remained approximately equal. In late November, however, most shoots had a few leaves of a new segment visible above the previous year's leaves and further growth of the new segment took place during December and January. It appears that few new leaves developed after early February 1962 and that the segments formed

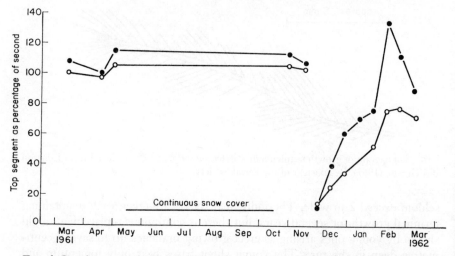

F IG. 6. Growing season for functionally sterile stems of *Polytrichum alpestre* from male turf in the study colony on South Georgia. The mean size of the uppermost segments on ten stems per collection is expressed as a percentage of the mean size of the second segments in terms of length (●) and the number of leaves (○).

during that particular summer had only 70% to 80% as many leaves as those from the year before. Moreover, despite some irregularity at the end of the season, the results for segment length provide no evidence of stem elongation after early February. These results thus indicate a slightly shorter growing season on South Georgia than reported earlier, when it was suggested that growth normally continues into March (Longton and Greene, 1967). The present data were obtained by comparing the size of the uppermost stem segments with that of the second segments in successive collections, a procedure which is considered more reliable than the earlier method of comparing only the uppermost segments, as it reduces discrepancies arising through variations in the annual growth rate in different specimens.

TABLE 3

Approximate Growing Season of *Polytrichum alpestre* in the Study Colonies

Station	Year	Sex of turf	Date of snow clearance	Growing season
South Georgia	1961–62	Male	Mid-October	Late November to early February
	1961–62	Female	Mid-October	Late November to mid-February or early March
	1964–65	Male	Mid-October	Mid-November to February
	1964–65	Female	Mid-October	Mid-November to February
Signy Island	1963–64	Female	Not known	Late November to early February
	1964–65	Female	October–November*	Late November to late February or early March
	1965–66	Female	October*	Late November to early February
Argentine Island	1965–66	Female	Early December	Mid-December to early February

* Temporary thaws preceded complete snow clearance.

The remaining results, which are summarized in Table 3, indicate that stem elongation and leaf production in *P. alpestre* took place mainly from the end of November to February at each station. In 1964, however, new growth was visible on South Georgia by 13 November, while slight delay in the first appearance of new segments was associated with late snow lie at the Argentine Islands in 1965. The new segments were not generally visible until several weeks after snow clearance, but qualitative observations suggest that the terminal bud may enlarge during the intervening period.

IV. Geographic Variation in Annual Growth

As each stem develops one segment per year, the size of the segments can be used to compare the annual growth of plants in different populations.

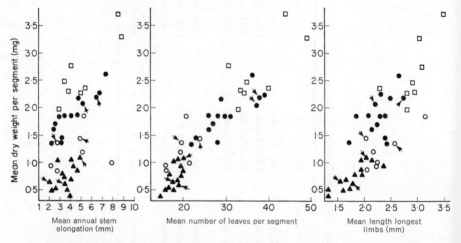

FIG. 7. Analysis of annual growth segments in specimens of *Polytrichum alpestre* from the Falkland Islands (□), South Georgia (●), Signy Island (▲) and the Argentine Islands (○). Arrows indicate specimens from the study colonies.

Growth segments were analysed in fifty-six collections from localities between the Falkland Islands and Marguerite Bay, and in seven specimens from Great Britain and Greenland. Measurements were carried out on the second and third segments from the apex of ten stems per collection, i.e. the partially complete uppermost segments were omitted. Records were kept of the stem elongation represented by each segment, and of the combined mass of the twenty segments from each specimen after drying to constant weight at 80°C. For two stems per collection, measurements were also made of leaf base dimensions for every third leaf, and of limb length for the five longest and five shortest leaves on each of the four segments. Due to the large number of leaves per segment on the British material, leaf base dimensions were measured for only five leaves from the bottom and five from the top of each segment, and for ten to fifteen leaves from the centre of the segment: limb length data for this material were based on the five longest and five shortest leaves in this sample.

The results from the Falkland Islands, South Georgia, Signy Island and the Argentine Islands are summarized in Fig. 7, expressed as mean values for each specimen. There was clearly considerable variation in the annual growth rate in different areas. Thus segment weight varied from approximately 0·4

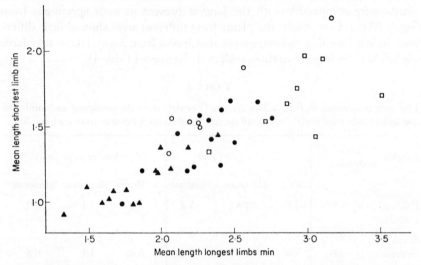

FIG. 8. Relationship between limb length of the longest and shortest leaves in specimens of *Polytrichum alpestre* from the Falkland Islands (□), South Georgia (●), Signy Island (▲), and the Argentine Islands (○).

to 1·1 mg on Signy Island, compared with 0·9 to 1·8 on the Argentine Islands, 1·3 to 2·6 mg on South Georgia and 2·0 to 3·7 mg on the Falkland Islands. The results cover several specimens from the sites where microclimatic data were recorded, and in general suggest that these sites may be representative of the more favourable habitats in the areas concerned. However, annual dry matter production per shoot in three specimens from the study colony on Signy Island varied from 0·6 to 1·1 mg, indicating that the growth rate may differ considerably within a few square metres. In general, the annual rate of dry matter production per shoot decreased with increasing latitude, but this trend was reversed at the two southernmost stations as mean segment weight on Signy Island tended to be lower than on the Argentine Islands.

On Signy Island, mean annual stem elongation ranged from only 2 to 5 mm. There was little difference in the lowest values recorded for other areas, but mean elongation of up to 9 mm per year was recorded at the Falkland Islands. Moreover, the greater annual dry matter production per shoot in more favourable areas was in general associated with increases in both leaf length and the number of leaves per segment (Fig. 7). However, some plants from the Argentine Islands had leaves as long as, or longer than, any collected on South Georgia.

Further data for leaf length are shown in Fig. 8, which demonstrates a positive correlation between the lengths of the longest and shortest leaves in different specimens. Indeed, the shortest limbs recorded on Falkland Island plants were comparable with the longest present in most specimens from Signy Island. Conversely, the plants from different areas showed little difference in leaf base dimensions, except that leaves from Signy Island may have slightly shorter bases than those collected elsewhere (Table 4).

TABLE 4

Leaf base dimensions in *Polytrichum alpestre*. The data show the maximum and minimum specimen mean values, and the overall means based on all specimens from each locality

Locality	Number of specimens	Base length (*mm*)			Base breadth (*mm*)		
		Mean	*Maximum*	*Minimum*	*Mean*	*Maximum*	*Minimum*
Falkland Islands	8	1·6	1·6	1·4	1·0	1·1	0·9
South Georgia	14	1·6	1·8	1·4	0·9	1·1	0·8
Signy Island	14	1·4	1·5	1·1	1·0	1·1	0·8
Argentine Islands	7	1·6	1·8	1·5	0·9	1·1	0·8

Data for the remaining specimens are summarized in Table 5. Most of the Southern Hemisphere plants were collected on the west coast of the Antarctic Peninsula, or on off-lying islands, between Jenny Island in Marguerite Bay and Hope Bay at the north-eastern tip of the Peninsula. The results for these plants generally fell within the range recorded for Argentine Island material, although the values for both segment weight and leaf length for a specimen from the Danco Coast were higher than for other plants from the Antarctic zone. In contrast, a specimen from Petermann Island had a mean segment weight of only 0·5 mg, which was comparable with the lowest values recorded for Signy Island, and a similar result was obtained for a collection from Laurie Island, which lies close to Signy Island in the South Orkney group. The final southern collection came from the outer zone of vegetation around a fumarole on Leskov Island, South Sandwich Islands. It gave a value of 1·4 mg per stem for annual dry-matter production, and its segments had an unusually large number of leaves in relation to their weight.

The few available results for plants from Britain and Greenland suggest that variations in the growth of *P. alpestre* in the Northern Hemisphere may follow a similar pattern to that demonstrated for the Southern Hemisphere. Thus the Greenland material was comparable, in terms of annual dry-matter production per shoot, stem elongation, leaf length and number of leaves, with many plants from South Georgia and the Argentine Islands. By contrast, segment weight for plants from the British mountains was in general even higher than values from the Falkland Islands, and many of the British specimens had correspondingly longer segments with a larger number of longer leaves.

V. Productivity in *Polytrichum alpestre* Communities

Communities dominated by *P. alpestre*, or by *P. alpestre* and *Dicranum aciphyllum*, form one of the most widespread vegetation types in the maritime Antarctic and a knowledge of their productivity is therefore essential for studies of energy flow in the terrestrial ecosystem. Mean net productivity per unit area in more or less pure stands of *P. alpestre* has been estimated by dividing the dry weight (w) of a sample of uniform depth by the number of growth segments in that depth (n) times the area of the sample (a). Thus:

$$\text{Mean annual net productivity per unit area} = \frac{w}{na}$$

The samples were either blocks of turf with a surface area of approximately 50 cm² or cylindrical cores with a surface area of 21 cm². They were cut to a uniform depth of between 1·5 and 2·0 cm, and the number of segments was counted from at least ten places in each sample, the results averaging six to seven segments in each case. Determinations have so far been made for specimens from the study colonies on South Georgia, Signy Island and the Argentine Islands, and for four additional samples collected within approximately 1 sq. m of another colony on South Georgia.

The results, which are indicated in Table 6, represent minimum values, as losses by decay are ignored. Even so, they demonstrate substantial annual net productivity in the *P. alpestre* communities, ranging from 342 gm/m² on Signy Island to 507 gm/m² on South Georgia, with intermediate values for the Argentine Islands.

TABLE 5

Growth Analysis in twenty specimens of Polytrichum alpestre

Collecting station	Latitude	Mean dry weight per segment (mg)	Mean annual stem elongation (mm)	Mean number of leaves per segment	Mean length of longest limbs (mm)	Mean length of shortest limbs (mm)	Mean length of leaf base (mm)	Mean breadth of leaf base (mm)
Leskov I., South Sandwich Is.	56°40'S	1·4	6·4	35·8	2·6	1·0	1·3	0·8
Laurie I., South Orkney Is.	60°44'S	0·5	3·5	17·2	1·6	1·1	1·3	1·0
Hope Bay, Trinity Peninsula	63°24'S	0·8	3·5	18·7	2·6	1·9	1·3	0·9
Hope Bay, Trinity Peninsula	63°24'S	1·1	3·9	17·4	2·3	1·5	1·6	1·0
Hope Bay, Trinity Peninsula	63°24'S	0·9	4·3	20·2	2·3	1·4	1·5	1·0
Norsel Pt., Anvers I., Danco Coast	64°46'S	1·5	3·7	20·2	2·6	1·7	1·7	1·1
Benenden Head, Danco Coast	64°46'S	1·3	3·5	17·4	2·2	1·6	1·6	1·0
Laggard I., Danco Coast	64°49'S	0·9	2·2	15·4	2·1	1·6	1·6	1·0

Coughtrey Peninsula, Danco Coast	64°55'S	2·1	5·9	21·7	3·1	2·3	1·9	1·1
Petermann I., Graham Coast	65°11'S	0·5	2·8	16·4	1·8	1·3	1·3	0·8
Cape Tuxen, Graham Coast	65°16'S	1·2	2·7	20·3	2·5	1·5	1·6	0·9
Jenny I., Fallières Coast	67°44'S	1·1	2·5	18·2	2·1	1·3	1·3	1·1
Jenny I., Fallières Coast	67°44'S	1·0	4·8	15·3	2·3	1·4	1·6	1·1
Cwm Idwal, Great Britain	53°07'N	4·9	6·5	56·0	4·0	1·7	1·7	1·0
Llyn Ogwen, Great Britain	53°08'N	8·3	15·1	82·5	3·7	2·1	1·7	1·2
Ben Lawers, Great Britain	56°32'N	3·7	5·4	44·2	3·8	1·3	1·8	1·0
Creag an Lochan, Great Britain	56°32'N	4·2	13·7	44·0	3·7	2·2	1·9	1·0
Disko I., West Greenland	69°15'N	1·3	2·9	19·5	2·8	2·1	1·5	0·9
Disko I., West Greenland	69°15'N	1·6	2·3	26·1	2·3	1·4	1·1	0·8
Disko I., West Greenland	69°15'N	1·7	3·4	23·9	3·1	1·9	1·6	0·9

TABLE 6

Mean Annual Net Productivity in Colonies of *Polytrichum alpestre*

Argentine Islands	Lat. 65°15′S	$\left\{\begin{array}{l}385 \text{ gm m}^2 \\ 421 \text{ gm m}^2\end{array}\right\}$	Study colony
Signy Island	Lat. 60°43′S	342 gm m²	Study colony
South Georgia	Lat. 54°17′S	$\left\{\begin{array}{l}462 \text{ gm m}^2 \\ 451 \text{ gm m}^2 \\ 455 \text{ gm m}^2 \\ 466 \text{ gm m}^2 \\ 507 \text{ gm m}^2\end{array}\right.$	Study colony Other colony

VI. Discussion and Summary

The growth of *Polytrichum alpestre* in colonies on South Georgia, Signy Island and the Argentine Islands has been related to the temperature regime, and the annual growth increments have been compared in these and other populations in cool temperate, Subantarctic and maritime Antarctic stations to the southern limit of the species known range.

Winter snow cover persisted for seven to eight months at the two Antarctic sites, but it was generally light, and temperatures at plant level fluctuated slowly with both short-term and long-term changes in air temperature, falling as low as −22°C at the Argentine Islands. However, there was relatively slow cooling to the winter minima, and as gradual warming took place in spring, rapid freezing and thawing of the plant tissue was prevented. This may aid winter survival, as slow freezing is thought to reduce the extent of intracellular ice formation in plants, while rapid thawing may increase the damage caused by extracellular ice (Levitt, 1956). Winter conditions in the South Georgian colony were also unlikely to cause severe frost damage, as deep snow cover stabilized the temperature at around or slightly above 0°C.

In summer, wide and rapid diurnal fluctuations in temperature were characteristic of the surface layers of the three study colonies. Mean temperature at plant level exceeded mean air temperature, but there was often rapid cooling from maxima of 10°C to 30°C in the early afternoon to around or below 0°C at night. However, it seems unlikely that extensive ice formation took place frequently within the plants during the growing season, as most daily minimum temperatures were above −1·75°C and some degree of undercooling normally precedes ice formation in plant tissues (Levitt, 1956).

The maximum temperatures near the surface of the *P. alpestre* colonies during periods of sunshine were often as much as 25°C higher than air temperature, and comparable differences have been recorded for other Antarctic mosses (Matsuda, 1964; Holdgate, 1964; Longton and Holdgate, 1967;

Sáiz *et al.*, 1970; this symposium). These high temperatures are not surprising, in view of the morphology of bryophyte communities. There is normally a complete overlap of several layers of plant tissue in the upper parts of the turf, reducing the amount of radiant energy lost by transmission, while *P. alpestre* and many other mosses have a large number of small leaves held obliquely, so that much of the radiation reflected from them will fall on other surfaces in the colony. The communities may thus be expected to absorb a high proportion of the incoming radiation within a layer only a few millimetres deep near the level of the growing points in the stem apices. Moreover, the rate of heat loss through wind action is likely to be low among the small, tightly packed leaves situated near the ground. Bryophyte colonies therefore seem structurally well equipped to absorb radiant light energy for photosynthesis and to benefit from heating through direct insolation. Indeed, this may be one reason for their success under the conditions of freely available moisture but low ambient air temperatures prevailing in the maritime Antarctic.

Stem elongation and leaf production in *P. alpestre* occurred mainly during a period of some three months at the warmest time of the year, normally beginning after the clearance of winter snow and ending in February. It is possible that net assimilation continued for a longer period, as mean temperatures remained above 0°C throughout much of February and March. However, Baker (1970: this symposium) has pointed out that some bryophyte communities on Signy Island become progressively drier during the summer. It is not clear whether shortage of water limits growth during February and March, but the period of several weeks between the end of the development of new plant parts and the advent of severe winter conditions could be important in allowing hardening of the young tissues, particularly if it is associated with some degree of dehydration.

The shoots of *P. alpestre* are segmented in appearance, as leaves developing early and late in the growing season have shorter limbs than those formed in high summer. An analysis of the growth segments demonstrated a progressive reduction in annual dry-matter production per stem passing from the Falkland Islands southwards to Signy Island. Higher results were recorded at the Argentine Islands than on the more northerly Signy Island, however, and it was shown that the summer microclimate at the former station was warmer than that on Signy Island during at least one season, despite slightly lower air temperatures. It may thus be significant that there is also evidence of reduced reproductive success in some mosses and flowering plants on Signy Island compared with the Argentine Islands and other stations near the west coast of the Antarctic Peninsula (Longton, 1966; Holtom and Greene, 1967).

The greater annual dry-weight increase per shoot in *P. alpestre* at the warmer stations resulted from the production each year of a greater number of longer leaves, combined, in many populations, with an increase in stem elongation. The reduction in leaf length at higher latitudes was associated with an overall decrease in plant size and with greater shoot density, thus leading to the development of more compact turf. At first sight the Antarctic populations therefore appeared to differ morphologically from temperate zone plants, but it is clear from the present results that the variation is continuous.

Net annual productivity values in *P. alpestre* communities followed a similar trend to those for individual shoots, the highest being recorded on South Georgia, while the results for the Argentine Islands exceeded those for Signy Island. It may be noted that differences between the study colonies in the estimated productivity per unit area were relatively smaller than the corresponding differences for individual shoots, the ratios for the study colonies on Signy Island and South Georgia being of the order of 1·0 : 1·4 for community productivity (Table 6), compared with at least 1·0 : 2·0 for mean segment weight (Fig. 7). This is to be expected in view of the higher shoot density on Signy Island, but more data are essential before valid comparisons of community productivity can be made. The main value of the present results lies in their demonstration that annual net productivity may reach the order of several hundred grams per square metre in bryophyte colonies at favourable sites in both Subantarctic and maritime Antarctic regions. As Holdgate (1967) has pointed out, however, in the latter area closed communities comparable with the type discussed here cover only a small proportion of the total land surface.

Considered overall, the present results clearly demonstrate a strong correlation between the growth rate of *P. alpestre* and the summer temperature regime at plant level, but a study of other microclimatic parameters in the field, and a comparison of plant performance in a range of controlled conditions in the laboratory, are necessary to confirm the importance of temperature relative to other factors in limiting growth. Experimental studies are also essential to determine whether different populations of *P. alpestre* show genetically controlled morphological or physiological adaptations to their diverse environmental regimes.

Acknowledgements

It is a pleasure to thank my colleagues on South Georgia, Signy Island and the Argentine Islands for obtaining thermistor readings and specimens in my absence, Mr G. C. S. Clarke for collecting some of the Northern Hemisphere material, and Mr E. P. Wright for assistance in analysing the temperature data.

References

Baker, J. (1970). Yeasts, moulds and bacteria from an acid peat on Signy Island. This symposium, 717–22.

Greene, S. W., Greene, D. M., Brown, P. D. and Pacey, J. M. (in press). Antarctic Moss Flora. I. The Genera *Andreaea, Pohlia, Polytrichum, Psilopilum,* and *Sarconeurum. Br. Antarct. Surv. Sci. Rep.* **64**.

Holtom, A. and Greene, S. W. (1967). The growth and reproduction of Antarctic flowering plants. *Phil. Trans. R. Soc.* B **252**, No. 777, 323–37.

Holdgate, M. W. (1964). Terrestrial Ecology in the Maritime Antarctic. *In* "Biologie Antarctique: Antarctic Biology" (Carrick, R., Holdgate, M. W. and Prévost, J. eds.) Hermann, Paris. 181–94.

Holdgate, M. W. (1967). The Antarctic Ecosystem. *Phil. Trans. R. Soc.* B **252**, No. 777, 363–83.

Levitt, J. (1956). "The Hardiness of Plants." American Society of Agronomy, New York.

Lewis, M. C. and Greene, S. W. (1970). A comparison of plant growth at an Arctic and Antarctic station. This symposium, 838–50.

Longton, R. E. (1966). Botanical Studies in the Antarctic during the 1963–64 and 1964–65 Seasons. *Br. Antarct. Surv. Bull.* **10**, 85–95.

Longton, R. E. and Greene, S. W. (1967). The growth and reproduction of *Polytrichum alpestre* Hoppe on South Georgia. *Phil. Trans. R. Soc.* B **252**, No. 777, 295–322.

Longton, R. E. and Holdgate, M. W. (1967). Temperature Relationships of Antarctic vegetation. *Phil. Trans. R. Soc.* B **252**, No. 777, 237–50.

Matsuda, T. (1964). Microclimate in the community of mosses near Syowa Base at East Ongul Islands, Antarctica. *Antarctic Rec.* **21**, 12–24.

Pepper, J. (1954). *The Meteorology of the Falkland Islands and Dependencies 1944–50.* Falkland Islands Dependencies Survey, London.

Podpěra, A. J. (1954). "Conspectus Muscorum Europaeorum." Práce Československé Akadamie Věd. Praha.

Sáiz, F. Hajek, E. R. and Hermosilla, W. (1970). The colonization of introduced litter by subantarctic soil and moss Arthropods. This symposium 897–907.

A Comparison of Plant Growth at an Arctic and Antarctic Station

M. C. LEWIS* AND S. W. GREENE
*Department of Botany, The University of Birmingham, England,
and British Antarctic Survey*

I. Introduction

The characteristic terrestrial vegetation of polar regions is relatively poorly developed, and it has been estimated that the amount of growth made each year (i.e. net annual primary production) is normally below 10% of that for temperate regions (Bliss, 1962). However, it is still uncertain to what extent these low values are due to climatic limitation of rates of growth during the growing season, which is short and cool although with a daily receipt of solar energy not very different from that of temperate regions, or to other factors such as soil deficiencies, water deficits or even substantial vegetative die back between successive growing seasons.

Further, the observation that Arctic ecosystems are comparatively much richer than their Antarctic counterparts has prompted much discussion as to whether the difference is due primarily to aspects of plant dispersal or to inequalities in conditions for plant growth between the two regions.

The investigation of these problems constitutes the primary objective of our Bipolar Botanical Project which forms part of the United Kingdom contribution to the International Biological Programme. The project involves the application of directly comparable methods to the study of the following aspects of both Arctic and Antarctic terrestrial vegetation:

(*a*) The environmental conditions under which the plants are growing.

(*b*) The natural and potential primary production of individual species and communities.

(*c*) Plant adaptation to polar conditions.

The field programmes are currently being carried out at Godhavn, Disko Island, West Greenland (lat. 69°15′N, long. 53°30′W) and Grytviken, Cumberland Bay East, South Georgia (lat. 54°17′S, long. 36°31′W). A comple-

* Present address: Department of Biology, The University of York, England.

mentary experimental programme under controlled environmental conditions is also being undertaken at Birmingham and York, England.

A variety of methods and procedures are being utilized in the project, including microclimatic monitoring, area biomass sampling and physiological comparisons. The present paper will be restricted to a consideration of some results obtained by the application of growth analysis techniques to selected test plants growing on a non-limiting medium in the open.

II. Material and Methods

At least during the early vegetative phase, the growth of a plant, as expressed by increase in dry weight, follows an exponential curve. This growth rate can be expressed as the rate of growth per unit of plant material or the "Relative Growth Rate" (R_W), as it is more commonly called. It may be expressed as:

$$R_W = \log_e \frac{W.t^{-1}}{W_0}$$

where $W_0 =$ initial dry weight

and $W =$ dry weight after time t

The relative growth rate of a plant is primarily dependent on two further parameters:

(i) The net photosynthetic efficiency of a unit area of leaf, which may be expressed as the rate of increase in dry weight of plant per unit area of leaf and is termed the "Net Assimilation Rate" (E_A). It may be expressed as:

$$E_A = \frac{W-W_0.t^{-1}.\log_e A}{A-A_0 \qquad A_0}$$

where $A_0 =$ initial leaf area and

$A =$ leaf area after time t, W_0 and W being as before.

(ii) The degree of leafiness of the plant which may be expressed as the ratio of the total leaf surface to the total plant weight and termed the "Leaf Area Ratio" (F_A). It may be expressed as:

$$F_A = \frac{\dfrac{A_0}{W_0} + \dfrac{A}{W}}{2}$$

where A_0, A, W_0 and W are as before.

In fact the "Relative Growth Rate" of a plant is the product of the "Net Assimilation Rate" and the "Leaf Area Ratio".

Relative growth rates, net assimilation rates and leaf area ratios have been determined for the early vegetative phase of commercial varieties of several crop plants at a number of sites in Greenland and South Georgia. The species and varieties tested were as follows: *Avena fatua* (oats, variety Astor), *Brassica rapa* (turnip, variety Green Top Stone), *Raphanus sativus* (radish, variety Saxa) and *Brassica napa* (rape, variety Salad).

The following procedures were adopted:

(*a*) The plants were grown throughout in 15 cm pots of vermiculite and freely supplied with water and nutrients, to provide a substrate. The nutrient solution used was modified Hoagland's, as follows:

Macronutrients		*Micronutrients*	
	g/l.		mg./l
KNO_3	0·51	H_3BO_3	2·90
$Ca(NO_3)_2.4H_2O$	1·18	$M_2CI_2.4H_2O$	1·81
$MgSO_4.7H_2O$	0·49	$ZnSO_4$	0·22
KH_2PO_4	0·14	$CuSO_4.5H_2O$	0·08
		$H_2MoO_4.4H_2O$	0·02
		$FeSO_4$ chelated	2·49
		in EDTA	

(*b*) Nine seeds were planted per pot, and when the seedlings had reached the three-leaf stage they were thinned to three per pot and the pots matched in pairs with respect to the size of the aerial parts of the plants, i.e. three plants in one pot were matched with three plants in a second pot.

(*c*) The first set of pots were harvested at this time and were washed free of vermiculite, care being taken to extract the roots intact. Leaf areas were obtained by the standard procedure of printing the leaf outline on ammonia-developed Diazo paper, cutting out and weighing the leaf silhouettes and estimating their area per plant, by extrapolating from the weight of pieces of paper of known area. The dry weight of the whole plant was determined after drying at 80°C.

(*d*) The remaining pots were placed at the test sites for seven to ten days and then harvested as before.

(*e*) Relative growth rates, net assimilation rates and leaf area ratios were calculated using individual pot means, so that ten independent values were obtained for each of the sites.

(*f*) Similar smaller-scale experiments were carried out at the primary site (see below) in Greenland and South Georgia in which oat seedlings were grown in pots containing local soil in place of the vermiculite.

The seedlings were watered as necessary, but no nutrients were added. They were harvested as described above.

(g) The significance of the between-site variation in relative growth and net assimilation rates has been determined using analysis of variance on within-site pot means. The levels of probability are shown in Tables 2 and 3 (*=5% level, **=1% level, ***=0·1% level).

A. SITES

At Godhavn and Grytviken a number of sites were chosen which were considered representative of the range of local variation of two major environmental factors, wind exposure and the amount and periodicity of solar radiation as influenced by the orientation and degree of slope. Details of the sites are given in Table 1. Microclimate variations were measured during the experiments but the results are unfortunately not yet available.

B. HARVEST DATES

In Greenland only one experiment was possible, this lasting for seven days during late August 1967 when weather conditions were normal. On South Georgia, two experiments were carried out each lasting ten days. The first was during mid-season in late January 1968, when many leaves were damaged by a particularly bad storm. The second was towards the end of the season, in March 1968, when the lowest night temperatures of the season were experienced. Precise dates were as follows:

	Experimental Period
Greenland	
All Plants	20–28 August 1967
South Georgia	
Expt. 1	
Oats	11–21 January 1968
Remainder	15–25 January 1968
Expt. 2	
Oats	8–18 March 1968
Remainder, including oats on natural soils	15–25 March 1968

III. Results

The values obtained for plants grown in vermiculite in Greenland are shown in Table 2. The values for relative growth rate vary considerably between sites, some of the differences being highly significant. The relationships between the sites are generally as expected with the highest growth

TABLE 1

Description and location of the test sites on Greenland and South Georgia. High insolation implies sloping surface. Normal insolation implies horizontal or near horizontal surface. Restricted insolation implies lacking direct sunlight for part of the day

Sites	Locality	Description	Insolation	Wind exposure
DISKO I., WEST GREENLAND				
1. Primary site	Østerlien, Godhavn	South-facing sub-arctic slope supporting luxuriant, closed vegetation of both herbs and *Salix* scrub	High, at times restricted	Low
2. *Salix herbacea* heath	Lyngmarksfjeldet, Godhavn	Sheltered, flat depression within exposed plateau area, supporting closed mat of *Salix herbacea*	Normal	Low–moderate
3. Cryptogamic heath	Godhavn	Level area with a small phanerogamic component in an essentially cryptogamic vegetation	Normal	Moderate
4. Fellfield	Lyngmarksfjeldet, Godhavn	Level, gravelly plateau with sparse, open vegetation	Normal	High
5. North-facing slope	Lyngmarksbugt, Godhavn	Steep, shaded slope, supporting a sparse vegetation of both phanerogams and cryptogams	Restricted, rarely normal	Low–moderate
CUMBERLAND EAST BAY, SOUTH GEORGIA				
1. Primary site	South shore of King Edward Cove	North-facing slope, supporting dense, tufted *Festuca erecta* grassland	High	Moderate
2. *Acaena* slope	South shore of King Edward Cove	North-facing slope, supporting a ± pure, closed sward of *Acaena adscendens*	High	Low
3. *Festuca* heath	East shore of Gull Lake	Level area supporting a closed, mixed community of *Festuca* and *Acaena*	Normal	Moderate–high
4. Fellfield	East shore of Gull Lake	Gentle boulder-strewn slope with sparse, open vegetation	Normal	High
5. South-facing slope	Hope Point	Ledge of ± vertical cliff face, supporting sparse *Festuca erecta* grassland	Restricted, at times normal	Moderate

TABLE 2

Mean values for *Relative Growth Rates, Net Assimilation Rates* and *Leaf Area Ratios* for plants grown in vermiculite at the five test sites in Greenland. Probability levels of between-site variation determined using analysis of variance. R_W = Relative growth rate in gm/gm wk. E_A = Net assimilation rate in gm/dm²wk. F_A = Leaf area ratio in dm²/gm

Site	Time in season	Oats			Turnip			Radish		
		R_W	E_A	F_A	R_W	E_A	F_A	R_W	E_A	F_A
1. Primary	Late	·45	·27	1·67	·95	·48	1·98	·47	·48	·98
2. *Salix herbacea* heath	Late	·49	·33	1·48	·44	·35	1·26	·29	·37	·78
3. Cryptogamic heath	Late	·27	·19	1·42	·52	·31	1·68	·46	·57	·81
4. Fellfield	Late	·46	·37	1·24	·34	·27	1·26	·34	·60	·57
5. North-facing slope	Late	·32	·27	1·19	·32	·19	1·68	·31	·45	·69
Probability of significant difference between sites for each species		**	***	***	***	*		NS	NS	

TABLE 3

Mean values for *Relative Growth Rates*, *Net Assimilation Rates* and *Leaf Area Ratios* for plants grown in vermiculite at the five test sites in South Georgia. Probability levels of between-site variation determined using analysis of variance. R_W = Relative growth rate in gm/gm wk. E_A = Net assimilation rate in gm/dm²wk. F_A = Leaf area ratio in dm²/gm

Site	Time in season	Oats			Turnip			Radish			Rape		
		R_W	E_A	F_A	R_W	E_A	F_A	R_W	E_A	F_A	R_W	E_A	F_A
1. Primary	Mid	·37	·46	·80	·50	·40	1·25	·36	·48	·75	·64	·60	1·07
	Late	·27	·27	1·00	·27	·24	1·13	·05	·03	1·67	·09	·11	·82
2. *Acaena* slope	Mid	·40	·37	1·08	·48	·43	1·12	·41	·52	·79	·56	·54	1·04
	Late	·36	·42	·86	·26	·22	1·18	·24	·27	·89	·22	·24	·92
3. *Festuca* heath	Mid	·32	·44	·73	·36	·33	1·09	·45	·63	·71	·47	·53	·89
	Late	·31	·35	·89	·15	·13	1·15	·16	·18	·89	·23	·23	1·00
4. Fellfield	Mid	·19	·36	·53	·44	·37	1·19	·21	·32	·66	·52	·45	1·16
	Late	·22	·24	·92	·09	·08	1·13	·11	·12	·92	·12	·09	1·33
5. South-facing slope	Mid	·31	·34	·91	·40	·34	1·18	·39	·44	·89	·51	·48	1·06
	Late	—	—	—	—	—	—	—	—	—	—	—	—
Probability of significant difference between sites for each species	Mid	**	NS		NS	NS		**	*		*	NS	
	Late	*	**		*	*		NS	NS		NS	*	

TABLE 4

Comparison of range of mid and end of season values for *Relative Growth Rates*, *Net Assimilation Rates* and *Leaf Area Ratios* for plants grown in vermiculite at the five test sites in South Georgia. R_W in gm/gm wk. E_A in gm/dm² wk. F_A in dm²/gm.

	Mid-season between-site ranges			Late season between-site ranges		
	R_W	E_A	F_A	R_W	E_A	F_A
Oats	·40—·19	·46—·36	1·08—·53	·36—·22	·42—·24	1·00—·86
Turnip	·50—·36	·43—·33	1·25—1·09	·27—·09	·24—·08	1·18—1·13
Radish	·45—·21	·63—·32	·79—·66	·24—·05	·27—·03	1·67—·89
Rape	·64—·47	·60—·45	1·16—·89	·23—·09	·24—·09	1·33—·82

TABLE 5

Comparison of mid and end of season site means of *Relative Growth Rate* and *Net Assimilation Rate* for Oats and Turnip grown in vermiculite in Greenland and South Georgia. R_W in gm/gm wk: EA in gm/dm² wk.

OATS

Greenland sites	Late-season		South Georgia sites	Mid-season		Late-season	
	R_W	E_A		R_W	E_A	R_W	E_A
1. Primary	·45	·27	1. Primary	·37	·46	·27	·27
2. *Salix herbacea* heath	·49	·33	2. *Acaena* slope	·40	·37	·36	·42
3. Cryptogamic heath	·27	·19	3. *Festuca* heath	·32	·44	·31	·35
4. Fellfield	·46	·37	4. Fellfield	·19	·36	·22	·22
5. North-facing slope	·32	·27	5. South-facing slope	·31	·34	—	—

TURNIP

Greenland sites	Late-season		South Georgia sites	Mid-season		Late-season	
	R_W	E_A		R_W	E_A	R_W	E_A
1. Primary	·95	·48	1. Primary	·50	·40	·27	·24
2. *Salix herbacea* heath	·44	·35	2. *Acaena* slope	·48	·43	·26	·22
3. Cryptogamic heath	·52	·31	3. *Festuca* heath	·36	·33	·15	·13
4. Fellfield	·34	·27	4. Fellfield	·44	·37	·09	·08
5. North-facing slope	·32	·19	5. South-facing slope	·40	·34	—	—

rates occurring at the more sheltered sites with higher insolation. However, the different species are influenced in different ways by the variation in micro-climate between the sites, e.g. the relative growth rate of the turnip is depressed to a larger extent by the greater exposure and resulting lower temperatures at the fellfield than is that of oats. On the other hand, the results would suggest that the turnip is able to take greater advantage of the more favourable conditions at the primary site than is the oat. The South Georgian data also indicate clear differences between the sites (see Table 3).

Those sites with the highest relative growth rates for a particular species are not necessarily those with the highest assimilation rates. It is not the intention to analyse this situation further at present except to say that it is brought about, at least in part, by a complex interaction of the differential effects of light and temperature on leaf expansion, assimilation rates and growth (Warren Wilson, 1966a, b).

The two harvests for South Georgia (Tables 3 and 4) serve to illustrate the extent to which growth rates are influenced by variations in climate through the growing season. The late season values are in general only a half of those obtained for the middle of the growing season. However, there are again con-siderable differences in the response of the various species. Oats, for example, are far less affected by the deterioration in conditions between mid and late season than are the other species.

In passing, it may be noted that comparisons were made under laboratory and field conditions between rape, turnip and radish plants with or without cotyledons, and no significant differences were obtained.

A comparison of mean figures for oats and turnip at the northern and southern station (Table 5) suggests that conditions for growth of these species are more favourable in Greenland than South Georgia. The late-season range of values for South Georgia is considerably lower than the range for a com-parable period of the growing season in Greenland. In fact, even at mid-season the southern figures do not significantly exceed the northern late-season values.

The relative growth rates of oats growing in natural soils were at least 20% below those for a non-limiting medium (Table 6), indicating that the primary site soils are nutrient deficient and exert a limitation on growth rate, but from these and other data (Warren Wilson, 1966a), there is no indication that the soils investigated are any more limiting than natural soils of temperate re-gions.

The range of relative growth and net assimilation rates of turnip in South Georgia and Greenland are comparable with those previously published by Warren Wilson (1966a) for Cornwallis Island (75°N) (Table 7). The growth of turnip at the Greenland primary site is considerably in excess of previously reported values for Arctic areas. However, relative growth and net assimilation

TABLE 6

Mean Values for *Relative Growth Rates*, *Net Assimilation Rates* and *Leaf Area Ratios* for Oats grown in Natural Soil and Vermiculite at Primary Sites in Greenland and South Georgia. R_W in gm/gm wk, E_A in gm/dm² wk and F_A in dm²/gm.

	R_W	E_A	F_A
GREENLAND			
Vermiculite	·45	·27	1·67
Natural soil	·35	·34	1·03
SOUTH GEORGIA			
Vermiculite	·27	·27	1·00
Natural soil	·12	·20	·60

rates for polar areas are considerably lower than for the same species growing under similar test conditions in temperate regions. Relative growth rates are depressed to a much greater extent than are assimilation rates, leaf expansion also being significantly reduced. It is interesting to note that values for 54°S lat. are demonstrably lower than those obtained at 69°N, which themselves are substantially less than those for 52°N.

IV. Discussion

The results draw attention to the large variation in microclimate existing between the sites and emphasize that if realistic growth rates are to be obtained for a region, experiments need to be carried out in as many ecologically diverse sites as possible. The results also show that it is essential to repeat the experiments throughout the growing season if annual changes in radiation receipt are to be taken into account. The desirability of extending the work over a number of seasons is equally obvious.

That such standardized techniques provide a useful quantitative basis for comparing the conditions for plant growth in widely spaced geographical areas is demonstrated by the values for Greenland and South Georgia. Similarly, comparisons with regions in other major climatic zones of the world should give some assessment of the severity of the polar habitats.

However, it should be remembered that the test plants used have been specially bred for growth in the agricultural habitats of temperate regions and are hence physiologically adapted to growth in warmer temperature regimes. Hence, comparable work with indigenous plants along the lines suggested by Warren Wilson (1966a) is necessary if a true insight is to be gained into the modes of plant adaptation to the cooler temperature regimes of polar environments. Data of this sort were collected during the course of the present work,

TABLE 7

Comparison of values for *Relative Growth Rates, Net Assimilation Rates* and *Leaf Area Ratios* for Turnip at Arctic, Antarctic and temperate stations. R_W in gm/gm wk, E_A in gm/dm² wk and F_A in dm²/gm

	Greenland (69°N) (late season)	South Georgia (54°S) (mid-season)	South Georgia (54°S) (late season)	Cornwallis Island (75°N)* (mid-season)	England (52°N)* (mid-season)
R_W	·95— ·32	·50— ·36	·27— ·09	·54	2·16
E_A	·48— ·19	·43— ·33	·24— ·08	·41	·68
F_A	1·98—1·26	1·25—1·09	1·18—1·13	1·39	3·19

* Values from Warren Wilson (1966a).

but the results have not yet been worked out. Comparisons of behaviour of bipolar species such as *Phleum alpinum* and *Montia fontana*, which grow both at the northern and southern stations would be of particular interest.

Similar methods are also being applied to native species growing *in situ* to provide information on their contribution to the productivity of natural communities. Direct measurements of the dry matter production of such comunities, when combined with detailed data for such climatic and edaphic factors as solar radiation, temperature, humidity and nutrient levels, should lead to a better understanding of the functional aspects of polar ecosystems.

Acknowledgements

We would like to acknowledge our indebtedness to the other members of the Bipolar Botanical Group—Mrs D. M. Greene, T. V. Callaghan, G. C. S. Clarke, and D. W. H. Walton, all of whom assisted in the collecting and processing of the results presented here. We would also like to thank the British National Committee for the International Biological Programme for sponsoring the project as part of the U.K. official programme. Finally, we acknowledge gratefully financial and logistic support from the Royal Society, the British Antarctic Survey and the Universities of Birmingham and Copenhagen.

References

Bliss, L. C. (1962). Adaptations of arctic and alpine plants to environmental conditions. *Arctic* 15, 117–44.
Warren Wilson, J. (1966a). An analysis of plant growth and its control in arctic environments. *Ann. Bot.* 30, No. 119, 383–402.
Warren Wilson, J. (1966b). Effect of temperature on Net Assimilation Rate. *Ann. Bot.* 30, No. 120, 753–61.

Productivity Studies on Macquarie Island Vegetation

J. F. JENKIN* AND D. H. ASHTON
*Antarctic Division, Department of External Affairs† and Botany School,
University of Melbourne, Australia*

I. Introduction

The early geographic and taxonomic surveys of Cheeseman (1919) and Hamilton (1926), and the work of Taylor (1955), have provided the basis for the present structural and productivity studies. If compared with physiognomically similar vegetation elsewhere, the luxuriance of the vegetation of the lower elevations of Macquarie Island and similar Subantarctic islands is comparable only with the herbaceous communities of the high tropical mountains (Troll, 1960). The present work is directed towards elucidating the reasons for this growth under the climatic conditions prevailing at Macquarie Island, with uniformly low temperatures, frequent strong winds, regular and frequent precipitation and low total radiation.

A limited comparison has been made between Macquarie Island grasslands and coastal grasslands on Phillip Island, Victoria, and montane and sub-alpine grasslands in Central Victoria. The herbfields are compared with the late-summer herbfield biomass at Mt Nelse in the Australian Alps.

A. ENVIRONMENT

Macquarie Island (54°30′S, 158°57′E) is an isolated rectangular plateau 220 to 433 m above sea-level. It has been glaciated, but is now free of permanent snow. The rocks of the island are all basic, and according to Taylor (1955) the type of soil formed is largely dependent on wind exposure. Where plant growth is not limited by wind velocity a peat soil is formed and where the wind retards plant growth, dry tundra soils form. Wind erosion, either occurring naturally, or where the sward has been broken by rabbit grazing, is a common feature.

The climate is uniformly cold, windy and wet. There is a mean annual precipitation of 101 cm occurring over 330 days; hence the island suffers no drought. The mean wind speed is 20 knots, and associated with this, there is

* Present address: Botany School, University of Melbourne.   † Now Department of Supply.

a considerable deposition of wind-borne salt. The mean annual temperature is 4·5°C, the mean annual range of variation 3·3°C, and the mean diurnal variation ± 1·6°C. The highest air temperature ever recorded is 12°C. Macquarie Island has the reputation of having one of the most uniform climates on earth (Landsberg et al., 1965). The generalized total radiation estimate by Landsberg is 78 Kcal/cm²yr; that recorded for 1967/68 was 75 kcal/cm²yr. (Radiation was measured by a "Rimco" Solar Radiation Integrator, wavelength response 0·4—1·1 μ calibrated against an Eppley Pyrheliometer.) Hours of sunshine comprise 18% of the possible maximum. (See Fig. 1a for climatic data.)

Microclimatic effects within the taller vegetation are not particularly marked, due to the lack of sunny calm weather. The air temperature around shoot bases in large tussocks of *Poa foliosa* may reach 1–3°C above maximum screen temperatures.

B. VEGETATION

Three main formations are present. Grasslands, which may be 1 to 1·5 m high, consist of pedestalled tussocks of *Poa foliosa* and the large-leaved co-dominant *Stilbocarpa polaris* (Ashton, 1965). These occur up to about 230 m where the *Poa* is small and dense. Above this altitude herbfields dominated by *Pleurophyllum hookeri* occur in relatively sheltered sites. A feldmark community dominated by *Azorella selago* and *Rhacomitrium crispulum* occurs on the more wind-exposed areas. The herbfield is found at all altitudes down to sea-level where either a high water table occurs or where landslips or screes provide the opportunity for succession. The development of a peat pedestal permits *Poa foliosa* to grow higher than *Stilbocarpa* or *Pleurophyllum* and thereby compete successfully for light.

The flora is relatively meagre with only thirty-five vascular species and has strong affinities with the New Zealand region, with Australia and with the circumpolar islands.

II. Methods

The standing biomass of grassland and herbfield was measured by harvesting five 1 m sq. quadrats. Root weight was estimated from twenty 2 in (5 cm) diameter cores to depths of up to 2 ft 6 in (approx. 75 cm). Sites for intensive study were selected at the northern end of the island over the altitudinal range of both grassland and herbfield. Grassland was sampled at 20, 150 and 750 ft above sea-level (6, 45 and 230 m); herbfield was sampled at 30 ft and 770 ft (9 m and 235 m). The seasonal variation in standing biomass was sampled from grassland at 150 ft (45 m), and herbfield at 770 ft (235 m) by a series of harvests at approximately ten-week intervals. Selected quadrats were reharvested at intervals of up to two years to obtain estimates of re-growth. Leaf areas were estimated to obtain values of leaf area index (LAI), and numerous shoots were tagged and measured to provide information on leaf longevity and the length of the growing season.

TABLE 1

Comparative Biomass Data

Vegetation type and locality	Altitude (m)	Dominant species	Dry weight (kg/m²)		LAI (m²/m²)
			Above ground	Below ground	
GRASSLAND					
MACQUARIE ISLAND†	6	Poa foliosa	0·96	—	—
	45	Poa foliosa	0·92	1·70	7·23
	230	Poa foliosa	0·33	—	1·68
VICTORIA					
Coastal. Phillip Island	15	Poa poiformis	0·39	0·64	2·50
Basalt plain. St Albans (Groves, 1965)	30	Themeda australis	0·34	—	—
Montane. Wallaby Greek	610	Poa australis var. latifolia	0·13	—	—
Alpine. Lake Mountain	1370	Poa australis var. alpina	0·25	—	2·45
NEW SOUTH WALES					
Alpine. Kosciusko, (Costin, 1967)	1830	Poa caespitosa	0·13	—	—
NEW GUINEA					
Alpine. Mt Wilhelm (Walker, 1968) (a) Forb-rich	3530–4400	Ranunculus basilobatus— Deschampsia klossii	0·51—0·88	—	—
(b) Tussock	4400	Heirochloe redolens— Poa nivicola	0·36—0·58	—	—
HERBFIELD					
MACQUARIE ISLAND†	9	Pleurophyllum hookeri	0·76	—	7·13
	235	Pleurophyllum hookeri	0·47	0·67	1·42*
VICTORIA					
Alpine. Mt Nelse	1830	Celmisia longifolia	0·30	—	1·48

Replacement following harvesting

			Above ground only	Mean percentage replaced in one year‡
GRASSLAND				
MACQUARIE ISLAND†	45	*Poa foliosa*	0·75	91
	230	*Poa foliosa*	0·10	28
VICTORIA	15	*Poa poiformis*	0·31	79
HERBFIELD				
MACQUARIE ISLAND†	9	*Pleurophyllum hookeri*	0·23	30
	235	*Pleurophyllum hookeri*	0·11	23
VICTORIA	1830	*Celmisia longifolia*	0·41	137

* Value for *Pleurophyllum* only, which species represents on average 18% of the total biomass. Inclusion of all species including bryophytes would probably increase this to approximately 7.

† Macquarie Island figures are mean values from all harvests for which data is complete at present.

‡ Reharvest percentages are total reharvest as percentage of original harvest living material.

III. Results and Discussion

A. BIOMASS OF HERBFIELD AND GRASSLAND

The biomass of the Macquarie Island formations is high (see Table 1). The grassland is comparable with similar formations at Mt Wilhelm in New Guinea (Walker, 1968) and is two to three times greater than that of coastal grassland in southern Victoria. The herbfield at Macquarie Island has twice the biomass of alpine herbfield at 1830 m in north-eastern Victoria.

The root growth is also substantial. In the grassland there is a 20 to 1 variation from pedestal to inter-tussock space. Mean dry weights of live roots and rhizomes to 2 ft (approx. 60 cm) depth are about twice that of the tops. In the waterlogged herbfield the root and rhizome weight approximately equals that of the tops.

B. SEASONAL VARIATION IN PLANT DRY WEIGHT

The seasonal variation in the standing biomass shows a subdued curve with a statistically significant peak in late summer 1965 and indications of an early summer peak in 1966 (Fig. 1b). In *Poa* the peak of litter accumulation follows some time later, and the litter accumulates as a massive thatch-like collar around the base of the tussock (Fig. 2). In *Stilbocarpa* litter accumulation does not occur to any appreciable extent due to rapid decay. The same picture emerges for *Pleurophyllum* in the herbfields (Fig. 3), although its winter die-back is fairly marked. In early summer twenty to thirty leaves form the rosette, growth slackens off in late summer and by autumn only the small central leaves are green.

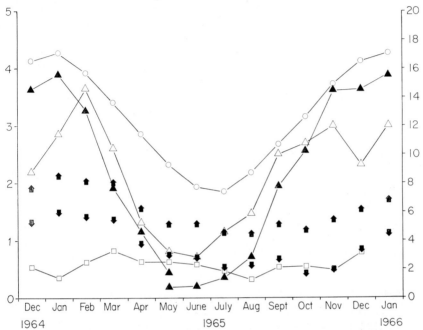

FIG. 1*a*. Environmental data for Macquarie Island. All results are daily means on a monthly basis. All data except radiation is from the Macquarie Island ANARE Meteorological Station records for the period indicated. The radiation figures are records from May 1967 to May 1968.

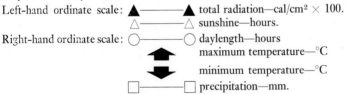

Left-hand ordinate scale: ▲———▲ total radiation—cal/cm² × 100.
△———△ sunshine—hours.
Right-hand ordinate scale: ○———○ daylength—hours
maximum temperature—°C

minimum temperature—°C
□———□ precipitation—mm.

C. GROWTH CHARACTERISTICS

Data from tagged shoots indicate that *Poa foliosa* has a very long growing season. An increase in leaf production is evident from late winter on to a peak in summer. Flowering short shoots terminate growth at any time throughout summer. Vegetative shoots slacken off growth in late autumn. The growing season of the grass is about ten months and for the rosette about eight months. Observations suggest that the longevity of grass leaves may be six months over summer and ten months over the winter period. This is considerably shorter than that of leaves of New Zealand tussock grass *Chionochloa rigida* (Mark, 1965). It is possible that replenishment of leaf area by new leaves maintains a high efficiency of photosynthesis.

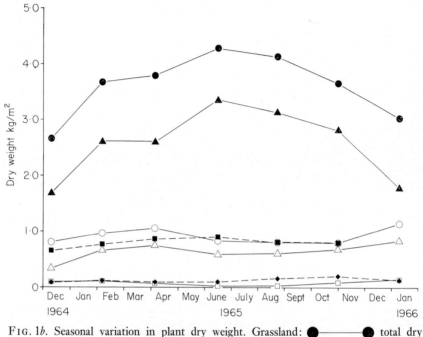

FIG. 1*b*. Seasonal variation in plant dry weight. Grassland: ●————● total dry weight—all species. ▲————▲ Litter—*Poa foliosa* only. ○————○ Total biomass —all species. △————△ Biomass—*Poa foliosa* only. Herbfield: ■-------■ total dry weight—all species. □-------□ Biomass—*Pleurophyllum hookeri* only. ◆-------◆ Litter—Pleurophyllum hookeri only.

The variation of growth for the consecutive summer periods is interesting, since the rapid increase in summer 1966 was preceded by an unusually sunny period in November. This warmer period may have had some influence on the mass germination of *Pleurophyllum* seeds observed in summer 1966. It is of interest that although the climate is very uniform and the vegetation well adapted to it, slight variations in the temperature and light regimes may have a very significant effect.

Studies by Dunstone and Evans (*personal communication*), using the CSIRO Phytotron at Canberra, indicate that *Poa foliosa* has a lower temperature range for optimum growth than do some other more temperate species of *Poa*, such as *Poa caespitosa* and *Poa pratensis*, i.e. 16–21°C as opposed to 22–27°C. The growth of *Poa foliosa* was less at 10–15°C, and it is not known whether its response falls greatly at its natural temperature range of 5–10°C. At 33–37°C its growth was extremely poor, as suggested by its behaviour in a Melbourne summer. The yearly growth rate of *Poa foliosa* grassland is approximately twice that of the winter growth of an improved mixed pasture at Yarragon (100 m) in Gippsland, Victoria. Mean winter

FIG. 2. Mature grassland at 45 m, Macquarie Island. Large pedestalled tussocks of *Poa foliosa* are interspersed by the large-leaved *Stilbocarpa polaris*. The mattock handle in the lower right corner is approximately 3 ft (approximately 0·9 m) in length.

temperatures at Yarragon are 5°C higher than the mean annual temperature at Macquarie Island. The mixed pasture comprised *Lolium perenne*, *Trifolium subterraneum* and *Dactylis glomerata*, and had received superphosphate at the rate of 250 kg/ha. Its growth was measured between 13 June and 9 September (Aitken, *personal communication*).

Studies on the rates of photosynthesis of the three dominants are not yet completed; preliminary indications are that rates are low.

The leaf area index (LAI) is high for the Macquarie Island communities and is much greater than comparable communities in Victoria. The penetration of light is quite considerable in the grassland. Incident light is only reduced to 20% at 30 cm in the grass, but to 3% in *Stilbocarpa* due to differences in leaf orientation. There is then a large leaf area for the interception of predominantly diffuse light.

FIG. 3. Herbfield at 235 m. *Pleurophyllum hookeri* with associated grasses, sedges and bryophytes.

D. CHLOROPHYLL CONTENTS

The chlorophyll contents of the three dominant species studied are high (Table 2).

It is generally considered that chlorophyll does not limit photosynthesis unless light intensity is low. However, Sestak (1966) indicated a definite relationship between chlorophyll content and photosynthetic rates at saturating light intensities in fodder cabbage and sugar beet. Friend (1961) has suggested that the linear relationship between leaf chlorophyll content and daylength in Marquis wheat is related to greater leaf thickness at longer daylengths. On average, *Poa foliosa* leaves are thinner in summer than in winter. The chlorophyll contents given in Table 2 are summer values; winter data are not yet available. Work by Mooney and Billings (1961) on

TABLE 2

Chlorophyll Contents of Macquarie Island Species

SPECIES	Chlorophyll mg/gm FW
Poa foliosa	0·22 sheath 1·41 blade
Stilbocarpa polaris	0·59
Pleurophyllum hookeri	0·43
cf. Celmisia longifolia (Victorian Alps)	0·36

Oxyria digyna suggests that the higher chlorophyll content in Arctic, as compared with Alpine, races may be a compensation permitting maintenance of comparable rates of photosynthesis in both areas. While more work is necessary, the implication is that greater chlorophyll contents may permit higher rates of photosynthesis than would otherwise occur, given the prevailing conditions at Macquarie Island.

E. CALORIFIC VALUES AND EFFICIENCY OF ENERGY UTILIZATION

Relative efficiences of utilization of incident energy provide a useful parameter in the comparison of different communities. For a given time

TABLE 3

Calorific Values of Macquarie Island and Other Species (corrected for sulphur and moisture)

SPECIES	CALORIFIC VALUES IN KCAL/GM DRY WEIGHT				
	Lamina	Petioles	Rhizome	Root	Total mean
Poa foliosa	4·71	4·33	4·79	4·62	4·60
Stilbocarpa polaris	4·10	3·97	4·00	4·10	4·05
Pleurophyllum hookeri	4·28	—	4·35	4·20	4·28
Celmisia longifolia	4·55	—	—	4·39	4·47
20 Alpine herbs (Bliss, 1962)	—	—	—	—	4·14—4·90
Zea mays (Lieth, 1968)	—	—	—	—	4·2
Helianthus annuus (Lieth, 1968)	—	—	—	—	4·3

interval, the calorific equivalent of the vegetation growth per unit area may be expressed as a percentage of the radiation incident on that area.

Macquarie Island species were analysed for calorific content (Table 3). Values obtained are of the same order as those quoted for other comparable plants and communities.

TABLE 4

Percentage Efficiency of Nett Annual Above-ground Production

Vegetation type and locality	Dominant species	Total yearly radiation Kcal/cm²yr	Percentage efficiency*
SUBANTARCTIC			
Macquarie Island			
Grassland (altitude 45 m)	Poa foliosa	75	0·46
(altitude 230 m)	Poa foliosa	75	0·06
Herbfield (altitude 9 m)	Pleurophyllum hookeri	75	0·13
(altitude 235m)	Pleurophyllum hookeri	75	0·06
TEMPERATE			
Victoria (lat. 38°S)			
Grassland. Coastal	Poa poiformis	138	0·10
U.S.A. Minnesota (lat. 45°N)			
Grassland. Native, mature	Andropogon scoparius	128	0·09
Marsh	Typha sp.	128	0·46
(Bray et al., 1959; Bray, 1962)			
ALPINE			
Victoria			
Herbfield (altitude 1830 m)	Celmisia longifolia	140‡	0·13
U.S.A. New Hampshire (lat. 45°N)			
Mt Washington (altitude 1840 m)			
Sedge meadow	Carex bigelowii	110†	0·05§
(Bliss, 1966)			
ARCTIC			
U.S.A. Alaska (lat. 75°N)			
Cape Thomson. Wet meadow	Carex aquatilis	75†	0·09§
(Bliss, 1966)			

* Based on total yearly radiation.

† Radiation figures are estimates derived from Landsberg et al. (1965). The figure for Alaska is probably reasonably accurate, that for Mt Washington less so because of differences in incident radiation due to increased altitude and differing cloud cover. Hence the latter efficiency is only an approximation.

‡ Estimate only; the comments re altitude in † above are applicable here.

§ These figures are based on data presented by Bliss (1966), and are not actually quoted by that author.

Lieth (1968) suggests that from an ecological point of view it is preferable to use total radiation rather than only that within the visible spectrum, and that total yearly radiation figures are most useful when considering different widely separated natural communities. However, regardless of the spectral range or time interval used, comparisons of percentage efficiency may involve percentages of different total amounts of radiation. Such comparisons are therefore most useful when made between areas receiving similar total amounts of radiation; this will not always be possible.

Percentage efficiency figures derived for Macquarie Island are approximations, as they are based on the yearly regrowth of previously clipped quadrats (see Table 1). The extent of regrowth is variable, but is high for the lower-altitude grassland. The upper grassland is at its altitudinal limit and the regrowth reflects its reduced vigour there. The lower values for the herbfield are thought to reflect the more severe effects of clipping on herbfield vegetation than on grassland. Similarly the figures for the Victorian communities are based on regrowth. Further, the Macquarie Island percentages refer to above-ground regrowth only, and do not include root growth or the depletion of stored reserve material. However, given these limitations, the results (Table 4) nevertheless show a relatively high efficiency, higher than many communities previously reported. For the grassland the efficiency is comparable to that of a *Typha* marsh (Bray, 1962). The value for *Typha* is quoted by Bliss (1966) as exemplifying a high efficiency in a natural herbaceous community.

IV. Conclusion

The vegetation of Macquarie Island comprises relatively few species, which range over a considerable variety of habitats. Competition is important in the restriction of the various communities, and the height, growth, biomass and productivity of grassland exceeds that of herbfield. Only where waterlogging is severe can herbfield become dominant.

The luxuriance of the grasslands is related to long growing seasons and a relatively depressed temperature optimum. The dominants have high chlorophyll contents and are well adapted morphologically to a climate which has little direct sunlight. Leaf area indices are high, new leaf production is sustained over much of the year and leaf longevity is prolonged. Utilization of incident energy appears to be relatively efficient.

Acknowledgements

This study is part of a joint programme under the auspices of the Antarctic Division, Commonwealth Department of Supply and the Botany School, University of Melbourne. Grateful acknowledgement is made to the Division and to Professor J. S. Turner, Head of the Botany School, for support in this programme. One of us (J.F.J.) was a member of the 1965 Australian National Antarctic Research Expeditions (ANARE) party on Macquarie Island and subsequently spent the summer months of 1966 and 1968 on the island. D.H.A. has visited the island annually since 1962 with the December relief expedition. Our special thanks go to the members of the Macquarie Island parties, whose willing assistance has been invaluable. The permission of the Commonwealth Bureau of Meteorology to use their data for Macquarie Island is gratefully acknowledged.

References

Ashton, D. H. (1965). Regeneration pattern of *Poa foliosa* Hook f. on Macquarie Island. *Proc. R. Soc. Vict.* 79, No. 1, 215–33.

Bliss, L. C. (1962) Caloric and lipid content in Alpine tundra plants. *Ecology* 43, No. 4, 753–7.

Bliss, L. C. (1966). Plant productivity in Alpine microenvironments on Mount Washington, New Hampshire. *Ecol. Monogr.* 36, No. 2, 125–55.

Bray, J. R. (1962). The primary productivity of vegetation in Central Minnesota, U.S.A., and its relationship to chlorophyll content and albedo. *In* "Die Stoffproduktion der Pflanzendecke" (Lieth, H., ed.), Gustav Fischer Verlag, Stuttgart. 102–16.

Bray, J. R., Lawrence, D. B. and Pearson, L. C. (1959). Primary production in some Minnesota terrestrial communities for 1957. *Oikos* 10, No. 1, 38–49.

Cheeseman, T. F. (1919). The vascular flora of Macquarie Island. *Australas. Antarct. exped. Rep.* Ser. C 7, No. 3.

Costin, A. B. (1967). Alpine ecosystems of the Australasian region. *In* "Arctic and Alpine Environments" (Wright, H. E., Jr. and Osburn, W. H., eds.), Indiana University Press. 55–87.

Friend, D. J. C. (1961). Control of chlorophyll content by daylength in leaves of Marquis wheat. *Can. J. Bot.* 39, No. 1, 51–63.

Groves, R. H. (1965). Growth of *Themeda australis* tussock grassland at St Albans, Victoria. *Aust. J. Bot.* 13, No. 2, 291–302.

Hamilton, H. (1926). Ecological notes and illustrations of the flora of Macquarie Island. *Australas. Antarct. exped. Rep.* Ser. C 7, No. 5.

Landsberg, H. E., Lippmann, H., Paffen, K. H. and Troll, C. (1965). *In* "World Maps of Climatology" (Rodenwaldt, E. and Jusatz, H. J., eds.), Second Edition. Springer-Verlag, Berlin.

Lieth, H. (1968). The measurement of calorific values of biological material and the determination of ecological efficiency. *In* "Functioning of Terrestrial Ecosystems at the Primary Production Level, Proceedings of the Copenhagen Symposium, 1965" (Eckhardt, F. E., ed.) UNESCO, Paris. 233–42.

Mark, A. F. (1965). The environment and growth rate of narrow-leaved snow tussock, *Chionochloa rigida*, in Otago. *N.Z. J. Bot.* 3, No. 2, 73–103.

Mooney, H. A. and Billings, W. D. (1961). Comparative physiological ecology of Arctic and Alpine populations of *Oxyria digyna*. *Ecol. Monogr.* 31, No. 1, 1–29.

Sestak, Z. (1966). Limitations for finding a linear relationship between chlorophyll content and photosynthetic activity. *Biologia Pl.* 8, No. 5, 336–46.

Taylor, B. W. (1955). The flora, vegetation and soils of Macquarie Island. *A.N.A.R.E.* Rep., Ser. B 2·

Troll, C. (1960). The relationship between the climates, ecology and plant geography of the southern cold temperate zone and of the tropical high mountains. *Proc. R. Soc.* B **152**, 529–32.

Walker, D. (1968). A Reconnaissance of the Non-arboreal Vegetation of the Pindaunde Catchment, Mount Wilhelm, New Guinea. *J. Ecol.* **56**, No. 2, 445–66.

Discussion

Vegetation

HABITATS AND VEGETATION

G. A. LLANO

The contrast between the Antarctic Peninsula and the rest of the continent has emerged strikingly from this session. Few people have worked in both; perhaps as a result some important factors have tended to be ignored. The country around Wilkes station seems to me to be rather like the Peninsula, in having lush lichen vegetation and abundant snow algae. It may well be that *Deschampsia* or *Colobanthus* might be established if transplanted to Wilkes, and this might be more interesting than the importation of non-polar species.

There are habitats around McMurdo that have received insufficient attention. For example, the pits of scoriaceous volcanic rocks almost all have small thalli growing in them, although there are no macro-lichens. On the old crater slopes a layer of lichens is present under rocks. Archaeologists have described how stone layers in deserts were once used to trap condensed water, and these stones are a parallel case in that they trap snow which melts slowly and produces favourable conditions for vegetation within what appears to be a loose scree.

Haupt Nunatak, near Wilkes, has a top which is almost flush with the ice and over almost all the rock pinnacles ice has melted to leave a space roofed over with clear ice like a greenhouse and supporting a rich vegetation. In the Wilson Piedmont area of Victoria Land weathering of marble outcrop produces layers of rock chips and below these a flora is to be found. These are just examples of favourable micro-habitats of great interest for understanding of plant adaptation.

PAST CLIMATES AND VEGETATION

I. M. LAMB

Dr Ahmadjian made an important point when he referred to endemic lichens. On the level of endemism hinges the argument for perglacial survival of the flora. The endemism, unfortunately, is hard to evaluate in the Antarctic as the taxonomic literature is so imprecise as to be almost useless. Critical modern studies, however, confirm that in some crustose genera in the Peninsula there is a high percentage of endemics. Many species, for example of *Buellia* and *Ramalima*, are nitrophilous. Nitrophilous endemics are restricted to areas strongly influenced by birds, and it would be strange if such a physiological adaptation has arisen suddenly since ice maximum. If these species were in Antarctica through glacial maximum we can assume they were nitrophilous. Were there, then, bird colonies on the continent?

B. STONEHOUSE

We have no exact picture of the shift of the climatic zones. But if at ice maximum these were only displaced four or five degrees north I do not believe there is any problem. The islands now fringing the Antarctic might have been ice covered, but breeding sites must have been available on the Peninsula or in Victoria Land. Snow petrels and skuas now breed 320 km inland in the Tottanfjella and bring in nitrate to such places. Even if displaced from their present sites they would have found others at comparable distance from the ice edge. It is a pity we have no fossil records of high Antarctic birds in the Subantarctic: this would test the degree of displacement, but remains are unlikely where the soils are so acid. The only well-known sub-fossil bird bone beds in the Falkland Islands might help, but nobody has looked at them.

It is interesting that James Eights in 1820 recorded King Penguins in the South Shetland Islands, while the birds are now found only north of the northern limit of pack ice. Either the life cycle was different in this South Shetland population, or there was less ice about the islands in winter.

L. IRVING

I have speculated on the past distribution of Arctic birds in relation to climate. It seems unlikely these birds acquired cold tolerance as an adaptive change in the short time since the Pleistocene deterioration of the climate. As a physiologist I cannot see how physiological systems could change that quickly: we must look instead for a latent persistent capability or a superfluous capability developed as a "preadaptation".

W. BENNINGHOFF

About 40 miles north of Thule (Greenland) the margin of a small ice cap is receding at an estimated 5 m/yr and mosses and lichens were found in viable condition from below ice that is believed to have covered them for several decades. The advance and retreat of this fluctuating ice margin did not scour away these small plants, because they were frozen into an "icefoot" that joined with the perennially frozen soils.

PENCILLIUM IN ANTARCTICA

J. BAKER

Dr Rudolph reported *Pencillium* from soils. Were these actively growing in the soil or contaminant spores from the station that began to grow only in culture?

E. D. RUDOLPH

They were within the soil material, but we have no information about their activity there, as is often the case in temperate regions. This still does not mean that the fungi did not come from human contamination.

Part XIII

TERRESTRIAL FAUNA

Terrestrial Fauna

In 1962, at the first SCAR Symposium on Antarctic biology, J. L. Gressitt (1964) pointed out that nearly all records of land invertebrates had come from two areas: Victoria Land and the Antarctic Peninsula. Within Victoria Land, ecological studies had been started by Gressitt and his colleagues and by H. Janetschek, and M. E. Pryor (1962) had given the first detailed account of the ecology of an Antarctic Collembolan, supplementing the earlier autecological account of the mite *Maudheimia wilsoni* by Dalenius and Wilson (1958).

Since 1964 taxonomic and biogeographic work has increased, but mainly within the two areas of pioneer study. Much of this work has been reviewed in a volume of the United States Antarctic Research Series entitled "Entomology of Antarctica" (Gressitt, 1967). In the present section, H. Janetschek, who contributed a major ecological paper to that volume, reviews the arthropod fauna of Victoria Land and its ecology, and his contribution may well stand as typical for continental Antarctica. Research on the ecology of land animals in the maritime Antarctic (the zones and subzones are defined in the introduction to Part XII) has been undertaken chiefly by P. J. Tilbrook and associated British scientists at Signy Island and by Chilean biologists on Robert Island (South Shetland Islands). In this section P. J. Tilbrook contributes a review paper invited by the editors to cover this work and supplement that by Janetschek. The paper by three Chilean scientists on the capacity of the Antarctic soil fauna to invade new substrata includes references to other descriptions of their investigations, while P. J. Tilbrook's second paper, on the ecology of *Cryptopygus antarcticus*, is an example of the detailed autecological research likely to be undertaken increasingly in future.

Like the land vegetation, the terrestrial fauna of Antarctica is closely dependent upon climate, water availability, and substratum. Much of the information in the two preceding sections is therefore closely relevant to this one. In continental Antarctica the water regime of the desert soils described by F. C. Ugolini in Part XI, and especially the critical relationship between depth of summer thaw and depth of the ice permafrost horizon, greatly influences the presence and abundance of the soil arthropods described by Janetschek. The richer fauna of the maritime Antarctic is likewise greatly influenced by water regime, as P. J. Tilbrook indicates in his review paper, and varies in abundance from one to another of the vegetation types described by C. H. Gimingham and R. I. L. Smith in Part XII. Finally, no discussion of the Antarctic land fauna can be complete without some consideration of its origin and history, and this has been reviewed at length by L. R. Brundin in Part I. Taken together these papers give reasonable coverage of what is now known of the ecology of terrestrial invertebrates in Antarctica.

References

Dalenius, P. and Wilson, O. (1958). On the soil fauna of the Antarctic and of the Sub-antarctic Islands. The Oribatei (Acari). *Arkiv. Zool.* 2, 11, 393–425.

Gressitt, J. L. (1964). Ecology and biogeography of land arthropods in Antarctica. *In* "Biologie Antartique: Antarctic Biology", (Carrick, R., Holdgate, M. W. and Prévost, J., eds). Hermann, Paris.

Gressitt, J. L. (1967) (ed.). "Entomology of Antarctica." *Antarct. Res. Ser.* 10. American Geophysical Union.

Pryor, M. E. (1962). Some environmental features of Hallett Station, Antarctica, with special reference to soil arthropods. *Pacif. Insects.* 4, 681–728.

Environments and Ecology of Terrestrial Arthropods in the High Antarctic

HEINZ JANETSCHEK

Institut für Zoologie, Universität Innsbruck, Austria

I. Introduction

This paper is concerned with the ecology of terrestrial arthropods in South Victoria Land, and with research initiated by the author in 1961–62 and continued subsequently by staff of the Bernice P. Bishop Museum, Hawaii (Janetschek, 1963, 1967a; Wise *et al.*, 1964; Wise and Spain, 1967). In this region, away from the immediate coastal strip (where a cryovegetation and cryofauna should also be possible) terrestrial life is only found in the areas that are ice and snow free either permanently or during the short polar summer. The author knows of no cryocoenoses on glaciers and snowfields in Victoria Land.

II. Environmental Conditions

Terrestrial life in these high southern latitudes depends primarily on the availability, at least at certain times, of water as liquid or as moisture. For this the microtemperatures of the soil and its surface must rise above $0°C$, at least during a certain number of days during the season. Such an increase of microtemperatures above zero is probably also required for the active life of most of the terrestrial arthropods of the area. Obviously there must also be the correlated occurrence of primary production as food-base for the arthropods. Nearly all of the South Victoria Land arthropod species can be considered to be primary consumers, feeding especially on microphytes and detritus. Mites of the family *Rhagidiidae*, which is represented by one single species only in the very northern parts of South Victoria Land (*Coccorhagidia keithi* Str.), are, however, certainly predators.

A. TEMPERATURE REGIME

Even in the southernmost area with observed arthropod life, near to 86°S, there is still a diurnal change in the angular elevation of the sun above the horizon. The radiation-dependent parameters as well as the behaviour of the animals show a corresponding diurnal variation. Such a variation is demon-strated by a series of microtemperature readings at a locality on the edge of the polar inland ice sheet at about 77°S and 1830 m above sea-level (Fig. 1.). With air temperatures between about −5° and −15°C, the diel mean of the subsur-face of fine soil is above zero and the upper parts of the soil remain more or less above 0° during the greater part of the twenty-four-hour day. The graph of temperature distribution in such a soil (Fig. 2.) demonstrates clearly that the heat balance is potentially adequate for active life by terrestrial animals.

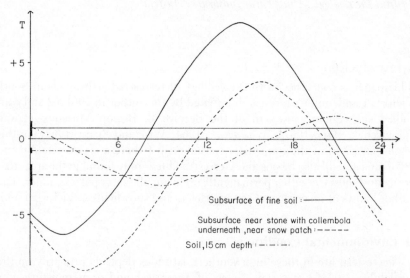

FiG. 1. Diel temperature variations and means at different depths in a chalikosystem soil at a mountain site near the polar plateau (Springtail Point, head of Mackay Glacier, 77°10′07′ ′S 1830±m, 12—14.1.1962). Data smoothed by Fourier analysis. (After Janetschek, 1967a).

Under good weather conditions, the critically important 0°C line reaches generally as deep as 10–15 cm in the soil, but in some parts of the dry valleys it may descend to about 1 m.

Air temperatures at the South Pole are of the same order in December and January as they are in winter at McMurdo. Approaching the pole, one may therefore reach areas where even during days with pronounced radiation under a clear sky, the highest microtemperature values remain below 0°C. The author's southernmost readings near Plunket Point at more than 85°S and about 2600 m above sea-level examplify this (Janetschek, 1967a). Because of their low temperatures, such localities lie outside the potential range of permanent soil life.

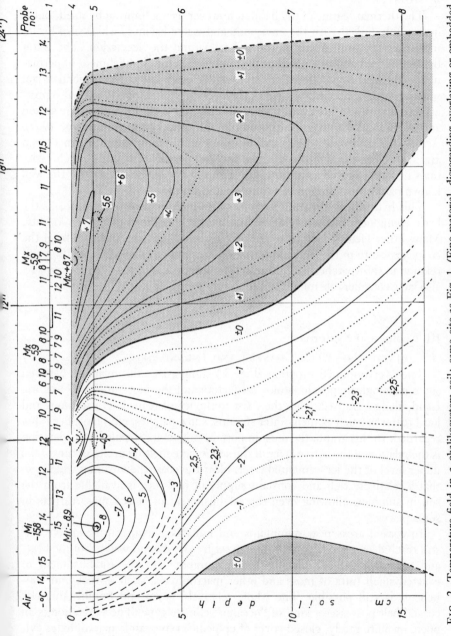

FIG. 2. Temperature field in a chalikosystem soil; same site as Fig. 1. (Fine material, disregarding overlaying or embedded stones.) (After Janetschek, 1967a.) Mi = minimum, Mx = maximum temperature.

B. Moisture

The thermal régime of the habitat, however, is not limiting by itself, but is inseparably linked with the environmental water balance, which also has to meet the minimum needs of the soil fauna and the vegetation. The water balance of the habitats, as well as the lower limits for establishment of permanent arthropod populations, are still insufficiently known. In general, a soil water content of about 2% seems to be necessary; arthropods were also present at one series of sites with a mean reading of 1% during part of the season and such localities may be transitorily tolerable (Wise and Spain, 1967). Actually the soil water content varies considerably from site to site in a given area, as well as through the seasonal and diel periods of melting. Such variations in space, as well as in time, are certainly one of the reasons for the well known patchy distribution of vegetation and animal life.

This hydrothermal regimen of the soil, which limits active life, forms the basic component of the overall environmental conditions in a given locality. Many other factors such as orographic features, altitude, distance from the coast, exposure to the prevailing winds, screening, exposure, inclination and relation to snowpatches and glaciers, thus determining the degree of seepage, also have considerable influence.

III. Ecological Systems

A. Variation between Coastal and Inland Sites

The oversimplified ecogram (Fig. 3.) summarizes the relations between some pedological and climatological factors and the biota in South Victoria Land, along a transect from the coast to the ice plateau. Diel variations and local patterns (such as melt-water streams, snow patches, etc.) have been disregarded. In this graph, the most important subject for detailed consideration is the relation of the active layer of the soil, where melting cycles occur, to the upper level of the ice-cemented layer. Near the coast they overlap widely, so that a relatively rich and constant supply of moisture is available from the soil in summer, allowing even the establishment of closed moss carpets in some places.

In coastal areas near mountains and nunataks, temperatures above 0°C still reach deep enough into the soil to set free ice-bound water, but the heat- and water-budget are already less favourable. Yet the establishment of isolated small tufts of moss and other macrophytes, such as rock-and soil-lichens, is still possible. The whole relatively warm and humid Antarctic coastal belt possesses a kind of "oceanic" climate-type. The vegetation is an open, or more rarely, closed cover of epipedic cryptogamic macrophytes evident to the naked eye. The floristic composition has not yet been studied in detail. The animal part of this ecosystem consists of a vegetation-water community (especially moss-water community) of protozoans, rotifers, nematodes and tardigrades occupying this special niche which does not occur in a comparable form elsewhere in the area. Population densities and frequencies of occurrence of Collembola and mites are often relatively high, and there may

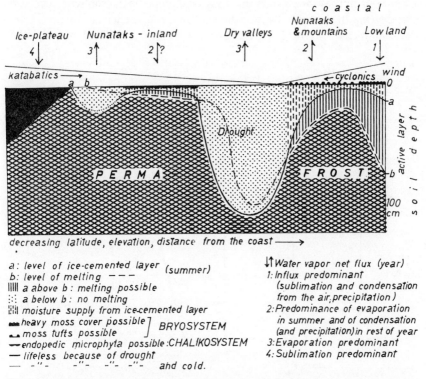

F IG. 3. Simplified ecogram, showing relations between some pedological and climatological factors and biota in South Victoria Land along a transect from the coast to the ice plateau (diel variations and local patterns disregarded). (After Janetschek, 1967a).

also be characteristic animal species (like the coastal collembolan *Gomphiocephalus hodgsoni*): however, the composition of the fauna has not yet been well studied. This "Bryosystem" forms a scattered belt along the Victoria Land coast, including the coast near mountains, south as far as about 85°S and vertically to about 1400 m at about 77°S.

The dry valley area cannot in general support arthropod life. Even temperatures above 0°C in soil as deep as 1 m cannot liberate water because the water formerly present in these surface layers has been removed by evaporation over the past 60,000 years (Wilson, 1970: this symposium). There are, however, areas of inland nunataks many kilometres away from the coast, along the large outlet glaciers and more or less in the immediate neighbourhood of the ice-plateau itself where the ice-cemented layer is at a high enough level to be reached by the diel melting cycles during the summer, making a certain amount of free water available. Temperatures are, however, very low and overall conditions in these areas such that only an endopedic microphytic vegetation can develop in the topsoil. Even the very rare rock-lichens of this ecosystem are "endopedic" in that they grow in rock cracks and are difficult to find, if they

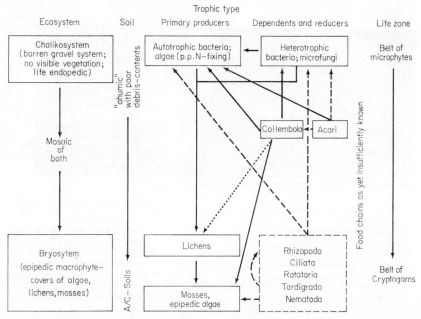

FIG. 4. Zonation of terrestrial Ecosystems in high Antarctica. (Food-webs simplified.) (After Janetschek, 1967a.)

occur at all. The surface seems completely barren and lifeless, but the endopedic microphytes (auto- and heterotrophic bacteria, algae, microfungi, etc.) can support animal life like microzoa, mites and Collembola. The floristic and faunistic components of this chalikosystem (chalix=gravel) are, as yet, poorly known. The mite species seem to be rather widely distributed, most of them occurring also in the Byrosystem; the Collembola, however, seem to be local endemics and some species (e.g. *Antarcticinella monoculata*) may be characteristic of the system. This pioneer chalikosystem represents the outmost belt and border of active life latitudinally southwards and vertically, inland from the coast. It extends southward as far as about 86°S and its arthropod populations occur in South Victoria Land up to somewhat over 2200 m. Around fumaroles there are micro-organisms (microphyta, some protozoans and rotifers) still at 3600 m (the highest known occurrence of life in Antarctica).

With increasing latitude, altitude or local drought arthropods disappear. It can be assumed that the endopedic microphytic life of the chalikosystem tolerates severer conditions, and its limits are still unknown. Farther inland and poleward, melting either does not happen at all or occurs very occasionally. Such areas lie beyond the hydrothermal border for activity and for the permanent establishment of life.

Soils, trophic types and food-webs, and the life zones of the two above ecosystems are summarized in Fig. 4. We can consider the two ecosystems described above also as a sequence of land life in time. The Chalikosystem could serve as a model for the physiognomic aspect of the ecosystem which developed in connection with the first colonization of dry land on earth in the past, and perhaps also for extraterrestrial life (Janetschek, 1964).

B. POPULATION DENSITIES AND BIOMASSES

Population densities and biomasses (Fig. 5.) are always very small: in the extreme chalikosystem soils up to 15 mg per l and more among some macrophytic carpets and topsoils in the Bryosystem, where there may be of the order of 10^2 individuals per square metre. In contrast, in the Maritime Antarctic moss carpet of Signy Island, there may be of the order of 10^4 individuals both of Collembola and Acari (Tilbrook, 1967).

Against every expectation, the peaks of population densities as well as of numbers of arthropod species found by the author, admittedly using rough methods, are not in the relatively warm and moist coastal lowlands, but on the higher slopes and ridges of mountains and nunataks not too far inland from the coast (Fig. 5b). These localities seem to lie near or above the highest level of the Pleistocene glaciation or are at least connected with localities which seem never to have been overrun by former extended glaciation. As mentioned in discussion (see p. 61), this, together with the restricted distribution of the most characteristic collembolan taxa (which seem to be local endemites), suggests a historical explanation for this phenomenon (Janetschek 1963, 1967a). The preglacial, pre-Pleistocene floristic and faunistic elements do not seem to have been extinguished completely: part of the Transantarctic Mountains seem to have acted as a refugia at ice maximum. The same phenomenon is well known for the European Alps. On the other hand, we have the fact that some arthropods in the high Antarctic are able to survive at present under very extreme environmental conditions. It therefore seems likely that the Pleistocene glaciations in the European Alps were never able to extinguish life completely, even in the central parts of these mountains,

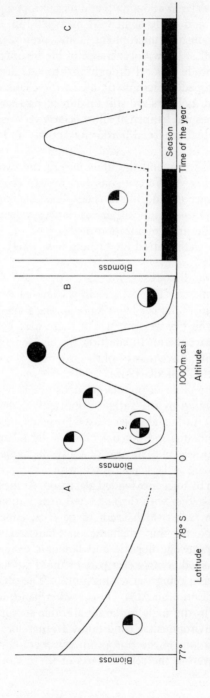

FIG. 5. Population density trends of collembola in South Victoria Land (schematized).

A: Latitudinal effect along the coastal lowlands.

B: Altitudinal effect along a transect from the coast to the head of Mackay Glacier, at about 77°S.

C: Seasonal population dynamics at coastal sites.

Scales are relative only and not comparable. Circles with black sectors indicate respective occurrences of the four Collembola species of the area, each sector representing a particular species.

since environmental conditions of the past were never more extreme than in the Antarctic today.

A comparison of population densities of collembolans at localities along the coast of South Victoria Land demonstrates a distinct latitudinal effect, populations decreasing with increasing latitude (Fig. 5a) (Janetschek, 1967a). Changing weather conditions (either from year to year or site to site) can mask the effect (Wise and Spain, 1967), but when samples taken under comparable weather conditions are considered the trend is visible. For example, fourteen samples taken at Lake Penny (78°16′S) between 12 November 1963 and 8 February 1964 gave a mean of 67 individuals per m², while eleven samples from Flatiron (Granite Harbour) at 77°00′S taken between 15 November 1963 and 12 February 1964 gave a mean of 95 individuals per m².

"Tin samples" without indication of volume (Wise and Spain, 1967) show the same trend. The means of twelve samples each are (sites arranged from south to north): Lake Penny, 4 individuals; Lake Péwé, 4; Marble Point, 30; Flatiron, 35. The figures published by Wise and Spain also demonstrate a high seasonal population peak of the coastal collembolan *Gomphiocephalus hodgsoni* in midsummer (Fig. 5c) at the time of maximum temperatures (Table 1).

TABLE 1

Individuals/m²† of *Gomphiocephalus hodgsoni* (*Collembola*) at Four Coastal Sites of South Victoria Land during the 1963–4 Season (calculated from the data of Wise and Spain, 1967)

Month	November	December	January	February
Number of samples	5	3	15	16
Number of sites	4	2*	4	4
Individuals/m²†	27	126	72	16

* Lake Penny (southernmost) and Flatiron (northernmost site) only.
† Figures are means of samples at all sites during each month.

Although the largest populations are met with at about 1000 m on mountains near the coast, it is also clear that populations decrease with further increases in altitude (Fig. 5b), but there is still insufficient quantitative information to permit more than a few general comparisons. To obtain reliable figures much more information is needed, since the distribution of arthropods in the soils of the area is very irregular and patchy. This seems primarily to be connected with the vegetation pattern of the Bryosystem, which forms a complicated open mosaic with many bare spots. But there are also real aggregations of the springtail *Gomphiocephalus hodgsoni* of from 80 to more than 800 individuals under a single stone (Wise and Spain, 1967). Such aggregation is well known in different groups of small soil animals elsewhere. Besides this primary reason for the patchy pattern, mentioned above, another could be the microbial milieu. Törne (1967a, b) demonstrated, with cellulose-decomposition experiments that the population dynamics of the species of Collembola he studied are regulated mainly by microbial influence on food material. Soils with qualitatively different microfloras showed different rates of reproduction in the experimental Collembola. He found further indications of qualitative differences in the intestinal microflora of different species of Collembola. While a specific intestinal microflora is usually maintained, animals can adapt themselves to their microbial surroundings to a certain extent. Törne concluded that aggregation is advantageous because the Collembola are better able to compete successfully against their microbial milieu when at a higher population density.

On the other hand, there is a relative decrease of collembolans and a relative increase of mites with increasing total biomasses (Janetschek, 1967a). In South Victoria Land Collembola are normally more or less predominant in relation to mites. In the Maritime Antarctic, e.g. at Signy Island, the ratio of numbers of individuals is 1:1 according to Tilbrook (1967). These differences might possibly be explained by:

1. Competition (high numbers of mites were found on an island near McMurdo where no collembolans occur).
2. Changes of the microphytic milieu in the habitats favouring the mites.
3. The macrophytic cover and the soil in the Maritime Antarctic show an increase in what has been termed "Strukturwiderstand": the texture of the vegetation and of the topsoil becomes more dense, and therefore moving around becomes more difficult for (eu- and) hemiedaphic Collembola. (There is only one collembolan species, in north Victoria Land, which may be an atmobios form: *Isotoma klovstadi*).

C. BIOGEOGRAPHICAL DIFFERENCES

Furthermore, there is a sequence and prevalence respectively of higher taxa even in the high-Antarctic itself. Mites especially show a latitudinal sequence corresponding to habitat development, which is roughly comparable with vertical sequences in high mountains elsewhere. First come the Trombidiformes (Prostigmata) as pioneers represented by the families Pachygnathidae, Tydeidae and Eupodidae. The predatory Rhadidiidae first appear relatively far north, with one species (*Coccorhagidia keithi*) in South Victoria Land at about 76°S and another (*C. gressitti*) in North Victoria Land. Oribatid mites (Cryptostigmata) only appear in North Victoria Land (*Maudheimia petronia*) (disregarding a single finding of an airborne specimen of *Alaskozetes antarcticus* on Ross Island). Yet Oribatids are quite common in the outer

Maritime Antarctic. The Collembola also belong to a few families which are also pioneers elsewhere (Onychiuridae, Hypogastruridae, Isotomidae).

D. TEMPERATURE RELATIONS AND OVERWINTERING

The length of time during which active life is possible in a season and the mode of overwintering are of particular significance in Antarctic arthropods. In the development of the author's graphic model of the voltinism of the coastal springtail *Gomphiocephalus hodgsoni* (Janetschek, 1967b) a mean of ninety days of activity proved to fit the population pattern at about 130 m on Cape Crozier (Ross Island). An active season of fifty-seven days fitted the population at about 1200 m on Mt England. Field observations along the South Victoria Land coast in the 1963–4 season suggested that *G. hodgsoni* populations there were active over ninety-six days, or for 26·3% of the year (Wise and Spain, 1967). This value is in agreement with the author's postulated mean active season of ninety days at Cape Crozier. Actually activity is possible only for a part of this time, when temperatures are near to or above 0°C. Most of the time is spent inactivated and/or hibernating. From the author's graphic model of voltinism he postulated that all stages should overwinter (Janetschek, 1967b). This assumption has been more or less confirmed by the field records now published by Wise and Spain. However, the distinct decline in population size towards the end of the season suggests that only a small part of the populations survive. Environmental conditions and the preferred habitats for overwintering are not yet known sufficiently, but overwintering seems to take place *in situ*, where the animals are immobilized by decreasing temperatures. Consequently those colonies survive which are in a sufficiently deep soil at the onset of diapause to escape intolerably low winter temperature minima. Winter minima of $-39°$ to $-43°$C have been measured on the ground in the area by enclosed maximum-minimum thermometers (Janetschek 1967a; Wise and Spain, 1967). Temperatures in the overwintering niches in the topsoil must be somewhat higher. Little is known about the frost resistance of the species involved, but short-term experiments suggest a lower limit of about $-28°$C (Janetschek, 1963, 1967a). *Isotoma klovstadi* from North Victoria Land, being rather an atmobios springtail, has a frost resistance of $-50°$ to $-60°$C (Pryor, 1962). Lethal and preferred temperatures of the high Antarctic mites and springtails need further investigation.

Among the many open questions concerning Antarctic arthropod ecology, there is one that especially forces itself upon the mind. Evidently whether or not the active layer of soil thaws out is of prime importance in determining the limits of life. But the question of the shortest tolerable duration of the season to allow establishment of permanent populations on the basis of a hydrothermal regimen seems to be just as important. According to the author's graphic models (Janetschek, 1967b), at Cape Crozier on Ross Island, two

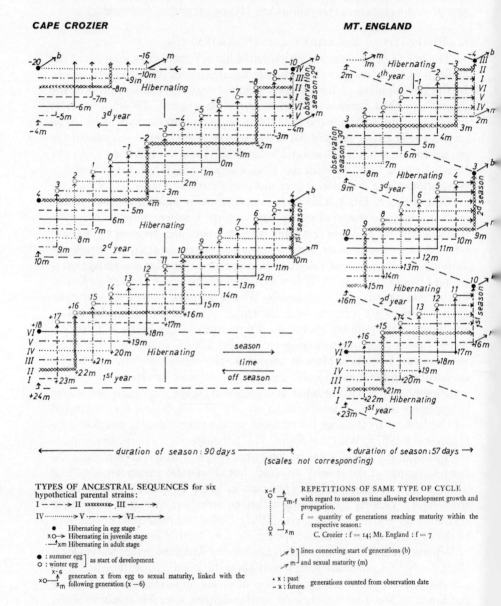

CAPE CROZIER

MT. ENGLAND

← duration of season: 90 days →   ← duration of season: 57 days →

(scales not corresponding)

TYPES OF ANCESTRAL SEQUENCES for six
hypothetical parental strains:
I – – – → II xxxxxxxxx> III – – – –→.
IV ·······→ V ·—·—·→ VI –––––→
• Hibernating in egg stage
xo–→ Hibernating in juvenile stage
–↑xm Hibernating in adult stage
• : summer egg ⎤ as start of development
o : winter egg ⎦
xo↑x-6 generation x from egg to sexual maturity, linked with the
   xm following generation (x –6)

REPETITIONS OF SAME TYPE OF CYCLE
with regard to season as time allowing development growth and
propagation.
f = quantity of generations reaching maturity within the
respective season:
   C. Crozier : f = 14; Mt. England : f = 7
⤷ b ⎤ lines connecting start of generations (b)
⤷ m ⎦ and sexual maturity (m)
+ x : past
– x : future generations counted from observation date

FIG. 6

generations of springtails (in the sense of direct parental sequence) should be able to develop in the course of one season (Fig. 6). Taking into account the six parental strains in the voltinism of *Gomphiocephalus hodgsoni*, nine "generations" should be possible. At a mountain site on Mount England, about 1200 m above sea-level, the respective numbers are only one and two respectively. This means that as the season becomes shorter the chance of an individual reaching maturity and laying eggs without having overwintered first becomes progressively reduced. For the individual specimen, the survival of an Antarctic winter must always be a matter of chance. The expectation of survival to produce future generations will thus be less if overwintering becomes necessary to reach maturity, and even worse if more than one winter must be passed, in areas with a very short active season. The colonization of an area and the maintenance of a population there will consequently be dependent on the active season exceeding the minimum tolerable length. A decrease in duration of season will be correlated with an increasing dissection of activity by inactive spells even during the summer, with increasing time to reach maturity (since development is temperature-dependent) and a requirement for greater frost resistance in the overwintering stages. The smaller the species, the shorter should be its life cycle. Besides other factors such as plasma peculiarities, determining the frost resistance, smaller species could hence be favoured in colonizing the most extreme environments at the border of life.

Disregarding for the moment possible sampling errors, the latitudinal sequence of the terrestrial trombidiform mites (Prostigmata) of Victoria Land seems to support this hypothesis (Table 2).

The Collembola do not fit as well and most of their species seem to be only locally distributed. Possibly their distribution is influenced by historical factors, reflecting conditions of the past, more than by ecological conditions at present.

Systems analysis (Petrusewicz, 1967; Odum, 1968) should next concentrate on structures, to provide a sound basis for analysis of functions in the systems. Future research should hence try to determine the duration of the

---

FIG. 6. Model of assumed generation sequence of the springtail *Gomphicephalus hodgsoni*. Each generation is graphed from beginning of development to the commencement of reproduction, disregarding later eggs laid. The left-hand graph is for the Cape Crozier population (Ross I., appr. 77°30′S, 170±m), over two years, and the right-hand one for that from Mt England (appr. 77°03′S, 1200±m), over three years. Horizontal stripes correspond with time needed to reach maturity. Arrows from lower to higher lines join generations F with the appertaining F_1, each at the time when F reached maturity. Corresponding with assumed maturity in the sixth instar, there are six intertwined ancestral lines. (After Janetschek, 1967*b*.)

active season at the southernmost and highest sites still supporting life, and also to investigate the life-cycles of the species involved, as well as their resistance to frost and desiccation. The results would do much to complete the picture of terrestrial life at its polar borderline.

TABLE 2

Latitudinal Sequence of Terrestrial Prostigmata (Trombidiformes) in Victoria Land

Species	Body length* (μ)	Southernmost record*
Nanorchestes antarcticus	240	85°32′
Tydeus setsukoae	340	84°40′
Protereunetes maudae	450	84°47′
Stereotydeus shoupi	450	84°40′
S. mollis	500	78°40′
Coccorhagidia keithi	800–950	76°12′
C. gressitti	1140	73°25′

* Data after Strandtmann (1967).

References

Janetschek, H. (1963). On the terrestrial fauna of the Ross-Sea area, Antarctica (Preliminary report). Pacif. Insects 5, 305–11.

Janetschek, H. (1964). Die Mikrophytenstufe. (Ein neuer Begriff und ein Programm). Anz. öst. Akad. Wiss. Math.-Nat. Kl. 9, 1–6.

Janetschek, H. (1967a). Arthropod Ecology of South Victoria Land. Antarct. Res. Ser. 10, 205–93.

Janetschek, H. (1967b). Growth and maturity of the springtail, Gomphiocephalus hodgsoni Carpenter, from South Victoria Land and Ross Island. Antarct. Res. Ser. 10, 295–305.

Odum, E. P. (1968). Energy flow in Ecosystems: A historial review. Am. Zoologist 8, 11–18.

Petrusewicz, K. (1967). (ed.). "Secondary Productivity of Terrestrial Ecosystems (Principles and Methods)" Vols. I, II, Państwowe Wydawnictwo Naukowe. Warszawa Krakow.

Pryor, M. E. (1962). Some environmental features of Hallett Station, Antarctica, with special reference to soil arthropods. Pacif. Insects 4, 681–728.

Strandtmann, R. W. (1967). Terrestrial Prostigmata (Trobmidiform Mites.) Antarct. Res. Ser. 10, 51–80.

Tilbrook, P. J. (1967). The terrestrial invertebrate fauna of the Maritime Antarctic. Phil. Trans. R. Soc. B 252, 261–78.

Törne, E. v. (1967a). Beispiele für indirekte Einflüsse von Bodentieren auf die Rotte von Zellulose. Pedobiologia 7, 220–7.

Törne, E. V. (1967b). Biespiele fur mikrobiogene Einflüsse auf den Massenwechsel von Bodentieren. *Pedobiologia* 7, 296–305.

Wilson, A. T. (1970). The McMurdo Dry Valleys. This symposium, 21–30.

Wise, K. A. J., Fearon, C. E. and Wilkes, O. R. (1964). Entomological Investigations in Antarctica, 1962–63 season. *Pacif. Insects* 6, 541–70.

Wise, K. A. J. and Spain, A. V. (1967). Entomological Investigations in Antarctica, 1963–64 season. *Pacif. Insects* 9, 271–93.

The Terrestrial Environment and Invertebrate Fauna of the Maritime Antarctic

P. J. TILBROOK
British Antarctic Survey, Biological Unit, Monks Wood Experimental Station, Abbots Ripton, Huntingdon, England

I. Introduction

The Maritime Antarctic region considered here includes the western coastal fringe of the Antarctic Peninsula and adjacent islands, South Shetland Islands, South Orkney Islands, South Sandwich Islands and Bouvetøya. Although the coastal areas of East Antarctica were included within the Maritime Antarctic zone by Tilbrook (1967b) they are omitted from this account, as they are transitional, in climatic and biotic characteristics, between the Maritime and Continental situations and are to some extent considered by Janetschek (1970: this Symposium).

Work on terrestrial invertebrates in this region has expanded greatly since 1960, but most of it has been concerned with making basic collections, especially of arthropods. Very little is yet known about the biology of particular species or about their interrelationships. Nevertheless it is useful at this stage to review the situation so that priorities for future work may be better established. This paper summarizes current knowledge of the terrestrial invertebrates in this Maritime Antarctic region, drawing attention particularly to relevant work published since the last Symposium in 1962 (Gressitt, 1964). It therefore complements the contribution by Janetschek (1970: this Symposium) dealing with the Continental Antarctic Ecosystem.

II. Habitats

The total area of the Maritime Antarctic region is difficult to measure, as much of it consists of small islands and its eastern boundary on the Antarctic Peninsula is hard to define. Approximately, however, it covers an area of 40000 km², roughly 90% of which consists of permanent ice or snowfields. Some 4000 km² of ground is therefore free of ice or snow cover for part of the year and, taking into account the mountainous topography, this amounts to about 5000 km² of ground surface. Some of this is in the form of nunataks and the highest point in the region is 2824 m, but the mean height of the snow-free area is probably only some 200 m, so the majority of this surface can be regarded as available for colonization by plant and animal life.

The character of the exposed land surface ranges from bare rock through pure mineral soil and varying proportions of mineral matter and vegetation to entirely vegetation. Much chemical and physical analysis has taken place and there have been several attempts to classify the terrestrial habitats in this region both on soil types and vegetation. Nutrient availability does not appear to be limiting (Allen and Northover, 1967; Northover and Allen, 1967; Northover and Grimshaw, 1967) and it is climate and substrate stability which are the dominant factors controlling both the establishment of vegetation and the development of soils (Allen *et al.*, 1967). The climate of the region is oceanic and data have been summarized by Pepper (1954), Longton (1967) and others. Microclimatic conditions, however, frequently differ considerably, as demonstrated by Chambers (1966b), Tilbrook (1967b), Longton and Holdgate (1967) and Greene and Longton (1970: this Symposium). The extent and effect of solifluxion phenomena have been examined by Chambers (1966a and b, 1967). Areas devoid of macroscopic vegetation (Chalikosystem of Janetschek) range from lithosols to fine glacial debris (Allen and Heal, 1970: this Symposium).

In many places rock and soil surfaces have a more or less continuous cover of vegetation and locally there are substantial peat deposits. Due, however, to the slow rate of decomposition and the lack of root-bearing plants and burrowing invertebrates, there is little mixing of the surface vegetation with the soil immediately beneath. A brown earth soil is formed only locally, below patches of the two phanerogams *Deschampsia antarctica* and *Coloban-thus quitensis* (Holdgate *et al.*, 1967). The vegetation of the Maritime zone has received much attention since Holdgate's preliminary survey in 1961–62 (Holdgate, 1964) and his classification based on the Signy Island flora has been developed and extended to include communities throughout the Antarctic Peninsula by Longton (1967) and most recently Gimingham and Smith (1970: this Symposium). There are eight basic subformations. That dominated by grass and cushion plant is typical of sheltered north-facing slopes, but although widespread throughout the region it is rarely extensive. Five other subformations consist of bryophyte and lichen communities and one of the most widespread in this region is the lichen and moss cushion subformation. On the borders of sea-bird and mammal colonies where trampling is not excessive there is an organically rich soil which frequently supports extensive mats of the thallose alga *Prasiola crispa*.

In addition to these widespread habitats there are others which do not fall within the above classification. A distinctive and luxuriant vegetation is found in the warmer, more humid conditions around active fumaroles in the South Sandwich Islands (Longton, 1967; Longton and Holdgate, 1967). In penguin colonies and seal wallow areas the rich organic soil is bare of vegetation due to the activity of the animals. The more isolated nests and nest burrows of other birds produce more specialized local niches and other such transient habitats are bird and animal carcasses, and seaweeds in the upper shore regions and lake edges. No account has been taken of the distribution of the microflora and in areas lacking macroscopic vegetation these organisms are clearly important in providing the basis for simple food chains (Janetschek, 1970; this Symposium).

It is not possible to gauge the overall extent of the various habitat divisions within this region, but some details from Signy Island give an indication of the relative proportions. Of a total area of 19·4 km², approximately 13 km² is snow free in summer and this probably represents 16·5 km² of actual ground surface. Detailed mapping of the vegetation of the island by Holdgate in 1962–64 indicates the following cover by the respective habitat divisions.

Habitat	Area (km²)	% of total surface
Fruticose lichen and moss cushion		
continuous cover (over 50% of ground surface)	3·5	21
sparse cover (under 50% and often only about 5–10%)	5·0	30
Moss turf	1·0	6
Moss carpet and moss hummock		
continuous cover	1·25	7·5
sparse cover	0·75	4·5
Biotically formed organic soil	0·65	4·0
Grass and cushion plant	0·0001	—
Bare rock and mineral soil (with or without crustose lichen)	4·25	26
Penguin nests and seal wallows	0·1	0·6
Other birds' nests	0·0005	—

It is clear that a considerable amount of information is available on the characteristics of the terrestrial habitats in this region.

III. Fauna

The main groups represented in the region are Protozoa, Rotifera, Nematoda, Tardigrada and Arthropoda. Enchytraeid annelids are found amongst seaweed and other decaying organic matter along the upper shoreline and occasionally in moss just above high-water mark and Turbellaria have been reported from the edges of freshwater pools (Gressitt, 1965). Because work to date has tended to concentrate on particular groups rather than on the total fauna within one habitat, a group treatment will be adopted here.

A. PROTOZOA

Very little is known of this group within the region. Heal examined the Testacea in samples from Signy Island (Heal, 1965; Heal *et al.*, 1967) and recorded eighteen species all known from temperate soils. As pointed out by Stout and Heal (1967), however, species are defined on morphological grounds and genetic interchange is rare or confined to distinct varieties which may have geographical or ecological limitations. More intensive work now being carried out at Signy Island by H. G. Smith has so far revealed fifty-seven species of testate and six naked amoebae, fifty-six ciliates and twenty-three flagellates (exceeding 10μ) from a variety of habitats (*personal communication*). This compares with twenty-six testate and five naked amoebae, twenty-three ciliates and nine flagellates reported by Sudzuki (1964) from moss water of East Antarctica.

Heal (1965) found that of eighteen testacean species in *Deschampsia* grassland, *Corythion dubium* constituted 72% of the live individuals, but the preliminary results of Smith (*personal communication*) indicate that the proportion of this species may be much lower. In the top horizon of *Deschampsia* soil with thirty-three testacean species present, it was only 11%, and in moss peat with thirty-five species it was 30%. Apart from the Testacea the peat also contained ciliates (mostly Gymnostomatida and Hypotrichida) and small flagellates, but no naked amoebae. Soil from a penguin colony was devoid of Testacea in summer, but naked amoebae, ciliates and a flagellate were present. In a morainic soil the protozoan fauna consisted almost entirely of flagellates and ciliates (mostly Hypotrichida).

The only data available on numbers and biomass concern the Testacea, which is the dominant group in vegetated habitats. From soil below *Deschampsia*, Heal (1965) calculated the numbers of Testacea as $890 \pm 150 \times 10^6/m^2$ with an approximate biomass of $2 \ g/m^2$. In numbers of both species and individuals the Signy Island soils approximate to those of temperate woodland and moorland. There is, however, considerable variation between different habitats at Signy Island, which tends to support the view that soil and vegetation type have a greater influence on the micro-organisms than does climate in this region (Heal *et al.*, 1967). The true role of the Protozoa has not been established, but the majority of soil forms feed on bacteria and to a lesser extent on yeasts, algae and fungal spores and mycelia (Stout and Heal, 1967).

B. ROTIFERA

These are organisms requiring a water film in which to swim, but in periods of drought many are able to encyst and so resist both desiccation and low temperatures (Kühnelt, 1961). There has been no specific study made of this group within the Maritime Antarctic. Sudzuki (1964), working on moss-water communities of East Antarctica separated thirteen species of Rotifera, ten of which belonged to the more common soil-dwellers, the Bdelloidea. The Baermann funnel technique is known to be an efficient method of extracting Rotifers (Nielsen, 1948) and many were collected by the author while using a slight modification of this technique to study the nematodes of various habitats at Signy Island. In most cases only presence or absence was noted for each sample and none was identified. It can be stated, however, that Rotifers were common in mosses throughout the region and seemed to be more abundant in the wetter communities. In samples of *Pohlia nutans* from Signy Island a density of $5 \cdot 0 \times 10^4/m^2$ was recorded and the larger individuals were 250 μ in length. Soil-dwelling bdelloid Rotifers may feed on plant or animal remains and also on living Protozoa (Kühnelt, 1961).

C. NEMATODA

The presence of soil nematodes in this maritime region has been reported on many occasions, but nothing has been published on their taxonomy. Work in progress on a variety of habitats at Signy Island indicates that at least twenty-seven species of nematode are represented (V. Spaull, *personal communication*). The only abundance data so far published are those given by Tilbrook (1967a and b), but they refer to total numbers of nematodes with no division either on taxonomic or feeding-group criteria. Nevertheless, they serve to demonstrate the relatively large numbers of these organisms in a variety of habitats throughout the region; an abundance similar to that in a temperate moorland locality. As far as the bryophytes are concerned, the greatest densities were found in the wetter communities. Thirty-four cores taken from a *Pohlia nutans* mat between March and December 1962 gave a mean figure of approximately 10×10^5 individuals/m². This must only be taken as an order of abundance, however, as there was considerable within-site variation between samples, and results have not yet been subjected to statistical treatment. Although based on fewer cores, figures for *Deschampsia* clumps, *Colobanthus* cushions and soil from a seal-wallow area indicate a greater abundance of nematodes in these habitats. This is supported by preliminary results from the more detailed and specific study by Spaull. Mean figures from four 6 cm deep cores taken in February 1968 from *Deschampsia* and *Colobanthus* give 42 and $52 \times 10^5/m^2$ respectively. Densities are even higher in localized favourable habitats. The top 2 cm of soil from a *Daption capensis* nest area and a chinstrap penguin colony gave figures of $23 \times 10^5/m^2$ and $39 \times 10^5/m^2$ respectively with single-species dominance evident in these more specialized niches (Spaull, *personal communication*). As yet, no significant seasonal variation in numbers has been demonstrated for bryophyte habitats, but the division of each 6 cm deep core sample into upper and lower halves has revealed a seasonal vertical effect (Tilbrook, 1967b). During the summer some 70% of the population inhabited the top 3 cm, but during the winter the proportion in the 3–6 cm layer increased until it even exceeded that in the upper layer. This was probably due to differential mortality. Like the total numbers present, this pattern of vertical distribution varied between different bryophyte subformations and appeared to be correlated with depth of snow cover which serves to insulate in winter and yet retard ground warming at the onset of summer. It is likely that in the more specialized habitats seasonal variation will be more dramatic and this has been demonstrated in soil from a penguin colony at Macquarie Island (Bunt, 1954). Laboratory experiments have indicated that freeze tolerance of nematodes is generally accomplished by preliminary dehydration and that immature forms are the most resistant (Meryman, 1966).

Nothing has been published on the feeding habits of these Antarctic forms, but it has been stressed that nematodes in general feed on plant or animal "protoplasm" and do not take dead organic matter (Nielsen, 1967). As so little is known of the interrelationships within the Maritime Antarctic terrestrial ecosystem, it is of interest to record that probably three species of predatory fungi have been observed with nematode prey by R. I. L. Smith during microscopic examination of bryophytes at Signy Island (*personal communication*).

D. TARDIGRADA

This group also has yet to be studied specifically in this region. Like rotifers and nematodes these organisms require a water film for movement, but it is known that some species are able to form cysts and so resist desiccation as well as low temperatures (Kühnelt, 1961). Murray (1910) found that both adults and eggs of species of *Macrobiotus* from Victoria Land were particularly tolerant in this way. Eleven species, of four genera, are listed from Maritime Antarctic localities by Murray (1910) as compared with six species of two genera from East Antarctica (Sudzuki, 1964). The only data available on numbers of individuals present are those obtained during extraction of nematodes from Signy Island vegetation (Tilbrook, 1967b). The Baermann funnel technique used, however, is known to be inefficient for the extraction of tardigrades (Nielsen, 1948), so the figures represent minimum numbers present. Of three bryophyte communities sampled over a long period, the tardigrades were most abundant in the wetter *Pohlia nutans* where the mean figure for thirty cores was $88 \times 10^3/\text{m}^2$. The largest individuals measured were 500 μ in length. The role of these animals is uncertain, but soil forms have been reported as feeding on minute plant debris and living moss cells (Kevan, 1962), as well as rotifers and nematodes (Kühnelt, 1961).

E. ARTHROPODA

Of all the invertebrate groups the arthropods have received most attention in this region. Consequently the taxonomy is well advanced, and in view of the intensive collecting from many localities throughout the region it is likely that the majority of species are now known. By far the most numerous and important arthropods are the Collembola and Acari, but two species of Diptera are locally abundant and representatives of other groups have been recorded (Balfour-Browne and Tilbrook 1966; Covarrubias, 1966*a*; Saiz *et al.*, 1970; this Symposium). These latter records should be treated with caution, however, as often only isolated individuals have been reported and there is a danger that they may have been collected in areas of human habitation or even accidentally introduced during extraction. There are similarly unsubstantiated reports of mites and Collembola. Omitting these doubtful records, twenty-five species of free-living terrestrial mites and seven species of Collembola are known at present from this region. These are mostly listed by Gressitt (1967*a*) and Tilbrook (1967*a*) and more recent additions are given by Strandtmann and Tilbrook (1967). Many of the species are widely distributed both geographically and ecologically, e.g. *Cryptopygus antarcticus* (Tilbrook, 1970; this Symposium) but most exhibit some habitat preference which can be demonstrated by their percentage frequency (Tilbrook, 1967*a* and *b*) or percentage abundance (Covarrubias, 1966*a*; di Castri *et al.*, 1967). Adopting an information-theory approach, di Castri *et al.*, (1967) suggest that the different values for biotic diversity shown by communities of different habitats represent stages in an ecological succession. Nests and faeces would be the pioneer stages, indicating an initial dependence on marine influence, with diversity increasing through soils, terrestrial algae and lichens to mosses. Further ecological notes on individual species are given by Strong (1967) and Gressitt (1967*b*).

There have been a number of attempts to estimate the density of arthropod populations or communities in various habitats within this region (Tilbrook, 1967*a* and *b*; di Castri *et al.*, 1967; Covarrubias, 1966*a*), but unfortunately the different results are rarely intercomparable due to the considerable variation in sampling and extraction techniques. Furthermore, the figures often represent means of very few samples with no indication of the standard error and as it is known that most of the arthropods show a highly aggregated distribution. Consequently, the data are of limited application. There is no doubt, however, that in spite of a relatively low species diversity when compared with ecosystems in lower latitudes, the density is frequently of a similar magnitude. di Castri *et al.*, (1967) claim that this represents the adaptation of the system to combat the constant abiotic (climatic or edaphic) "interference" predominant in this region. Numerically the entomobryoid Collembola and prostigmatic mites are dominant throughout the region and other mites and

Collembola exceed them in abundance only in the more specialized niches. Covarrubias (1966a), for example, gives a figure of approximately $3 \times 10^5/m^2$ for oribatid mites from terrestrial algae, representing some 81% of the total meiofauna. For reliable quantitative data on the arthropod fauna on an area basis certain bryophyte communities, from which accurate replicated cores may be taken, offer the most suitable substrate in this region. Covarrubias (1966a) gives figures of $21 \times 10^4/m^2$ for Collembola and $2 \times 10^4/m^2$ for mites from 'mosses' in the South Shetland Islands. Data given by Tilbrook (1967a), however, suggest that not only does the density vary considerably between different bryophytes but also between the same bryophytes throughout the region. Furthermore, repeated sampling over two years has shown that there is a temporal fluctuation in numbers showing little regular seasonal effect.

The majority of arthropods are found in the upper layers of the soil or vegetation; 75–100% in the top 3 cm (Tilbrook 1967a; Schlatter et al., 1968). Schlatter et al., (1968) also claim that although arthropod density decreases with altitude in soils, there is an increase in the index of diversity and Covarrubias (1966b), working on moss and lichen habitats, reports a diversity at the top of mountains similar to that at the base. This implies a relatively high stability in these high altitude communities and to some extent parallels the situation reported for East Antarctica by Janetschek (1967), though the altitudinal range is much less.

IV. Conclusion

The mountainous topography of the Maritime Antarctic region and its effect on the physical environment ensures discontinuity of vegetation cover and the admixture of different habitat types over relatively small areas. This, together with the broad habitat tolerance shown by many of the terrestrial invertebrates, has resulted in a general faunal homogeneity. Adopting the macrohabitat divisions described previously, however, some preference is apparent with most species and this is likely to be more evident when the "aquatic" element has been better studied. Figures so far available suggest that extrapolation of numerical data obtained from one locality is invalid to the region as a whole. Many of the terrestrial organisms are present in large numbers and exhibit substantial temperature tolerance and in some cases adaptation. This is consistent with the suggestion of Dunbar (1968) that temperature is one of the least important factors in the development of polar ecosystems. He maintains that their present structure is largely a reflection of their youth and immaturity.

In a valuable paper by Holdgate (1967), a synthesis of information on the terrestrial Antarctic ecosystem includes biomass data for some invertebrate groups. The figures are extremely broad estimates, but there is still insufficient information to permit any significant refinement and they do indicate the low standing-crop of invertebrates as a whole, even in the more favourable habitats. The apparent paucity of herbivorous invertebrates, also noted by Holdgate, serves to emphasize the importance of the decomposer organisms in the soil cycle and the need to study them in conjunction with the invertebrate groups in any trophic investigation.

It is clear that in spite of the increased effort over the last eight years terrestrial zoology is still at an early stage of development in the Maritime Antarctic. It has often been stated that the Antarctic terrestrial system is a simple one and it is implicit that this refers to the restricted number of species present and perhaps the restrictions on growth and activity caused by the more severe climate. It should be remembered, however, that the groups found in the Antarctic present some of the greatest difficulties to study. The tardigrades and rotifers, for example, are poorly known taxonomically and in many cases techniques to evaluate respiration, assimilation etc. are not yet available. It is important that a taxonomic and distributional knowledge of the lesser-known groups be built up, but there is now a need for more autecological studies with a view to attaining a better understanding of the interrelationships of the Antarctic fauna and the flow of energy or nutrients through the system. Meaningful correlation of data on different organisms or groups can best be achieved by concentrating attention on selected habitat sites.

Acknowledgements

I am very grateful to H. G. Smith, R. I. L. Smith and V. Spaull for permission to quote from their unpublished results and to Dr M. W. Holdgate for making available his vegetation map of Signy Island.

References

Allen, S. E. and Heal, O. W. (1970). Soils of the maritime Antarctic zone. This symposium, 693–6.

Allen, S. E. and Northover, M. J. (1967). Soil types and nutrients on Signy Island. *Phil. Trans. R. Soc.* B **252**, No. 777, 179–85.

Allen, S. E., Grimshaw, H. M. and Holdgate, M. W. (1967). Factors affecting the availability of plant nutrients on an Antarctic island. *J. Ecol.* **55**, 381–96.

Balfour-Browne, J. and Tilbrook, P. J. (1966). Coleoptera collected in the South Orkney and South Shetland Islands. *Br. Antarct. Surv. Bull.* **9**, 41–43.

Bunt, J. S. (1954). The soil-inhabiting nematodes of Macquarie Island. *Aust. J. Zool.* **2**, No. 2, 264–74.

Chambers, M. J. G. (1966a). Investigations of patterned ground at Signy Island, South Orkney Islands: I. Interpretation of mechanical analyses. *Br. Antarct. Surv. Bull.* 9, 21–40.

Chambers, M. J. G. (1966b). Investigations of patterned ground at Signy Island, South Orkney Islands: II. Temperature regimes in the active layer. *Br. Antarct. Surv. Bull.* 10, 71–83.

Chambers, M. J. G. (1967). Investigations of patterned ground at Signy Island, South Orkney Islands: III. Miniature patterns, frost heaving and general conclusions. *Br. Antarct. Surv. Bull.* 12, 1–22.

Covarrubias, R. (1966a). Observaciones Cuantitativas sobre los invertebrados terrestres Antárticos y Preantárticos. *Inst. Antárt. Chile. Publnes.* 9, 1–53.

Covarrubias, R. (1966b). Estructura de las Zoocenosis terrestres Antarticos. *In* "Progresos en Biologia del Suelo". Monografias I. UNESCO. Montevideo. pp. 343–57.

Castri, F. di., Covarrubias, R. and Hajek, E. (1967). Soil ecosystems in sub-Antarctic regions. *In* "Symposium on Ecology of Sub-Arctic Regions". Natural Resources Research. UNESCO. Paris. In press.

Dunbar, M. J. (1968). "Ecological Development in Polar Regions. A Study in Evolution". Prentice-Hall, New Jersey.

Gimingham, C. H. and Smith R. I. L. (1970). Bryophyte and lichen communities in the Maritime Antarctic. This symposium, 752–85.

Greene, S. W. and Longton, R. E. (1970). The effects of climate on Antarctic plants. This symposium, 786–800.

Gressitt, J. L. (1964). Ecology and biogeography of land arthropods in Antarctica. *In* "Biologie Antarctique: Antarctic Biology". (Carrick, R., Holdgate, M. W. and Prévost, T. eds) Hermann, Paris. p. 211–22.

Gressitt, J. L. (1965). Terrestrial animals. "Antarctica". Methuen, London. pp. 351–71.

Gressitt, J. L. (1967a). Introduction. *In* "Entomology of Antarctica". American Geophysical Union, *Antarct. Res. Ser.* 10, 1–33.

Gressitt, J. L. (1967b). Notes on arthropod populations in the Antarctic Peninsula—South Shetland Islands—South Orkney Islands area. *In* "Entomology of Antarctica". American Geophysical Union, *Antarct. Res. Ser.* 10, 373–91.

Heal, O. W. (1965). Observations on testate amoebae (Protozoa, Rhizopoda) from Signy Island, South Orkney Islands. *Br. Antarct. Surv. Bull.* 6, 43–47.

Heal, O. W., Bailey, A. D. and Latter, P. M. (1967). Bacteria, fungi and protozoa in Signy Island soils compared with those from a temperate moorland. *Phil. Trans. R. Soc.* B 252, No. 777, 191–7.

Holdgate, M. W. (1964). Terrestrial ecology in the Maritime Antarctic. *In* "Biologie Antarctique: Antarctic Biology" (Carrick, R., Holdgate, M. W. and Prevost, J. eds.). Hermann, Paris, pp. 181–94.

Holdgate, M. W. (1967). The Antarctic Ecosystem. *Phil. Trans. R. Soc.* B 252, No. 777, 363–83.

Holdgate, M. W., Allen, S. E. and Chambers, M. J. G. (1967). A preliminary investigation of the soils of Signy Island, South Orkney Islands. *Br. Antarct. Surv. Bull.* 12, 53–71.

Janetschek, H. (1967). Arthropod ecology of South Victoria Land. *In* "Entomology of Antarctica". American Geophysical Union, *Antarct. Res. Ser.* 10, 205–93.

Janetschek, H. (1970). Environments and ecology of terrestrial arthropods in the high-Antarctic. This symposium, 871–85.

Kevan, D. K. McE. (1962). "Soil Animals". Witherby, London.

Kühnelt, W. (1961). "Soil Biology". Faber and Faber, London.

Longton, R. E. (1967). Vegetation in the Maritime Antarctic. *Phil. Trans. R. Soc.* B **252**, No. 777, 213–35.

Longton, R. E. and Holdgate, M. W. (1967). Temperature relationships of Antarctic vegetation. *Phil. Trans. R. Soc.* B **252**, No. 777, 237–50.

Meryman, H. T. (1966). Review of Biological Freezing. *In* "Cryobiology". Academic Press, London. pp. 1–114.

Murray, J. (1910). Tardigrada. *Rep. Sci. Invest. Br. Antarct. Exped. 1907–9* **1**, Part 4, 81–185.

Nielsen, C. O. (1948). An apparatus for quantitative extraction of nematodes and rotifers from soil and moss. *Natura jutl.* **1**, 271–7.

Nielsen, C. O. (1967). Nematoda. *In* "Soil Biology". Academic Press, London. pp. 197–211.

Northover, M. J. and Allen, S. E. (1967). Seasonal availability of chemical nutrients on Signy Island. *Phil. Trans. R. Soc.* B **252**, No. 777, 187–9.

Northover, M. J. and Grimshaw, H. M. (1967). Some seasonal trends in nutrient content of the soils of Signy Island, South Orkney Islands. *Br. Antarct. Surv. Bull.* **14**, 83–88.

Pepper, J. (1954). *The meteorology of the Falkland Islands and Dependencies, 1944–1950.* London, Falkland Islands and Dependencies Meteorological Service.

Schlatter, R., Hermosilla, W. and Castri, F. di (1968). Distribucion altitudinal de los artropodos terrestres. *Inst. Antart. Chile. Publnes.* **15**, 1–26.

Stout, J. D. and Heal, O. W. (1967). Protozoa. *In* "Soil Biology". Academic Press, London. pp. 149–95.

Strong, J. (1967). Ecology of terrestrial arthropods at Palmer Station, Antarctic Peninsula. *In* "Entomology of Antarctica". American Geophysical Union, *Antarct. Res. Ser.* **10**, 357–71.

Strandtmann, R. W. and Tilbrook, P. J. (1967). Some Prostigmata (Acari) from Signy Island, South Orkney Islands and Deception Island, South Shetland Islands. *Br. Antarct. Surv. Bull.* **17**, 51–57.

Sudzuki, M. (1964). On the microfauna of the Antarctic region I. Moss-water community at Langhovde. *JARE Scient. Rep.* E **19**, 1–41.

Tilbrook, P. J. (1967a). The terrestrial invertebrate fauna of the Maritime Antarctic. *Phil. Trans. R. Soc.* B **252**, No. 777, 261–78.

Tilbrook, P. J. (1967b). Arthropod ecology in the Maritime Antarctic. *In* "Entomology of Antarctica". American Geophysical Union, *Antarct. Res. Ser.* **10**, 331–56.

The Colonization of Introduced Litter by Subantarctic Soil and Moss Arthropods*

FRANCISCO SÁIZ, ERNST R. HAJEK AND
WLADIMIR HERMOSILLA†
Universidad de Chile, Santiago, Chile

I. Introduction

The Antarctic ecosystem is structurally very simple and presents many unique peculiarities. In addition, the role Antarctica has played in past ages, as a bridge or a dispersal centre for flora and fauna, has interested many scientists in investigating its problems. The study of the Subantarctic mesofauna would provide a better understanding of the relationships between the Chilean fauna and that of the Subantarctic regions and would help in the evaluation of the characteristics of the Chilean edaphic biocenosis from the evolutionary and biogeographical point of view.

The Ecology Section of the Instituto de Higiene y Fomento de la Producción Animal, in collaboration with the Instituto Antártico Chileno, has arranged some long-term investigations of soil biology, which were started in 1964–65. This paper results from the third year of the programme and the authors took part in the twenty-first Chilean Antarctic Expedition (1966–67). Papers by Covarrubias (1966a, 1966b), di Castri et al., (1967), Hermosilla et al., (1967), Schlatter (1967), Saiz and Hajek (1968) and Schlatter et al., (1968) have already presented results of this series of investigations.

In this study we have considered the colonization of diverse types of litter by the moss mesofauna, leaving for later examination the analysis of the situation created by the introduction of other substrata (soil, faeces, etc.). These examinations will together provide a complete picture of the selective characteristics of colonization by these invertebrates.

II. Materials and Methods

The principal aim of the present investigation was the study of the

---

* This paper is the fourth in the series under the general title "Ecological Research on Robert Island (South Shetland Islands)".

† Also Instituto Antártico Chileno.

reaction displayed by the components of the Subantarctic moss mesofauna when confronted with new habitats provided by a range of introduced litter. The basic methodology for the investigation was suggested by Prof. Dr Francesco di Castri.

A wide flat area on Robert Island was chosen as the research site, because it was a good example of the isothermic Subantarctic tundra.* The average thickness of moss was 9 cm.

Five different kinds of introduced litter were analyzed experimentally, namely:

(a) Litter of *Araucaria araucana*
(b) Litter of *Nothofagus obliqua* var. *macrocarpa*
(c) Litter of *Drimys winteri* var. *chilensis*
(d) Litter of *Populus alba*
(e) Litter of *Betula* sp.

The intention of this selection was to provide the Subantarctic moss mesofauna with both litter of plants previously existing in the Antarctic zone and now present in Chile (*Araucaria* and *Nothofagus*), and litter of trees that never existed in Antarctica. The latter material included *Drimys* (an autochthon Chilean genus) and *Populus* and *Betula*, both introduced to Chile. *Betula* is of particular interest as a primary colonist of Arctic regions. In each case, the litter used was obtained from a single tree from the Chilean Central Zone, dried in the sunshine and later sterilized in an autoclave. The samples were sterilized inside round metal boxes, made with an inner capacity of 50 cc and closed laterally with a wire mesh to allow the free circulation of the mesofauna (Fig. 1). In total 200 boxes were prepared, forty for each substratum.

The boxes were arranged in the field in a rectangle directed east-west, of five parallel rows, 20 cm apart. In each series there were boxes located horizontally on the surface, buried to half their height and others buried vertically at a depth of between 5 and 10 cm (Fig. 1). Thermistors were placed in the middle box of each series and also located directly in the moss at similar depths to the boxes. The thermistor probe used was Yellow Springs Instrument Co., Ohio, No. 401, linked to a twelve-contact bridge and graduated from $-17°C$ to $+47°C$.

A microclimatological station was located near the experimental area to record other parameters. This station was equipped with minimum and maximum thermometers, psychrometer, capillary hygrometer, thermo-

---

* The authors of this paper, in applying the term "Subantarctic" to the South Shetland Islands are making it more nearly synonymous with the "Maritime Antarctic" of Holdgate (1964) than is usually the case. The definition of these zones is discussed in the Introduction to Part XII.
EDITOR

hygrograph, actinograph, anemometer (at 200 cm and 10 cm above the ground), and soil thermometers placed at −20, −10, −5, −2 cm and on the surface. These instruments were read every six hours, at 0.00, 6.00, 12.00, and 18.00 hours, local time.

The boxes were removed in accordance with the following sequence:

Boxes of rows 1 to 6 inclusive, each 24 hours
Boxes of rows 7 to 12 inclusive, each 48 hours
Boxes of rows 13 to 19 inclusive, each 96 hours.

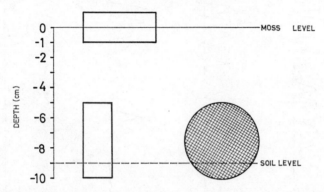

FIG. 1. Arrangement of sample containers in the field. (The lower box is represented both in side and front view.)

The standard time for removal of the samples was 18.00 hours. Once taken from the field the contents were poured in small Berlese-Tullgren funnels for the separation of the fauna, remaining in them during ninety-six hours under constant heat and light. Moss samples were taken simultaneously with the removal of boxes from rows No. 1, 12, 15 and 19, and from the same depths, to provide data on the variations in the composition and density of mesofauna during the period of study. Each control consisted of five samples.

III. Results and Discussion

A. MICROCLIMATE

Figure 2 shows the temperatures registered in the surface boxes containing *Araucaria* and *Nothofagus* litter and in the controls, together with the temperatures observed in the meteorological station. The temperatures measured on the surface (boxes as well as controls) evidently differ from those measured in the meteorological station and this is due to direct solar radiation, heat concentration in the upper layers of moss, differences in water content, and to radiation from the moss surface.

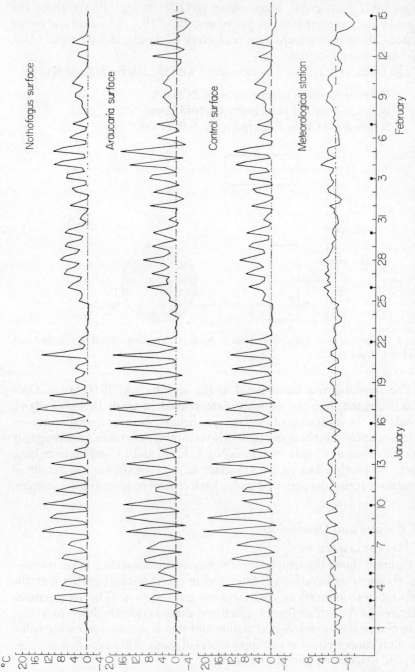

FIG. 2. Temperature records for boxes placed on the moss surface, and for a near-by meteorological station. Solid circles indicate days on which samples were removed.

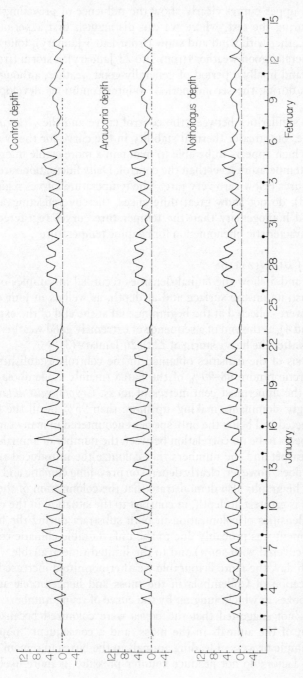

FIG. 3. Temperature records for sample boxes at a depth of 5 to 10 cm.

The three upper curves clearly show the influence of prevailing climatic conditions during the test, where we can distinguish first a period of unfavourable weather with wind and snow (from 1 to 3 January), followed by a period of generally good weather (from 3 to 22 January), a storm (from 23 to 25 January), and finally a period of generally good weather, although not as favourable as during the second period. Winter conditions developed after 13 February.

There are similarities between the control curve and the *Araucaria* substratum curve, but greater thermal stability in the curve for the *Nothofagus* substratum which appears to be able to maintain a more stable microclimate and a higher temperature level than the control. Daily fluctuations are smaller and temperatures below zero very rare. The temperature curves registered at depth (Fig. 3), do not show great differences, thereby reflecting a greater constancy and homogeneity than the temperature curves registered on the surface: a characteristic phenomenon for edaphic temperatures.

B. FAUNAL COLONIZATION

Figures 4 and 5 show the faunal densities recorded in samples of the introduced substrata on the surface and at depth, as well as in four controls. These latter were collected at the beginning and at the end of the experiment (samples 1 and 4), at the end of a sequence of extremely good weather days (2) and four days after the heavy storm of 22 to 26 January (3).

The analysis of the densities obtained in the controls establishes that in this Subantarctic tundra 98–99% of the fauna (mainly Collembola) is concentrated in the uppermost centimetres of moss. *Cryptopygus antarcticus* is overwhelmingly dominant, making up more than 95% of all the faunistic material collected and being the only species encountered in many samples.

There appears to be no correlation between the number of animals present in the moss carpet and the numbers that colonize the introduced substrata. Colonization does, however, clearly depend on prevailing climatic and physical conditions. The graphs also demonstrate that the colonization of the experimental boxes is greatest at depth, in contrast to the situation in the controls.

The low densities of colonization in both substrata during the first days of the experiment was probably due to the unfavourable climatic conditions (the site was covered with snow) and to the limited time available. After the fourth or fifth day, the more favourable weather permitted increased activity and multiplication of Collembola in the moss and hence accelerated their entry to the boxes in which, judging by the curve of rising numbers, they remained. It is not suggested that the boxes were colonized because of the multiplication of the animals in the moss, and a consequent "population" pressure; a simple process of leading animals in the boxes to remain there, as long as other factors do not produce counter-pressure, is more likely. Rates

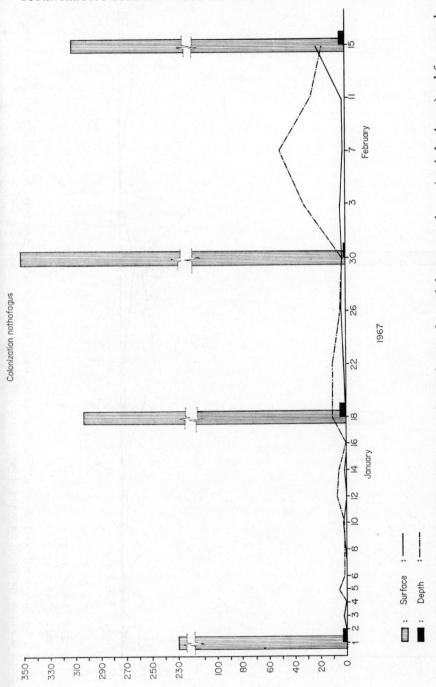

FIG. 4. Numbers of arthropods extracted from control cores from surface and deeper moss layers (vertical columns) and from sample boxes at surface and depth containing *Nothofagus* litter (continuous curves).

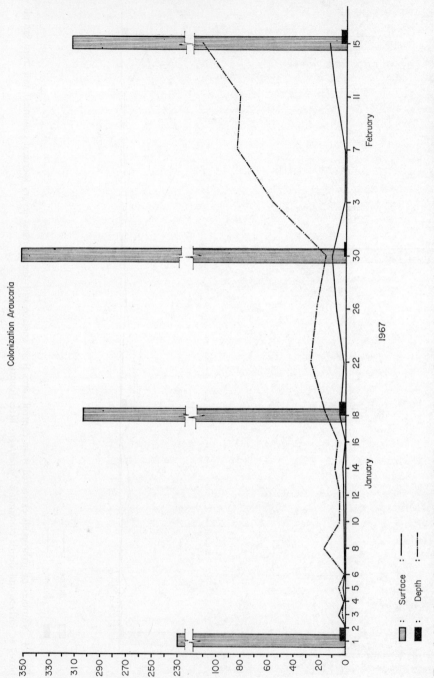

Fig. 5. Numbers of arthropods extracted from control cores from surface and deeper moss layers (vertical columns) and from sample boxes at surface and depth containing *Araucaria* litter (continuous curves).

of colonization increased until 22 January, when the heavy storm affected the animals even at depth: thereafter the animal population appeared disturbed and there was no recovery in the rate of colonization.

The minor irregularities in the curves may be explained by the fact that the animals colonizing the different boxes were drawn from populations of different sizes, as is shown by the unequal values of the five control samples considered on each occasion. Moreover, the data are not precise enough (there is insufficient replication) for it to be assumed that the number of animals obtained in the later samples correspond precisely to the number of animals obtained in the last preceding sample, plus an increment introduced in the subsequent period. It is better to think of the curves as all starting independently from an initial point and ending in each collection, so that the general curve for all boxes can be represented as rising steadily. The curve drawn would only show the final level of colonization for each box with increasing time. The most important concept expressed by the curves may be summarized in the following general statements.

1. Colonization by the surface fauna is restricted by climatic parameters (especially temperature) and also by such other influences as the drainage of rain- and meltwater, and wind, which can act mechanically to control the passage of colonizing animals through or over the moss mat.

2. At depth, colonization is more rapid because the boxes are the most favourable microclimatic environments available for the animals: under natural conditions there is almost no fauna at such depths. In the boxes an aerated and spongy environment is created, with a better drainage than that of the surrounding moss, thus producing an environment similar to the favourable surface moss layers.

The rising curve of densities in the deep samples between 30 January and 7 February shows once more the effects of favourable periods of time on the rate of colonization. The absence of snow and rain, and therefore of waterlogging, would permit the downward movement of the fauna as favourable microclimatic conditions extended into the lower layers where, also, conditions would be more stable than on the surface because of the "filter" effect of the upper moss layer.

Perhaps the different degrees of colonization of deep samples of *Araucaria* and *Nothofagus* litter at the end of the experiment may be explained by the complete flooding of the boxes of *Nothofagus* by drainage water which only moistened the samples of *Araucaria*.

Another factor that could be thought of altering or impeding the colonization of surface samples is the frequent freezing of the uppermost centimetres of the moss. This is not, however, thought likely to be very important, since the fauna is adapted to these conditions and it is precisely at these depths in which under normal conditions the whole fauna lives. Samples cut directly from frozen blocks of moss and extracted in Berlese-Tullgren funnels, provide a fauna no different in number and composition from that coming from dry moss. Freezing probably acts only by reducing the time during which the fauna is free to move and colonize new habitats.

Finally, two further considerations seem important. First, the faunal density in the control (mean of five samples) and its relationship with periods of bad weather (especially thawing) suggests that there is a more or less stable population of Collembola in the moss, which, when the climate becomes more favourable (control 2), increases to a certain extent. Secondly, downwash by melt- and rainwater and exposure to wind, add (control 3) individuals to the moss population from sources located at higher levels, such as areas covered by lichens and terrestrial algae, in which the fauna may show population increases of an explosive type (Covarrubias, 1966a). Rainwater and meltwater can also wash out and so reduce the colonizing fauna.

In conclusion, we believe the penetration of animals into the boxes is an active phenomenon and related to favourable climatic conditions. The increase in density in the control situations during bad weather is conversely believed to be a passive phenomenon due to the transport of animals by moving water. There is thus no relationship between the two processes.

C. NEW FAUNAL RECORDS FOR THE SOUTH SHETLAND ISLANDS

The faunistic poverty of the Subantarctic region, and especially of the moss and soil mesofauna is well known (Covarrubias, 1966a and b; di Castri et al., 1967; Schlatter et al., 1968). Consequently the capture of groups hitherto unrecorded, or rarely reported in the region, deserves notice. The following were collected during the present investigation:

(a) Araneida. A young specimen was found in a control moss sample at a depth of 5 to 10 cm. Covarrubias (1966a) recorded another specimen in humus-rich sandy soil.

(b) Psocoptera. Specimens were found in three control moss samples. Covarrubias (1966a) recorded the group for the first time with a single specimen found among lichens. These further findings appear to establish the group almost certainly as occurring under natural conditions in the Subantarctic region.

(c) Thysanoptera. In a surface moss sample collected as a control nine winged specimens of this Order were captured. It has not been described previously for these latitudes.

(d) Coleoptera. Balfour-Browne and Tilbrook (1966) described Coleoptera (Lathridiidae) for the first time in the Subantarctic region. Schlatter et al., (1968) again found specimens of this family. In two control moss samples twelve and one specimens of larvae which we suppose belong to the Family

Lathridiidae were collected respectively. This fact evidently indicates a certain degree of Subantarctic adaptation in the group.

References

Balfour-Browne, J. and Tilbrook, P. J. (1966). Coleoptera collected in the South Orkney and South Shetland Islands. *Br. Antarct. Surv. Bull.* **9**, 41–43.

Castri, F. di, Covarrubias, R. and Hajek, E. (1967). Soil ecosystems in subantarctic regions. Symposium on Ecology of Sub-arctic regions. UNESCO. Helsinki.

Covarrubias, R. (1966*a*). Observaciones cuantitativas sobre Invertebrados terrestres antárticos y preantárticos. *Inst. Antart. Chile. Publnes.* 9.

Covarrubias, R. (1966*b*). Estructura de las zoocenosis terrestres antárticas. Monografias I, UNESCO. 343–7.

Hermosilla, W., Covarrubias, R. and Castri, F. di (1967). Estudio comparativo sobre la estructura de los zoocenosis edáficas en el Trópico y en la Antártixa. IX Reunión Anual de Sociedad de Biologia de Chile. Valparaíso.

Saiz, F. and Hajek, E. (1968). Estudios ecológicos en Isla Robert. I. Observaciones de temperatura en nidos de Petrel gigante (*Macronectes giganteus* Gmelin). *Inst. Antárt. Chile. Publnes.* **14**.

Schlatter, R. (1967). Observaciones ecológico-cuantitativas de los Artrópodos terrestres en la Isla Robert (Antártica Chilena). Tesis Univ. de Chile. Santiago.

Schlatter, R., Hermosilla, W. and Castri, F. di (1968). Estudios ecológicos en Isla Robert (Shetland del Sur). 2. Distribución altitudinal de los Artrópodos terrestres. *Inst. Antart. Chile. Publnes.* **15**.

The Biology of *Cryptopygus antarcticus*

P. J. TILBROOK
British Antarctic Survey Biological Unit, Monks Wood Experimental
Station, Abbots Ripton, Huntingdon

I. Introduction

Cryptopygus antarcticus is a common Maritime Antarctic collembolan and has a circumpolar distribution in the Subantarctic. In many areas it is not only numerically the dominant arthropod but, because of its biomass and activity, is one of the most important components in the energy cycle of the terrestrial ecosystem.

It is the type species of the genus and was first described by Willem (1902) from a collection made during the voyage of the *Belgica* in 1897–99. Since then it has been recorded from many localities, but as with most Antarctic terrestrial arthropods, there is still little known of its ecology or general biology.

During a study of the arthropods at Signy Island and other Scotia Arc localities, some information was obtained on the distribution and abundance of this species and recently, whilst attempting to establish cultures in Britain for later experimentation, a few details of its life history have been noted. This paper is an attempt to draw together this rather fragmentary information and, by incorporating data available from other sources, to provide a comprehensive summary of what is at present known of this species.

II. Taxonomy and Morphology

Following the classification of Salmon (1964) the systematic position of *C. antarcticus* within the Collembola is:

Sub-order	—	Arthropleona
Super-family	—	Entomobryoidea
Family	—	Isotomidae
Sub-family	—	Anurophorinae

Since Willem's original description there have been several others, all listed by Wise (1967). No further description will be given here, but a number of scanning electron microscope photographs (Figs 1 and 2) demonstrate features of the external morphology, some of which cannot be seen clearly with the light microscope. The specimens photographed all came from Signy Island, but were not selected as particularly characteristic of the Signy form.

The hemiedaphic habit of this species is indicated by the presence of a furcula, fairly long antennae, dense pigmentation and well-developed eyes.

III. Geographical Distribution

The genus *Cryptopygus*, at present represented by twenty species (two as yet undescribed), is restricted to the Southern Hemisphere (Fig. 3). The distribution of *C. antarcticus* is also shown in this figure. It is widespread in the Antarctic Peninsula and the islands of the Scotia Ridge and has also been found on Bouvetøya, Archipel de Kerguelen and Heard Island. Although previously recorded from Balleny Islands and North Victoria Land (Pryor, 1962; Gressitt et al., 1963), Wise (1967) found that specimens from these areas differ constantly in some characters and so raised a new species, *C. cisantarcticus*. There is a doubtful record from Tasmania, but *C. antarcticus* can be truly termed circumpolar, since it has recently been collected at Macquarie Island.

IV. Habitats

In the Maritime Antarctic the species has been found in almost all terrestrial habitats free from permanent snow and ice. At South Georgia it is somewhat more restricted, perhaps due to the occurrence of other collembolan species and the generally more diverse fauna. This would also seem to be the case on Heard Island, where it has been reported as few in number amongst decaying *Azorella* roots and *Poa* grass (Brown, 1964).

V. Abundance and Horizontal Distribution

A measure of the relative abundance of *C. antarcticus* can be obtained by expressing the numbers found in each habitat as a percentage of the total arthropods. In most cases the number of samples taken from each habitat division in each area is too small for the figures to be very meaningful, but the indications are clear. Throughout the Antarctic Peninsula/Scotia Arc area, apart from South Georgia, the species shows a high degree of dominance, making up 70–90% of the fauna in moss habitats, though the figure is lower at about 50% in the South Shetland Islands. This may reflect the more diverse collembolan fauna there. In lichen habitats relative abundance is frequently as low as 5–20%, and this can be correlated with a greater degree

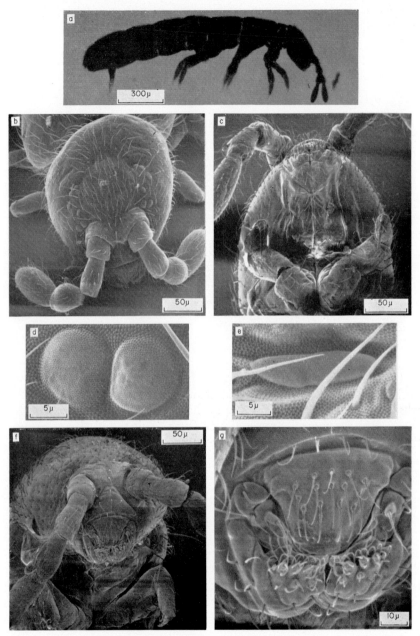

FIG. 1. *a*. Lateral view of *C. antarcticus* as seen under the light microscope to show normal body form. *b.–g*. Scanning electron microscope pictures of *C. antarcticus*. *b*. Dorsal view of head. *c*. Ventral view of head. *d*. Two eyes. *e*. Post-antennal organ. *f*. Anterior aspect of head. *g*. Close-up of mouth parts.

FIG. 2. Scanning electron microscope pictures of *C. antarcticus*: *a*. Antenna showing position of antennal organ on segment III. *b*. Antenna III sense organ. *c*. Cuticle surface and setal insertion. *d*. Claw. *e*. Male genital aperture. *f*. Retinaculum and attachment plates on furcula. *g*. Latero-ventral view whole specimen. *h*. Anus and female genital aperture.

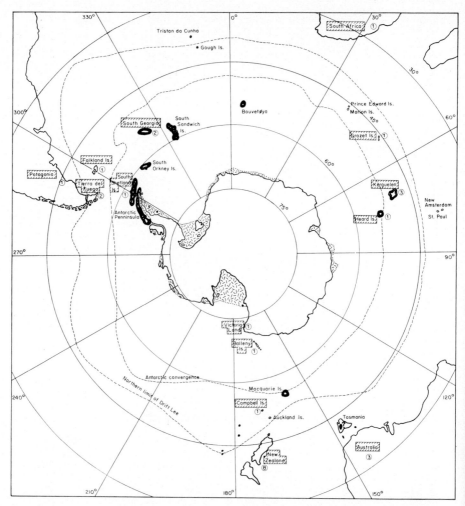

FIG. 3. Distribution of *Cryptopygus*. The present distribution of *Cryptopygus antarcticus* is shown (areas surrounded by black) and the place names surrounded by cross-hatching indicate where other species of the genus *Cryptopygus* occur. The numbers in circles denote the number of species other than *C. antarcticus* found at each area.

of exposure and a lower relative humidity. The dominance of the species in other habitat divisions is very variable from region to region, but in general, percentage abundance is very high and may be from 90% to 100% in such specialized niches as penguin colonies, bare rock and soil. The important factor again appears to be the humidity, and in the drier habitats certain mites are able to tolerate conditions better. At South Georgia relative abundance is much reduced, and even in moss habitats is only between 20% and 30%.

Accurate absolute abundance figures are only available for certain vegetated habitats and some data have been given elsewhere (Tilbrook, 1967a and b). Fortnightly sampling over twenty months at Signy Island showed how total numbers varied both spatially and temporally within and between three adjacent bryophyte types each superficially homogeneous. Monthly mean figures for cores approximately 10 cm² in surface area and 6 cm deep ranged between approximately five and thirty individuals, but the frequency distribution of sample unit values closely resembled the negative binomial, so confirming that aggregation exists. Furthermore, the coefficient of dispersion is frequently large, indicating that the degree of aggregation is high. This is a common feature of soil arthropod populations and suggests either localized, more favourable niches, poor dispersal after hatching from large clumps of eggs, or an actively gregarious habit. It is noteworthy that in the uniform conditions of a culture jar, aggregations are still formed.

VI. Vertical Distribution

At the main bryophyte sampling site on Signy Island, over two years, a mean 24% of the *C. antarctius* population in the top 6 cm occurred in the 3–6 cm layer, but there was significant variation between different moss types. As might be expected, the percentage in the lower layer was less in the more closely textured and frequently waterlogged *Pohlia* mats than in the drier, looser *Polytrichum* and *Dicranum*. This correlation of depth distribution with available pore space was very strikingly demonstrated at other Signy Island localities, and elsewhere throughout the area and in the mineral soils the lack of any truly burrowing invertebrates frequently restricted 95–100% of this species to the upper 3 cm layer.

VII. Temperature

C. antarcticus overwinters in all life stages, but the actual temperature tolerance of any stage is not known. It has, however, been shown with other collembolan species that the smaller stages are less cold resistant than the adults (Agrell, 1941).

A crude experiment carried out at Signy Island, primarily to determine the vegetational preference of *C. antarcticus*, did throw some light on its temperature tolerance. Known numbers of individuals taken at random from bulk collections were introduced into four containers each with four different moss cores. Two of these were then kept in a Stevenson screen and two in a greenhouse and a thermograph gave a continuous temperature trace in both situations. By extracting the animals at the end of a known period, some measure of the relationship between mortality rate and temperature was obtained. Five sets of experiments were carried out and, although the number of individuals introduced varied between 100 and 1000 and the duration between one and two weeks, the mortality rate was very similar in all the Stevenson screen examples. It varied between 29% and 37% mortality per week, whilst the overall temperature range was between $-23°C$ and $+3°C$. In the greenhouse the higher mean and maximum temperature resulted in a more variable mortality rate. On four occasions with the temperature range between $-1°C$ and $+33°C$ the mortality extremes were 16% and 44%. On the fifth occasion, however, the temperature range was between $+5°C$ and $+43°C$ and 100% mortality resulted. It seems that the temperature causing heat death is somewhere between 33°C and 43°C, which is similar to other collembolan species.

VIII. Life Cycles

As yet, only sparse information is available on the life cycle of *C. antarcticus*. Eggs were observed in the field in batches of several hundred, but almost certainly these were the result of laying by many animals. Evidence from eggs laid in culture suggests that the individual egg batch size is small—three to fourteen. The only female to lay in isolation deposited four eggs. Eggs have been laid in cultures in July or early August except for one batch deposited between 22 April and 2 May. At 2·5 cm in a moss mat at Signy Island the mean temperatures for July in 1962 and 1963 were $-0·98°$ and $-3·38°C$ and the maximum for both years only $+0·04°C$. It has been stated (Hale, 1967) that in Arctic or Subarctic climates, Collembola have only one or two generations a year. Eggs were not extracted during the field study, but if a definite annual laying period exists, one would expect a similarly defined hatching period when conditions allow. With sampling at two-weekly intervals this should result in a significant increase in the numbers of the smallest size group at one time, but the only such occasion was on 28 December 1962, when 300 small individuals were extracted from one core. This was almost certainly the result of a recent hatch from a large aggregation of eggs and correlated quite well with the onset of higher summer temperatures which might have promoted hatching of overwintered eggs. In fact, however, first size group individuals were common in samples throughout the year, and it therefore seems more likely that hatching, and presumably laying, takes place over the whole year when microhabitat conditions permit.

The eggs themselves are creamy white and spherical (approximately 140μ diameter) when laid. If fertile, each egg enlarges, splits the chorion in half, and gradually alters shape to a flattened spheroid. It also becomes more translucent and the deeply pigmented eye spots of the embryo are clearly visible through the wall before hatching. It is known that the egg development period varies with temperature (Hale, 1965) but of three egg batches to produce young in culture, two took between fifteen and twenty-eight days for all to hatch and the other between thirty-five and ninety-one days, although in each case they were kept at approximately $+7°C$.

When the first instar emerges from the egg it is almost colourless, but a purplish pigment soon develops over the whole body. The colour deepens as body size increases, until by the time the animal is approximately 1000μ long, the body looks black with a metallic sheen. On extraction, however, the pigment is seen to be a deep magenta colour.

In any assessment of the role of a species in a community in terms of biomass or respiration it is important to know the age structure of the population. Growth in Collembola is accomplished by a series of moults which continue throughout life, even after maximum size has been attained, but the number of instar stages occurring before both sexual maturity and maximum size are reached varies between species. During analysis of material from the main ecological study at Signy Island, *C. antarcticus* was divided into five equal, but arbitrary, size classes. Various authors have, however, calculated the size range of each successive instar stage, either from laboratory cultures or from field collections. Agrell (1948) measured certain body parameters, notably head length, of various Collembola species in collections from Lapland and by plotting the percentage frequency of each size a number of peaks were produced which represented the number of instar stages before attainment of maximum size. He also found that the growth factor between successive instars was a constant for each species, and so conformed to Dyar's rule. Hale (1965) verified this, but more recently Janetschek (1967) found that Dyar's rule did not apply to growth of total body length in the endemic Antarctic collembolan *Gomphiocephalus hodgsoni*, and claimed that this species showed regular growth of 90μ per moult. During examination of *C. antarcticus* it was found that measurement of total body length was as valid as the more time-consuming measurement of head length, and could be carried out on unmounted specimens with no significant loss of accuracy. From a collection extracted from *Marchantia* at Signy Island, 600 randomly taken individuals were measured and their frequency distribution is shown in Fig. 4. Clearly, there is only one peak of the expected form and this indicates that the first instar individuals have a mean body length of 500μ. The absence of further peaks may reflect inaccurate measurements in the larger size groups, or it may be that more specimens must be measured. Alternatively, if the different generations which were almost certainly represented in the sample each grow in a regular manner, but differ from each other, the overall picture would be similarly obscured. Nevertheless, this example suggests that under field conditions, and even within the microhabitat, post-embryonic growth is not by regular increments in this species but that after the hatching of a fairly constant first instar it becomes much more variable. Healey (*personal communication*) has found that in culture developing Onychiurid Collembola will moult with negligible size increase if feeding conditions are unfavourable. There is also some geographical variation in the size range of *C. antarcticus*. In the South Sandwich Islands and Bouvetøya the first instar is of similar size to the Signy form, but does not develop to the same maximum size.

It is not clear at which stage sexual maturity is reached, though the one individual known to lay eggs was approximately 1250 μ in total body length.

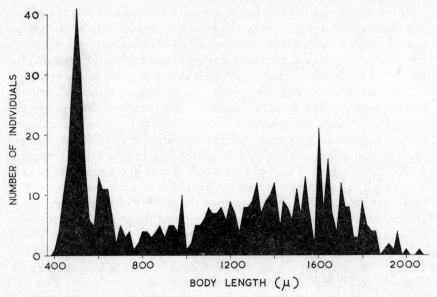

Fig. 4. Frequency distribution of 600 body-length measurements from a field population of *C. antarcticus*.

Of the fifty adult specimens which have been sexed during measurements, a third were males, the largest measuring 1722 μ, whilst of the remaining females a half exceeded this length and the largest reached 2060 μ. Although it is difficult, if not impossible, to speculate on the longevity of a species in the field from information obtained under culture conditions, there would seem to be no other means available at present. It may be of interest to note that five individuals have been kept in culture at $+7°C$ for twelve months.

IX. Food

The mouth parts of *C. antarcticus* are of a common collembolan type with a grinding area on the mandibles. Examination of gut contents suggests that many different types of food are taken, though fungal spores are the only well-defined structures that have been observed. When offered a variety of fungi isolated from Signy Island soil and vegetation some were taken readily and others ignored. Also, food accepted on one occasion was often rejected on another. It is well known that Collembola in general are non-selective in their feeding habits and indeed that many things are taken into the gut which are either of no nutritional value or pass out unchanged. In some cases this may, however, represent just a residue, after any bacteria and fungi present have been digested. During starvation *C. antarcticus* has also been observed feeding on living but inactive *Nanorchestes antarcticus* (Gressitt, 1967). When judging the effect of this species within the system, it is important to know both what is consumed and what of this is assimilated, but it seems at present that only food-tagging experiments with radioactive tracers will provide meaningful data.

X. Conclusion

C. antarcticus is widely distributed in the Maritime Antarctic and Sub-antarctic region and is most numerous in the colder parts of its range. In these areas it is found in most terrestrial habitats and is frequently the dominant member of the arthropod fauna. It is concentrated in the surface layer and is clearly able to withstand both very low temperatures and broad diurnal fluctuations. Whilst apparently not limiting the distribution of this species, however, the severe climate, by restricting activity and development, does diminish its contribution to the energy flow.

It is impossible to assess the true role of *C. antarcticus* within the ecosystem until its food intake in the field has been established. It probably takes in microphytes and detritus, but may also be important because organic matter which passes through its gut may be made more readily available to the decomposers. Although the mesostigmatic mite *Cyrtolaelaps racovitazai* has been seen consuming *C. antarcticus*, the proportion of this species supporting higher trophic levels must be very small. Its return to the system is probably mainly via the decomposers.

Clearly, many of the points made in this paper are based on very limited data and must be substantiated. Nevertheless, it is suggested that the autecological approach adopted here is the logical extension of community sampling when investigating the functioning of an ecosystem, even one as comparatively simple as the Antarctic terrestrial one.

Acknowledgements

Culture studies in this country have relied on the supply of fresh material from the Antarctic, and for this I am very grateful to Mr D. G. Bone of the

British Antarctic Survey. I am also indebted to Cambridge Scientific Instruments Limited for allowing me time on one of their Stereoscan microscopes and to Mr P. N. Lawrence and the British Museum (National History) for advice and assistance with the preparation of specimens. Finally, my thanks go to Mr J. R. Beck, Dr I. N. Healey and Mr E. A. Smith for commenting on the manuscript, and to my wife for typing the initial drafts. Mr K. A. J. Wise kindly made available unpublished distributional data.

References

Agrell, I. (1941). Zur ökologie der Collembolen. *Opusc. ent.* 3, 1–236.
Agrell, I. (1948). Studies on the Postembryonic Development of Collemboles. *Ark. Zool.* 41A, No. 12, 1–35.
Brown, K. G. (1964). The Insects of Heard Island. *A.N.A.R.E. Rep.* B 1, No. 73, 1–39.
Gressitt, J. L., Leech, R. E. and Wise, K. A. J. (1963). Entomological investigations in Antarctica. *Pacif. Insects.* 5, No. 1, 287–304.
Gressitt, J. L. (1967). Notes on arthropod populations in the Antarctic Peninsula—South Shetland Islands—South Orkney Islands area. *In* "Entomology of Antarctica". *Antarct. Res. Ser.* 10, 373–91. American Geophysical Union.
Hale, W. G. (1965). Post-embryonic development in some species of Collembola. *Pedobiologia* 5, No. 3, 228–43.
Hale, W. G. (1967). Collembola. *In* "Soil Biology" (Burges, A. and Raw F., eds.). Academic Press, London and New York. pp. 397–411.
Janetschek, H. (1967). Growth and maturity of the springtail, *Gomphiocephalus hodgsoni* Carpenter, from South Victoria Land and Ross Island. *In* "Entomology of Antarctica". *Antarct. Res. Ser.* 10, 295–305. American Geophysical Union.
Pryor, M. E. (1962). Some environmental features of Hallett Station, Antarctica, with special reference to soil arthropods. *Pacif. Insects,* 4, No. 3, 681–728.
Salmon, J. T. (1964). An Index to the Collembola. *R. Soc. N.Z., Bull.* 7, 2 vols, 1–651.
Tilbrook, P. J. (1967a). The terrestrial invertebrate fauna of the Maritime Antarctic. *In* "A Discussion on the Terrestrial Antarctic Ecosystem". *Phil. Trans. R. Soc.* B 252, No. 777, 261–78.
Tilbrook, P. J. (1967b). Arthropod ecology in the Maritime Antarctic. *In* "Entomology of Antarctica". *Antarct. Res. Ser.* 10, 331–56. American Geophysical Union.
Willem, V. (1902). Collemboles. *Résult. Voyage S.Y. Belgica,* Rapp. Sci. Zool. pp. 1–19.
Wise, K. A. J. (1967). Collembola (springtails). *In* "Entomology of Antarctica". *Antarct. Res. Ser.* 10, 123–48. American Geophysical Union.

Discussion

Terrestrial Fauna

M. W. HOLDGATE

Did Dr Hermosilla study the rate at which his sterile litter substrata were colonized by fungi or micro-organisms? It may well be that Collembola and Acari feed largely on these rather than directly on litter, so that the imported substrata might not be available initially as a food source. Differences in the number of animals recorded on the various materials might consequently be expected to be correlated with differences in microflora, rather than any intrinsic variation in their "attractiveness" to Antarctic arthropods.

W. HERMOSILLA

Only the mesofauna were studied, but it may be possible to develop the investigation along these further lines.

M. J. DUNBAR

What was Mr Tilbrook's evidence for saying that *Cryptopygus antarcticus* lay eggs all through the year?

P. J. TILBROOK

Conditions over most of the year allow eggs to hatch and the time for development from laying to hatching appears short. If all the eggs were laid at one time—say in autumn, with a winter diapause or dormancy—then one would expect a big, synchronous, hatch in spring or when conditions became favourable. It is true that on one occasion a large number of first instar individuals were extracted from one core in spring, so indicating a near-synchronous hatching of a batch of eggs, but apart from this, first instars were present in similar numbers throughout the year.

Part XIV

CONSERVATION

Conservation

The relative lack of disturbance of Antarctic ecosystems (and particularly of terrestrial and freshwater systems) has impressed and influenced most of those who have worked there. The impression has been deepened by the proximity, in Antarctic waters, of two industries which, though separated by a century in time, have provided classic examples of the mismanagement of valuable natural resources. Antarctic sealing, between about 1790 and 1830, so depleted the stocks of southern fur seals that only now are sizeable populations re-establishing themselves. Antarctic whaling, between 1930 and 1966, and especially in the last fifteen years of this period, likewise depleted the populations of the larger southern baleen whales, bringing the largest animal known to have lived on earth, the blue whale, to the verge of extinction. The difference between these two industries was that the former was conducted in ignorance of the life tables and potential sustainable yield of the animal resource that was being cropped, whereas the whaling industry had the benefit of expert scientific and statistical advice, based on many years of research, and chose to ignore it for short-term commercial reasons. There is a social lesson in this somewhere, for what good is it to pay scientists to study natural resources if their discoveries are not used to improve management?

Biologists have been determined that the other living resources of the Antarctic shall not be needlessly devastated by disturbance, pollution or human wastefulness and from the beginning of the post-I.G.Y. period of expansion of research have been pressing proposals for conservation measures. In this they have had the ready support of governments, who included conservation as one of the aims of the Antarctic Treaty and have moved forward vigorously to find an internationally acceptable common ground for it. Indeed, there have been times when the representatives of the governments have pressed the biologists, through SCAR, to greater activity. In this section, the review paper by M. W. Holdgate therefore tells a success story, but at the same time looks to the broader issues of how the international harmony attained in the Antarctic can be applied as a basis for comparable achievements in areas with more complex problems. In his supporting paper J. Shimoizumi deals with the local issues that arise in any national programme where a manned station is set next to vulnerable areas that must not be damaged. Taken together these papers and the following discussion indicate one field of practical achievement, based on science but interpreted as policy, in which work in the Antarctic has contributed toward the wiser management of the world environment.

Conservation in the Antarctic

M. W. HOLDGATE

The Nature Conservancy, Belgrave Square, London, England

I. Definitions

The word *conservation* is used by biologists, planners and landscape architects to mean:

- (*a*) the management of natural resources for the benefit of mankind, so that their available production is harvested without unnecessary or irreversible harm to the system (*resource conservation*);
- (*b*) the protection of plant and animal species and of samples of the natural ecological systems they compose (*wild life conservation*);
- (*c*) the protection of visually important features of the landscape, for aesthetic reasons (*conservation of amenity*).

Resource conservation is the broadest in scope, and encompasses the other two because the preservation of samples of natural ecosystems for research, education, maintenance of soil resources, or retention of genetic diversity, or of samples of wild landscapes for recreation, are in themselves wholly justifiable forms of land use and must be included in any plan for the rational management of the environment. There is, however, a difference in approach.

Wild life conservation (like conservation of amenity) manages an ecosystem in order to maintain a particular natural or semi-natural complex of plants and animals and to derive a return of knowledge, enjoyment, or potential for future development. It is thus concerned not to alter the character of the system. Resource conservation manages the system to maintain an output of an economically utilizable product at the optimal sustainable level and can readily accept changes from the initial natural condition. Both, however, are alike in demanding a conscious policy for the ecosystem, and both may involve active management: conservation is in this sense an applied science. Conservation involves a plan which employs scientific knowledge but is inevitably shaped by judgement of relative values.

II. The Objectives of Conservation in the Antarctic

The objectives of conservation in the Antarctic regions have never been set out clearly, but it is evident from the records of the Antarctic Treaty Consultative Meetings (Anderson, 1968; Carrick, 1964), the SCAR Working Group on Biology, the International Whaling Commission and other bodies that the following have been generally recognized:

1. The general protection of the scenic beauty of the Antarctic regions south of 60°S latitude, and of their birds, mammals, and terrestrial and freshwater life.

2. The protection of the remaining undisturbed ecosystems of the Subantarctic and temperate oceanic islands north of 60°S latitude, and as far as possible the restoration or stabilization of those island ecosystems that have been disrupted by man and by the alien species he has imported (Holdgate, 1968).

3. The wise management of the biological resources of the southern ocean, so that a protein crop can be taken without irreversible damage to the ecosystem or the undue depletion of populations of the cropped species (Carrick, 1964; Murphy, 1964; Gulland, 1970; this symposium).

No policy has been spelled out for the use of the resources of the Antarctic land, largely because although major mineral deposits occur there, including the world's largest coalfield (Adie, 1970; this symposium), their exploitation must involve great political and economic difficulties. An explicit, positive policy for the planned development of the recreational use of Antarctica is also lacking, although tourist visits to the region are increasing.

III. The Present State of Antarctic Ecosystems

A. LAND AND FRESH WATER SOUTH OF 60°S

Except in areas formerly exploited by sealers and in the immediate vicinity of present stations and sites of intensive research, the scenic and biotic resources of Antarctica remain in a substantially natural condition. The continent is the only great tract of land on earth of which this can be said. None the less, man has had, and is still having some effect on the ecosystem.

In the past, sealers overcropped the breeding stocks of fur seals (*Arctocephalus tropicalis gazella*) in the South Shetland, South Orkney and South Sandwich Islands so drastically that an initial population of about a million animals was virtually eliminated by 1830. Elephant seal (*Mirounga leonina*) were also taken, and penguin populations probably suffered through the killing of birds for food if not for oil. Roberts (1958) lists the known Antarctic sealing expeditions and makes the magnitude of this impact evident. Although these depredations ceased long ago fur seals are only now beginning to re-colonise their former range (Aguayo, 1970: this symposium; Bonner, 1968). More recently, cropping of seals for dog food may have led to local reductions in Weddell Seal (*Leptonychotes weddelli*) populations, even though the totals taken are trivial as a proportion of the Antarctic stock as a whole.

Today, the most obvious and publicised threats to the Antarctic land ecosystem arise from the construction of stations, with their associated fuel storage, power generating, aircraft landing and ship docking facilities. These must involve local disruption of the ecosystem, and because many stations are placed on rocky sites in coastal areas where the biota is richest, may have a relatively more serious impact than might be expected from their small area. Such stations also contaminate the ecosystem locally with waste, disposal of which is difficult in a region where burial is generally impossible, and decomposition slow: at most stations refuse and sewage are dumped into the sea with noticeable small-scale effects.

These local influences are, of course, negligible when considered in the total context of Antarctica. A more significant threat is posed by the move-ment and activities of men (especially scientists) in the field. Vehicular, and even pedestrian travel can break up vegetation and desert pavements and cause erosion. Sampling of soil and moss carpets for botanical and zoological studies leaves gaps in the ground cover which can also be widened by erosion. Two factors combine to aggravate this danger. First, Antarctic vegetation even in the Maritime zone grows slowly and scars take years to heal. Secondly, although the Antarctic regions are of vast extent, only a tiny proportion of the land surface is snow free and supports vegetation or soil and this comes under a disproportionate pressure both from scientists and travellers. In the neighbourhood of stations there is a real danger that trampling and sampling will ultimately come to hamper future research.

Disturbance of bird and seal colonies is another localized threat. Heli-copters are known to have caused diminished breeding success among penguins in the "show" colony at Cape Royds (Stonehouse, 1970: this symposium) and the relative disturbance due to flights at different altitudes is described by Sladen (1970: this symposium). In areas where helicopters and aircraft are used intensively, there is a distinct risk that the validity of data on bird breeding success will be reduced.

B. LAND AREAS NORTH OF 60°S

The impact of men on the oceanic islands of the southern circumpolar belt has been reviewed by Holdgate and Wace (1961), Dorst and Milon (1964) and Holdgate (1968) and is summarized in Table 1 (based on the latter paper). These islands are particularly vulnerable to human impact because their ecosystems have been developed within the isolation of an ocean barrier, and are species-poor, lacking many groups and species of plant and animal that are dominant in continental situations. Mammalian predators and herbivores are generally absent: when they are imported, the island vegetation is often drastically changed by grazing and their vast seabird breeding colonies cannot withstand the impact of such animals as rats or cats. Disturbance of the vegetation by burning, grazing or construction aids the spread of alien plants (especially ruderal weeds) which are less able to invade closed communities (Wace, 1968). Imported invertebrates often spread readily into niches that have no native occupant, especially in areas where the native vegetation is also disturbed and alien plants are spreading.

Like the Antarctic islands, those of the southern temperate zone were the scene of intensive sealing from about 1780 to 1830 and again between 1860 and 1880. At South Georgia about 1,200,000 fur seals were killed in the former period. Archipel de Kerguelen, Macquarie Island, Iles Crozet, Prince Edward Islands, Gough Island, Tristan da Cunha, Beauchêne Island, the Cape Horn archipelago and the New Zealand shelf islands all supported considerable stocks and were visited many times. On many of them elephant seal were also killed for blubber, as were King penguins at Macquarie Island. Male elephant seal continued to be cropped on a sustained yield basis at South Georgia until 1964/65 and an industry continues at Archipel de Kerguelen.

Although Table 1 shows that man has had a considerable influence on the majority of these islands, it does not reveal an even more important fact: that oceanic islands elsewhere have been more severely disturbed. Current reviews, organized by the CT (Conservation terrestrial) section of the International Biological Programme, have demonstrated that only a very few of the islands in the Pacific Ocean have escaped disruption while in the western Indian Ocean only Aldabra among the atolls retains a substantially natural ecosystem (Stoddart, 1967). Because of the high scientific interest of oceanic islands, with their species-poor disharmonic biotas and theoretical importance in biogeography (Wallace, 1895; Macarthur and Wilson, 1967), the conservation of the remaining Subantarctic and southern temperate islands is particularly urgent.

IV. Marine Ecosystems

The Antarctic oceanic ecosystem has been disturbed by the removal from it of a high proportion of its original baleen whale population (Zenkovich, 1970: this symposium; Mackintosh, 1970: this symposium). It is not clear how much this has been followed by increases in the populations of penguins, seals or fishes, all of which feed on the krill once taken by the whales. Sladen (1964) has suggested an increase in the chinstrap penguin, *Pygoscelis*

TABLE 1

Human Settlement, Feral Mammals and Degree of Damage on the Islands of the Circum-Antarctic Seas

Islands	Zone	Human population	Feral vertebrates	Condition
South Sandwich Islands (eleven islands)	Maritime Antarctic	Formerly sealers, for short periods. Small scientific station for a few summers on one island. A few scientific parties for short periods	None	Undamaged
Bouvetøya	Maritime Antarctic	None (weather station planned)	None	Undamaged
South Georgia (with outliers)	Subantarctic	Sealers from 1796 and many whalers from about 1910–65. Now only small scientific station	Reindeer (two herds) Rats	Local damage around stations and where reindeer grazing is heavy. Outlying islands undamaged
Marion Island	Subantarctic	Sealers formerly active. Now only weather station	Cats	Vegetation undamaged, but cats damaging avifauna
Prince Edward Island	Subantarctic	None	Formerly a few sheep	Undamaged
Iles Crozet	Subantarctic	Sealers formerly active. Weather station since 1963	Pigs on Ile aux Cochons, 1820–60, now extinct. Rabbits, goats said to have been present but now also extinct. Rats (?)	Vegetation substantially undamaged, especially probably on Ile de l'Est. Surveys required
Archipel de Kerguelen	Subantarctic	Sealers formerly active (1800–30). Weather station since 1949, with own farm	Rabbits (abundant), sheep, reindeer, pigs (local) cats, rats	Vegetation of main island damaged by rabbits. Local damage by sheep. Avifauna on main island damaged by cats and rats. Outlying small islands undamaged
Heard Island	Subantarctic	Sealers formerly. Scientific station 1947–54	None	Undamaged
Macquarie Island	Subantarctic	Sealers active 1820–80. Scientific station since 1945	Rabbits, imported in 1880, now abundant. A few sheep. Formerly a few goats and horses now extinct. Cats, rats, and predatory ground-living bird *Gallirallus* numerous	Widespread severe damage to vegetation by rabbits, and to smaller birds by predators

Falkland Islands	Temperate	Settled since eighteenth century. Now used for sheep ranching	Sheep farmed over much of land. Cattle locally feral in interior. Guanaco, feral on one island. Cats, rats, mice, widespread	Vegetation substantially altered by grazing except on smaller off-lying islands. Bird fauna probably substantially affected but remains rich
Gough Island, Inaccessible Island, Nightingale Island	Temperate	Sealers formerly. Weather station on Gough Island since 1955. Visits by Tristan Islanders to other two islands since 1810	Mice (on Gough Island)	Substantially undamaged
Tristan da Cunha	Temperate	Small settlement since 1810	Goats formerly (now extinct). Domestic stock maintained on lower grazings: cattle and sheep semi-wild in some areas. Cats, rats, mice widespread	Vegetation altered in heavily grazed areas, and bird fauna reduced by predators and man
Ile St Paul	Temperate	Fishing base, 1843–1914, and intermittently since. No present inhabitants	Rabbits abundant until 1957: later rare or ? absent. Cats, rats, mice	Rabbit grazing caused former disturbance of vegetation: condition now uncertain. Bird fauna probably reduced by predation
Ile Amsterdam	Temperate	Fishery base, 1843–53: farmed, 1871. Weather station since 1950	Cattle (numerous), formerly goats, sheep (now extinct). Cats, rats, mice	Native vegetation greatly altered by grazing and avifauna severely reduced by predation
Campbell Island	Temperate	Sheep farming, 1890–1927. Whaling station, 1908–14. Weather station since 1941	Sheep (now greatly reduced). Some cattle, formerly goats, pigs, guinea fowl, game birds. Cats, rats present	Grazing formerly altered vegetation. Management now aiming at removing sheep and aiding recovery. Populations of smaller sea birds reportedly reduced by predators
Auckland Islands	Temperate	Settled by Maoris, 1841. Whaling station 1849–52. Evacuated 1856: subsequent spasmodic farming. Weather station 1941–45	Pigs, goats and cats on main island. Rabbits, cattle on Rose and Enderby Islands. None on Adams Island	Adams Island undamaged. Vegetation and fauna elsewhere variously affected
Snares Islands, Bounty Islands, Antipodes Islands	Temperate	Small summer field station on Snares Islands. None elsewhere		Substantially undamaged

antarctica, correlated with the reduction in whale numbers, but the data are insufficient to establish the position for bird populations as a whole (Holdgate, 1967). *Euphausia superba* has a central place in so many food chains that it seems improbable that a "surplus" of it, created by the elimination of one of its many consumers, will remain uncropped for long, and if this is so, the whaling industry must have set in motion a complex readjustment of the Antarctic marine ecosystem as a whole. The killing of fur seal, elephant seal and penguins on some of the southern islands must have caused similar local changes in balance. There is nothing unusual in this, for all the oceans of the world have been affected by exploitation and their present "equilibrium" (if there is one) is different from that preceding the development of fisheries, and must be adjusting continually to the increasing skill of man as a predator.

Pollution is the other major disturbance caused by man to oceanic ecosystems. In Antarctic waters it is unquestionably trivial compared with northern seas. Yet organochlorine pesticide residues have now been found in penguins at McMurdo and in euphausiids, penguins and seals at Signy Island. The world-wide dissemination of these persistent substances, even at very low concentrations, has given understandable cause for concern.

V. Conservation Measures in Antarctic and Subantarctic land Areas

The Antarctic Treaty (H.M.S.O., 1965), which came into force on 23 June 1961, is in conservationist's terms a Management Plan. It lays down certain rules which govern the management of the resources of the Antarctic south of 60°S latitude, for example prohibiting warlike activities and contamination with radioactive waste and opening the whole area for purposes of peaceful scientific exploration. In this, it assumes that the most useful "crops" available from the continent today are scientific knowledge and international harmony, and establishes a framework for their attainment. Moreover, like other enlightened conservation organizations, it provides for the periodic review of the management plan at regular consultative meetings of all the governments concerned.

A. Wildlife Conservation on the Antarctic Land

Wildlife conservation in the Antarctic has been provided for under the Antarctic Treaty by detailed conservation measures, termed the Agreed Measures for the Conservation of Antarctic Fauna and Flora. These are based on scientific advice provided by SCAR through its Working Group on Biology, so that SCAR, in this respect, acts as scientific adviser to the Governments signatory to the Treaty and participating in the Consultative Meetings. The Agreed Measures apply in the same area as the Antarctic Treaty itself, namely the entire area south of 60°S latitude, but because states rights on the high seas are reserved, fishing is not affected and it is likely that nations also retain the right to take whales, seals and birds at sea. Consequently the Agreed Measure has full force only on land and on shelf ice, which is explicitly included with the land in the text. The legislative principles involved in the Agreed Measures and the ways they are being implemented by different countries have been reviewed by Anderson (1968) and will not be considered further here. At the time of writing (Autumn 1968) the Agreed Measures have not yet become effective because some of the countries have still to enact the necessary legislation, but they are being applied as Guide Lines in the interim and are a practical reality.

The Agreed Measures provide for:

(a) overall protection from killing, wounding, capture or molestation for all native mammals (except whales), and native birds in the Antarctic, at all stages in the life cycle (including eggs);

(b) lifting of this protection by Governments, who may issue permits to allow selected individuals to kill or capture birds and mammals:

   (i) to provide indispensable food for men and dogs, in the Treaty Area, in limited quantities;

   (ii) to provide specimens for study, for Zoological gardens, for museums and for similar scientific, educational and cultural purposes.

Information on the numbers of each species taken under permit is required and these data are to be exchanged between the participating Governments. It is laid down that the numbers of a species taken under permit should not ordinarily exceed that which the population is capable of making good during the next breeding season, and that activities likely to disturb the balance of natural ecological systems should not be permitted. As Anderson (1968) says, these requirements have far reaching implications. "Molestation" not only includes the wilful disturbance of penguins and seals by chasing them or throwing stones at them, but probably includes corralling or otherwise capturing birds for banding, experimental transport to other parts of the Antarctic to test homing ability, and the fitting of telemetry devices to birds and mammals. Scientists, like everyone else, must expect to justify their demands on the Antarctic fauna and be answerable for their conduct. The killing of seals for dog food, the traditional and best as well as cheapest way of keeping husky teams in good condition, is evidently frowned on and nations are expected to make other arrangements if they can.

Besides these general measures, there are provisions for:

(i) The special protection of species which can be shown to require this because of their rarity, vulnerability or some other good reason. At present this special protection applies to the Ross seal, *Ommatophoca rossi*, and all fur seals (genus *Arctocephalus*). Specially protected species may be killed only for a compelling scientific purpose or in an emergency.

(ii) The special protection of areas. This provision is intended to safeguard outstandingly interesting or unique samples of vegetation, soil or habitat. Within these areas, plant collection and the collection of birds and mammals is permitted only for compelling scientific purposes that cannot be served elsewhere, or in an emergency. There is also a prohibition on driving vehicles across the areas, although landing by boats or helicopters is permissible. Pilots and navigators are expected to use care in their choice of landing place.

(iii) Reduction to a minimum of harmful interference with living conditions of the Antarctic fauna, for example by preventing dogs running free, or low flying of helicopters over penguin colonies. The same Article of the Agreed Measures requires reasonable steps to be taken to minimize pollution of inshore waters, e.g. by the pumping of ships bilges.

(iv) Prohibition of the import into the Antarctic of non-indigenous species of animals and plants, except under permit. Only laboratory animals and plants, domestic livestock (excluding poultry) and sledge dogs may be imported. Poultry are prohibited because of the danger of introducing bird diseases that might spread to the native avifauna. Dogs must be inoculated against specified diseases two months before import. All introduced animals and plants have to be kept under controlled conditions and eventually removed or destroyed.

B. FUTURE NEEDS FOR CONSERVATION ON THE ANTARCTIC LAND

The Agreed Measures provide so comprehensive a frame-work for Antarctic wild life conservation that they are most unlikely to require significant amendment. They are indeed, more complete than any other measures applying to a large region of the world. Future action is required largely in three fields: perfection of their application, especially to specially protected species and areas, development of a positive scheme for management, especially of specially protected areas, and adoption of "educational" means to make all personnel visiting the Antarctic, whether scientists or tourists, aware of the need for conservation.

1. Specially protected species

Ross seals and fur seals have been given special protection under the Agreed Measures. All present evidence points to the Ross Seal being more numerous than previously supposed (Ray, 1970: this symposium). Its habits, so far as these are known, rarely if ever bring it within the area of application of the Agreed Measures, since it lives in the pack ice and rarely hauls out on Antarctic land or shelf ice. For this latter reason, its inclusion as a Specially Protected Species under the Agreed Measures is not altogether easy to justify, especially now that there is substantial agreement on the regulation of pelagic sealing in the Antarctic, under which the species receives protection in its main habitat.

Conversely, fur seals breed on land and are vulnerable when doing so. They yield a valuable product and are therefore attractive to sealers. They are rare in the Antarctic zone where they are establishing small nuclei of repopulation (Aguayo, 1970; this symposium). Given special protection now, they may be expected to re-establish themselves securely in their former range.

Three criteria have generally been used by the Working Group on Biology of SCAR in bringing forward cases for special protection. These are:

(a) rarity, either in the world or in the Antarctic zone,
(b) vulnerability,
(c) capacity to benefit from special protection.

The Ross Seal, although listed in the IUCN "Red Book" of endangered species, may not meet the first criterion and, with its wide dispersion and low population density almost certainly does not meet the second. The third criterion also seems not to apply, except in so far as the scheduling of the species draws attention to the need for its protection. Fur seals, on the other hand, fulfil all three criteria. Probably no other species of mammal, and no bird species breeding in the Antarctic does so, unless it is considered justifiable to extend protection to those which just penetrate the region and maintain marginal breeding populations there. On this basis a case could be made for special protection for elephant seal (*Mirounga leonina*) which has a small breeding group in the South Orkney Islands, but is numerous in the South Shetland Islands, macaroni penguin (*Eudyptes chrysolophus*) with a similar distribution and black-bellied storm petrel (*Fregetta tropica*). All of these are, however, numerous to the north of 60°S latitude.

What is apparent from this review is that before a species is proposed for special protection, a careful assessment of its numbers, biology, and vulnerability is required, and that the schedule will need periodic revision as new data become available. Such ecological research as a basis for conservation was urged by Carrick (1964) and remains highly relevant.

2. Specially protected areas

The Article of the Agreed Measures governing the special protection of areas establishes two criteria, outstanding scientific interest and uniqueness (rarity) of the ecological systems, represented there. These criteria can be further refined:

(a) the series of specially protected areas should include representative samples of the major Antarctic land and freshwater ecological systems, and of the variations they display in relation to edaphic, climatic, or geographic variables;

(b) areas with unique complexes of species should receive special consideration, as should any areas which are the type, or only known, habitats for plant or invertebrate species, or contain outstandingly interesting breeding colonies or birds and mammals;

(c) areas which have been the scene of intensive scientific study and thus provide a baseline for long-term investigations should be eligible for special protection.

Criteria (b) and (c) are clearly compatible with those laid down in the text of the Agreed Measures. For criterion (a) to be acceptable, the sites proposed must have a certain "quality": they must be outstandingly good examples of the ecosystems they represent. The criteria are interrelated, for areas that satisfy (a) and (b) are likely also to be good research sites.

If this argument is valid, there are two logical conclusions. First, the series of specially protected areas envisaged under criterion (a) can only be chosen after careful field surveys. Secondly, a classification of the land and freshwater ecosystems of the Antarctic is required, against which surveys can be judged. At present, such a classification is available for vegetation in the Maritime Antarctic (Gimingham and Smith, 1970: this symposium), and to some extent for soils (Ugolini, 1970: this symposium; Allen and Heal, 1970: this symposium). The breeding ranges of bird and mammal species are also well enough known for the significance of particular colonies to be judged. But there is no adequate classification of invertebrate habitats or of lakes.

It is not surprising that the series of fifteen Specially Protected Areas so far established is not comprehensive. In contains four areas selected primarily for botanical purposes, seven areas selected primarily to protect breeding colonies of birds and mammals, and four areas selected as samples of ecological systems as a whole.

Analysis of the list (Table 2) suggests that:

(a) the series includes breeding grounds of emperor, Adélie and chinstrap penguins but may not include any substantial breeding ground of the gentoo penguin or one of the small colonies of the macaroni penguin within the Antarctic zone proper;

(b) the list includes breeding grounds of most Antarctic Procellariidae;

(c) the list also probably includes breeding colonies of Dominican gull, Antarctic tern and blue-eyed shag;

(d) It protects four breeding colonies of fur seal and includes Weddell Seal breeding colonies.

However the size of most of these colonies is quite unknown and we have no baseline data such as are desirable if these areas are to serve in any way as a long-term control.

Representative samples of most maritime Antarctic vegetation types are probably included. Very extensive cover of grass (*Deschampsia antarctica*) occurs on one area, Lynch Island, and the cushion plant *Colobanthus quitensis* probably also grows there. No proper botanical or invertebrate surveys have been done, nor has any attempt been made to protect a series of representative freshwater bodies. No area of "desert pavement" soil, with its associated sparse biota, as in the Victoria Land dry valleys, features in the list. None of the intensively studied lakes on Signy Island or in Victoria Land receives special protection.

This problem is not confined to Antarctica. Throughout the world, nature reserves (which is what the specially protected areas really are) have been selected subjectively, because of known interest, and a more objective approach seeking to protect representative series of sites has followed. During the International Biological Programme such an objective survey is being mounted by the CT section on a world wide basis (Nicholson, 1968; Peterken, 1968) and it would obviously be appropriate to use a modification of the IBP Check Sheet and classification in a careful survey of possible Antarctic specially protected areas.

3. Management

Management is an essential component of conservation, although its intensity varies. It does not always imply interference with the ecosystem, but does invariably mean that a positive plan is drawn up for conservation in a region or country as a whole, and for each reserve or special area established there.

In the Antarctic, the need for continued scientific consideration of conservation policies has been recognized by the Governments, who have welcomed SCAR's interest and encouraged its continuation. It remains for SCAR to consider its scientific objectives and to establish a framework for their attainment. These objectives might include:

(*a*) study of the distribution, numbers and biology of Antarctic birds and mammals so that any fluctuations in abundance are detected and any necessary amendment to the Agreed Measures and the schedule of Specially Protected Species have a sound scientific base;

(*b*) surveys of plant and invertebrate communities and freshwater ecosystems, and development of a comprehensive classification of them, so that the series of specially protected areas is soundly based;

(*c*) monitoring of the changes taking place in land and freshwater

TABLE 2

Specially Protected Areas and the Reasons for their Designation

Area	Latitude	Longitude	Reason for establishment
Taylor Rookery, Mac. Robertson Land	67°26′S	60°50′E	Protection of largest known colony of Emperor Penguin (*Aptenodytes forsteri*) breeding on land
Rookery Islands, Holme Bay	67°37′S	62°33′E	Protection of breeding colonies and habitat of all six bird species resident in Mawson area, of which Giant Petrel (*Macronectes giganteus*) and Cape pigeon (*Daption capensis*) breed nowhere else in region
Ardeny Island and Odbert Island, Budd Coast	66°22′S	110°25′E	Protection of breeding colonies and habitat of Antarctic petrel (*Thalassoica antarctica*) and Antarctic fulmar (*Fulmarus glacialoides*), together with other bird species
Sabrina Island, Balleny Islands	66°54′S	163°20′E	Protection of biologically richest sample of Balleny Islands group, including only known breeding site of chinstrap penguin (*Pygoscelsis antarctica*,) in Ross Sea sector
Beaufort Island, Ross Sea	76°58′S	167°03′E	Substantial and varied avifauna, representative of coastal Ross Sea area
Cape Crozier, Ross Island	77°32′S	169°19′E	Rich bird and mammal fauna, microfauna and microflora, with habitat of considerable interest. Includes emperor penguin and Adélie penguin (*Pygoscelsis adeliae*) colonies, skuas (*Catharacta skua maccormicki*), and Weddell seal (*Leptonychotes weddelli*)
Cape Hallett, Victoria Land	72°18′S	170°19′E	Ecosystem of outstanding interest, including large Adélie penguin colony, skuas, and small area of unusually rich and diverse vegetation dominated by bryophytes, and supporting a variety of terrestrial invertebrates
Dion Islands, Marguerite Bay	67°52′S	68°43′W	Protection of the only known breeding colony of emperor penguins on the west side of the Antarctic peninsula
Green Island, Berthelot Islands	65°19′S	64°10′W	Protection of an exceptionally luxuriant bryophyte vegetation locally overlying up to 2 m of peat, with its associated terrestrial fauna

Area	Latitude	Longitude	Reason for establishment
Byers Peninsula, Livingston Island	62°38'S	61°05'W	Diverse plant and animal life, with vegetation representative of western South Shetland Islands. Substantial population of elephant seal (*Mirounga leonina*) and small breeding populations of fur seal (*Arctocephalus tropicalis gazella*)
Cape Shirreff, Livingston Island	62°28'S	60°45'W	Diverse plant and animal life, substantial numbers of elephant seals and small colonies of fur seals
Fildes Peninsula, King George Island	62°12'S	58°58'W	Protection of a sample of a large, biologically diverse area with lakes that are ice free in summer. As amended in 1968, this Specially Protected Area includes only one large lake with the surrounding land
Moe Island, South Orkney Islands	60°45'S	54°41'W	Diverse vegetation, with samples of most of the main communities of the Maritime Antarctic, also convenient as a control in case intensive research alters the ecosystem on the adjacent Signy Island. Substantial bird population, including Adélie and chinstrap penguins
Lynch Island, South Orkney Islands	60°40'S	45°38'W	Protection of one of the most extensive areas of grass (*Deschampsia antarctica*) known in the Treaty Area, with associated soil and invertebrate fauna
Southern Powell Island and adjacent islands, South Orkney Islands	60°45'S	45°02'W	Protection of a range of Maritime Antarctic vegetation types, a considerable bird and mammal fauna including breeding Weddell seal, large numbers of elephant seal in summer, and a small colony of fur seal. A representative sample of the South Orkney Island ecosystem

ecosystems, so that any serious deterioration due to human impact is detected and a sound case made for remedial or preventive measures.

Inevitably, these tasks will require international planning but must be implemented at national level. They cannot be undertaken at once over the whole Antarctic. All can however be started in selected areas, and the monitoring described under (*a*) and (*c*), involving repeated censuses or surveys of key breeding colonies or sites, will have scientific interest in its own right as well as value in conservation. Returns of species killed or taken under permit should be analysed in relation to these long-term studies of species abundance and distribution.

For each specially protected area, it is desirable that a management plan is drawn up, preferably under the supervision of a member of the SCAR Working Group on Biology. This plan should include:

(a) A brief description of the habitat with sections on:
> topography (with a map)
> climate
> geology
> geomorphology
> pedology.

(b) A statement of the reasons for its special protection (as cited in the formal Recommendation of the Consultative Meeting).

(c) An account of its biological features, especially those responsible for its status, in the following order:
> microbiology
> botany: plant species and communities present
> invertebrate fauna
> vertebrate fauna.

(d) An account of the threats, if any, to which the area is vulnerable.

(e) A prescription for the activities that should be permitted in the area, including:
> access points (show preferred landing places on map);
> pedestrian routes (if soil or vegetation is very vulnerable these may be marked both on a map and on the ground);
> areas where scientific sampling may and must not take place, and guide lines on the extent of this sampling. This section should carefully discriminate between research that can only be done in the area and that which could be done elsewhere: the latter should generally not be permitted;
> areas for routine monitoring as an index of change;
> plans for any work to be done on the area to protect its scientific interest e.g. maintenance of route markers.

(f) References to published scientific work in the area.

Such plans should be kept up to date and copies should be exchanged between all SCAR nations. When activities take place in the area under permit a record of them should be kept as an annex to the plan. This record should include the location of collections, the numbers of each species taken, and any structural alterations caused to the habitat.

These proposals may seem needlessly formal, complex and restrictive under present conditions in Antarctica. None the less, experience elsewhere confirms the need to compile an accurate dossier of information about strictly reserved areas and of the changes which take place there. In the long term, when human impact on the Antarctic land will undoubtedly increase and when the cumulative disturbance of decades of scientific activity must become a local hindrance to research, these procedures will not appear so irrelevant.

4. Information

From the earliest stages, those concerned with the drafting of Antarctic conservation measures recognized the need to secure the willing support of all personnel (especially non-scientists) working in the region. Now that Antarctic tourism is justifiably expanding, the need for information about Antarctic wild life; its interest, its vulnerability, and the conservation measures drafted for its protection is even more acute. As in National Parks everywhere, an attractive booklet is needed, with the following content:

an account of the Antarctic flora and fauna, its history, adaptations, and the reasons for its scientific interest;
pictures and a key for identification of birds and seals;
explanation of why the flora and fauna are vulnerable to disturbance, and a list of activities to avoid;
explanation of the Agreed Measures, and especially of the Specially Protected areas, and of other conservation agreements, and a plea for their observance;
brief account of some of the biological research going on in the Antarctic, and why it is worth while;
references to popular and scientific literature as sources of further information.

Such a booklet could be supplemented by "handouts" about the work of regularly visited stations and by displays on board tourist vessels.

C. CONSERVATION ON THE SOUTHERN ISLANDS

The land areas north of 60°S, and within the area of interest of SCAR are not subject to the same universal conservation measures, and some indeed have no conservation legislation at all, despite their high scientific interest. Those listed as "substantially undamaged" in Table 1, extending from the young Antarctic volcanoes of the South Sandwich arc to the temperate islands of the Tristan da Cunha group and the New Zealand shelf form a series of high scientific interest, and the three smaller members of the Tristan group are probably the least modified group of temperate oceanic islands in the world. Little or no economic crop is likely from these islands, apart from fishery in some inshore waters and the harvesting of the surplus production of male fur seals once stocks have risen to an appropriate level. Conversely, the potential return to scientific knowledge is very great. It may be assumed that for these land areas, as for the land south of 60°S, conservation should be directed largely to the protection of this scientific interest.

The conservation measures required for such islands are not unduly complex. They include:

(a) prohibition of the killing, capturing or molestation of native birds and mammals except under permit for scientific and analogous purposes, at a level which will not cause serious disturbance of the populations, and regulation by permit of the collecting of other animals and plants;

(b) prohibition of the importation of all alien mammals, because of the vulnerability of island vegetation to grazing and bird populations to predation by mammals, both of which are absent from the natural situation;

(c) prohibition of the importation of alien plants and invertebrates, as far as this is possible;

(d) prohibition of any avoidable disturbance of the island habitat, because alien plants, with their associated invertebrates have been shown to spread chiefly in places where the native vegetation has been disrupted by grazing, burning or trampling. Such alien species invade undisturbed vegetation much less readily.

Of these measures, (b) is the most important. Native bird and mammal populations can withstand a substantial level of culling by man, but are rapidly and irreversibly reduced by predation by rats, cats, or dogs. Island vegetation, likewise, is well able to withstand a normal level of scientific collection, but liable to irreversible disruption, even with consequent erosion of soil, following grazing by rabbits, sheep or cattle.

It is evident that the general form of the Antarctic Agreed Measures could, with slight modification, likewise be applied to the uninhabited southern temperate islands, and South Africa has done this for Prince Edward and Marion Islands. It is desirable that nations exercising sovereignty over the other islands consider a similar step. The problem is, of course, a global one, and in this context it is significant that the CT section of the IBP is sponsoring a world-wide survey of oceanic islands of scientific interest, in which SCAR is being asked to participate. Such a survey will place the southern islands in a wider context and help confirm the priorities for conservation.

Management plans should be drawn up for these islands, as for Antarctic Specially Protected Areas. Such plans will be more complex than for the latter. On many oceanic islands there are weather stations that must be resupplied and whose members need access to the island as a whole and facilities for scientific work. On some islands also, feral mammals have already become established. While these populations have real scientific interest, it is not easy to justify the disruption of a unique oceanic island ecosystem in order to study the behaviour of feral domestic stock, and where possible consideration must be given to their removal. New Zealand biologists are already eliminating sheep from Campbell Island: the wild cattle of Ile Amsterdam and the reindeer of South Georgia are likewise targets for control, if not elimination. All such proposals should, of course follow a biological survey and assessment of the trends the island ecosystem is following, and the desirability and possibility of modifying them.

VI. The Conservation of the Southern Seas

Unlike the islands and mainland of Antarctica, the southern oceans contain valuable natural resources which have been exploited by man for a long period. The whaling industry, after several decades of overcropping and consequent reduction of the resource, has now fixed harvesting levels below the sustained yield figure, and a slow recovery of the stocks is predicted (Mackintosh, 1970: this symposium; Gulland, 1970: this symposium). Pelagic sealing has only recently started in Antarctic waters and guide lines for its regulation have been drafted in advance. Fish and krill have not yet been exploited commercially, but Moiseev (1970, this symposium) computed that the latter may have an available yield of about 45×10^6 metric tons/yr which would double world fishery landings, and many of the technical problems for such a fishery are being overcome.

A. GUIDE LINES FOR THE VOLUNTARY REGULATION OF ANTARCTIC PELAGIC SEALING

SCAR, at the request of the Antarctic Treaty Consultative Meetings, has so far been active only in one field of marine conservation, the preparation of guide lines for the conservation of seal stocks and the regulation of Antarctic pelagic sealing. Such sealing, following an exploratory voyage by the Norwegian vessel *Polarhav* in 1964–65 (Øritsland, 1970: this symposium), is most likely to centre on crabeater seals (*Lobodon carcinophagus*) in the pack ice zone. Leopard seal (*Hydrurga leptonyx*) might also be taken, but Weddell seal (*Leptonychotes weddelli*) and Ross seal (*Ommatophoca rossi*) seem less likely to be important because of the coastal habitat of the one and the rarity of the other.

In advising on conservation measures, the SCAR Working Group on Biology was hampered by a lack of reliable data on the numbers and distribution of these species, and of the age structure of their populations. The interim guide lines proposed in 1966 and extended in 1968 emphasize this and provide for adjustment of sealing levels as knowledge improves. The main principles of the guide lines are (Polar Record, 1967):

1. The Antarctic seal stocks are a resource of potential value, which should be used in a rational way.
2. Harvesting of seal stocks should be held at or below the maximum sustainable yield.
3. Sealing should be regulated at a level at which the natural ecological ecosystems are not seriously disturbed.
4. To this end, the following precise conservation measures should be adopted:

   (a) figures should be set, in an Annex to the guide lines, which represent the best estimates of maximum sustainable yield for the time being;
   (b) the Antarctic should be divided into a series of zones (the same as those used by the whaling industry) and these should be closed to sealing in rotation;
   (c) certain areas where seal populations are the subject of scientific study should be designated as seal reserves, and commercial sealing excluded;
   (d) a sealing season and a "close season" should be established, and for the Weddell seal the latter should protect the species while it is breeding in inshore waters, where local populations could readily be killed out by sealers;
   (e) certain species (Ross and fur seals) should be protected at all times;
   (f) animals should not be killed by sealers when in the water (because of the high rate of loss);
   (g) governments should keep and exchange records of the numbers of adult males, pregnant females and pups of each species killed, and should also encourage biological research on seals, so as to improve the data on which quotas and sealing zones are based;
   (h) if at any time the total harvest of seals in the area south of 60°S approaches the maximum sustained yield, or is disturbing the ecological system in any area, the Consultative Parties should consult together to plan a meeting to discuss steps to remedy the situation.

Like the Agreed Measures, these guide lines thus provide for the special protection of some species and areas, the proper record of numbers killed, and the regulation of an activity on the basis of scientific knowledge. There is a similar problem, because the guide lines had to be prepared in advance of really adequate information, and a similar need for new research.

B. The Need for Further Measures

The Guide Lines for the Voluntary Regulation of Pelagic Sealing in the Antarctic go as far as is reasonable at present, when knowledge is inadequate and an industry has yet to begin. Ultimately, they may require extension in two ways: in area of application so as to cover pack ice north of 60°S and in form of expression so as to become internationally binding rather than voluntary. More fundamental, however, is the need to apply scientific knowledge in a similar manner to the wise management of the other resources of the Antarctic ocean—krill and fish—and indeed to the management of oceanic resources generally (Gulland, 1970: this symposium). Krill lies at the centre of Antarctic food chains, and there is scarcely a species of bird or seal in the region whose population would not be liable to adjustment were krill greatly reduced in abundance by cropping. Perhaps even more seriously, excessive harvesting of krill could disturb the general balance of the Antarctic marine ecosystem. A critical scientific study of this situation, and the drafting of guide lines for the management of an industry based on krill, may be the most pressing task in Antarctic conservation today.

VII. Conclusion

One theme recurs through this whole field, as it does everywhere in conservation. This is the need for legislation to be a tool of management and for the management to be based on sound scientific knowledge and directed toward the attainment of set objectives. Generally speaking, conservation in the Antarctic is well advanced, and if it is to be consolidated it needs to be supported by more comprehensive research, and implemented by more precise planning. The landscape and wildlife of the Antarctic land are a resource of great aesthetic and scientific value, and the life of the ocean has great economic as well as scientific importance. The international agreements now secured demand the support of scientists, through SCAR, to ensure that policies continue to be guided by the best knowledge available.

References

Adie, R. J. (1970). Past environments and climates of Antarctica. This symposium, 7–14.
Aguayo, L. A. (1970). Census of Pinnipedia in the South Shetland Islands. This symposium, 395–97.
Allen, S. E. and Heal, O. W. (1970). Soils in the Maritime Antarctic Region. This symposium, 693–96.
Anderson, D. (1968). The conservation of wild life under the Antarctic Treaty. *Polar Rec.* 14, No. 88, pp. 25–32.
Bonner, W. N. (1968). The fur seal of South Georgia. *Br. Antarct. Surv. Sci. Rep.*, No. 56.
Carrick, R. (1964). Problems of conservation in and around the Southern ocean. *In* "Biologie Antarctique: Antarctic Biology" (Carrick, R., Holdgate, M. W. and Prévost, J. eds). Hermann, Paris.
Dorst, J. and Milon, P. (1964). Acclimatation et conservation de la nature dans les iles subantarctiques françaises. *In* "Biologie Antarctique: Antarctic Biology" (Carrick, R., Holdgate, M. W. and Prévost, J., eds). Hermann, Paris.
Gimingham, C. H. and Smith, R. I. L. (1970). Bryophyte and lichen communities in the Maritime Antarctic. This symposium, 752–85.
Gulland, J. A. (1970). The development of the resources of the Antarctic seas. This symposium, 217–23.
H.M.S.O. (1965). The Antarctic Treaty and the Recommendations of subsequent Consultative Meetings held at Canberra, 1961, Buenos Aires, 1962 and Brussels, 1964. Miscellaneous No. 23 (1965), Cmnd 2822.
Holdgate, M. W. (1967). The Antarctic Ecosystem. *Phil. Trans. R. Soc.* B 252, 777, pp. 363–83.
Holdgate, M. W. (1968). The influence of introduced species on the ecosystems of temperate oceanic islands. *Proceedings, I.U.C.N. 10th Technical Meeting, I.U.C.N. Publications, New Series, No. 9, pp. 151–76.*
Holdgate, M. W. and Wace, N. M. (1961). The influence of man on the floras and faunas of southern islands. *Polar Rec.* 10, No. 68, pp. 475–93.
Macarthur, R. H. and Wilson, E. O. (1967). "The Theory of Island Biography". Princeton (N.J.); Princeton University.
Mackintosh, N. A. (1970). Whales and Krill in the 20th century. This symposium, 195–212.
Moiseev, P. A. (1970). Some aspects of the commercial use of the Krill resources of the Antarctic seas. This symposium, 213–16.
Murphy, R. C. (1964). Conservation of the Antarctic fauna. *In* "Biologie Antarctique: Antarctic Biology" (Carrick, R., Holdgate, M. W. and Prévost, J., eds). Hermann, Paris.
Nicholson, E. M. (1968). "Handbook to the Conservation Section of the International Biological Programme". I.B.P. Handbook No. 5. Blackwell, Oxford.
Øritsland, T. (1970). Sealing and seal research in the south-west Atlantic pack ice, September–October, 1964. This symposium, 367–76.
Peterken, G. F. (1968). "Guide to the Check Sheet for IBP Areas". I.B.P. Handbook No. 4. Blackwell, Oxford.
Polar Record (1967). Report of fourth Antarctic Treaty Consultative Meeting, Santiago, Chile, 1966. *Polar Rec.* 13, No. 86, pp. 629–49.
Ray, C. (1970). Population ecology of Antarctic seals. This symposium, 398–414.
Roberts, B. B. (1958). A chronological list of Antarctic expeditions. *Polar Rec.* 9, No. 59, pp. 97–134 and No. 60, pp. 191–239.

Sladen, W. J. L. (1964). The distribution of the Adélie and chinstrap penguins. *In* "Biologie Antarctique: Antarctic Biology" (Carrick, R., Holdgate, M. W. and Prévost, J., eds). Hermann, Paris.

Sladen, W. J. L. and Le Resche, R. E. (1970). New and developing techniques in Antarctic ornithology. This symposium, 585–96.

Stoddart, D. R. (1967). Ecology of Aldabra Atoll, Indian Ocean. Atoll Research Bulletin, No. 118. Smithsonian Institution, Washington, D.C.

Stonehouse, B. (1970). Adaptation in polar and subpolar penguins (Spheniscidae). This symposium, 527–41.

Ugolini, F. (1970). Antarctic soils and their ecology. This symposium, 673–92.

Wace, N. M. (1968). Alien plants in the Tristan da Cunha Islands. *Proceedings, I.U.C.N. 10th Technical Meeting, I.U.C.N. Publications, New Series, No. 9.*

Wallace, A. R. (1895). "Island Life" (2nd Edition). Macmillan, London.

Zenkovich, B. (1970). Whales and plankton in Antarctic waters. This symposium, 183–85.

Conservation Around Showa Base

J. SHIMOIZUMI
Society of Biological Sciences Education, Tokyo, Japan

The Japanese Antarctic Research Expedition (JARE) began in 1956, and during the first expedition Showa base was built on East Ongul Island about 4 km off the coast of Antarctica (Fig. 1). Relatively few scientists and supporting staff visited the station during the first six annual expeditions because the ice-breaker *Soya* could not penetrate directly to the base. Only about forty to fifty people could therefore be engaged in operations in any one year and relatively few materials could be supplied. For the seventh expedition in 1966 the newly built high-performance ice-breaker *Fuji* was available and able to reach Showa directly, landing more than 250 people and many tons of materials. Since then the number of people visiting Showa has been increasing year by year.

Consequently, the problems of pollution and the destruction of natural balance due to human activity have arisen. The development of the base has inevitably conflicted with the protection of the Antarctic flora and fauna. Therefore from the point of view of conservation it is necessary to divide the area into two: the base area, influenced by man, and other areas which can be protected. At present we intend to declare two penguin colonies as our first sanctuaries, on Ongul Kalven Island and on Rumpa Island near Showa. In addition to the bird sanctuaries, we have to select areas for other terrestrial communities, for mosses and lichens, as soon as possible. We have some areas suitable for this purpose, as at Langhovde, Skallen, and Skarvsnes.

Before the establishment of the nature conservation areas, we need more detailed surveys and comparisons between sites. The extent of the influence of human activity has not been studied in detail. Carbon dioxide and other gases released in the air, excreta and waste from the base discharged as sewage, oil released from the ship into the sea, and materials dumped on land are all increasing every year and all will cause pollution. Consequently, we have applied strict regulations to protect the natural environment around Showa until the influence of the human activity has been well studied.

We consider that it is not only necessary to protect particular species, but

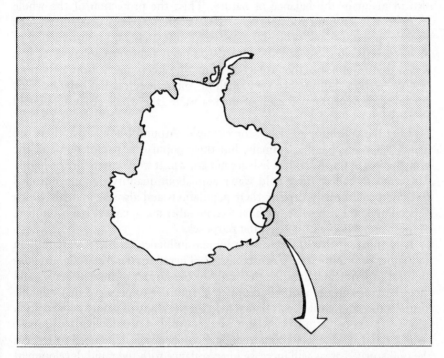

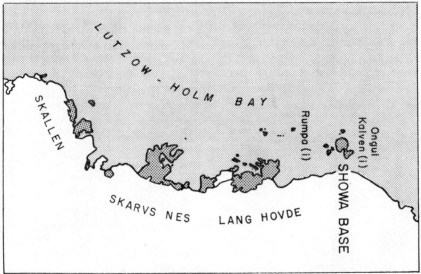

FIG. 1. The area around Showa Base. Parts shown grey are ice-free areas. (1:1,000,000)

also to maintain the balance of nature. This; the protection of the whole ecosystem, is our fundamental theme. Because the large-size consumers, such as seals, penguins, and other birds, depend ultimately on the production of phytoplankton in the ocean and directly on many fishes or euphausians, it is necessary to emphasize the protection of marine environment from pollution. Energy fixation and flow are very small in Antarctic terrestrial habitats, so if we fail to prevent the pollution of the sea water, the whole ecosystem could be at risk.

Take the collection of fishes for example. Around Showa base there are many fishes and benthic animals, but their population parameters and the growth rates of the individual fish are not known. It would therefore be highly dangerous to collect these cold water animals in quantity, for uncontrolled collection could easily destroy their populations and also the animals which depend upon the fishes. So, we have to remember not to collect large numbers of these animals even for scientific purposes.

It is apparent that there was no human influence on the Antarctic flora and fauna before the base was established. Therefore, the Antarctic provides an ideal experimental area for the study of the impact of human beings and their activities on the natural ecosystems. In order to preserve this valuable virgin nature and ideal experimental field for the study of nature conservation which cannot be found elsewhere in the world, I would like to propose stronger and more effective international co-operation. The need to reserve the undisturbed areas will increase in accordance with the rapid development of civilization in the Antarctic.

This is my conclusion: that we make the kind of effort we have made at and around Showa base, as widely as possible, and that this coming expedition be devoted to the study of Antarctic conservation.

Discussion

Conservation

IMPLEMENTATION OF MEASURES FOR ANTARCTIC CONSERVATION

B. B. ROBERTS

The "Agreed Measures on the Conservation of Antarctic Fauna and Flora" (negotiated at Brussels in June 1964) have so far been approved by Argentina, France, Norway, South Africa and the U.S.S.R. The United Kingdom will approve them next week.

The Annexes which deal with Specially Protected Species and Specially Protected Areas (negotiated at Santiago in November 1966) have been approved by Argentina, France and South Africa, and will be approved by the United Kingdom next week.

The "Interim Guide Lines for Voluntary Regulation of Antarctic Sealing" (negotiated at Santiago in November 1966) have been approved by Argentina, Australia, Belgium, France, Norway and South Africa, and will be approved by the United Kingdom next week.

The reason for the delays is that each government must go through their own constitutional procedures to enable them to bring these measures into effect. In the United Kingdom, for example, it has been necessary to get a Bill through Parliament. For United Kingdom citizens, the "Antarctic Treaty Act 1967" came into force on 1 July 1968.

These proposals for conservation cannot be binding on any government until they have been approved by all twelve Antarctic Treaty governments, but meanwhile, we have negotiated an "informal" agreement to go ahead as far as possible; each government regarding the proposals as "guide lines" during the interim period. All the governments have started the appropriate administrative action.

We have no reason to be dissatisfied with the progress made. Very few international agreements involving so many diverse nations have achieved success in such a short period. It is only ten years since the Antarctic Treaty was negotiated. But, equally, there is no time for complacency. We must press on as quickly as possible.

Governments have had some very valuable advice from SCAR and they have all recognized SCAR as the appropriate organization to advise on conservation. It should be possible to continue this happy relationship if SCAR biologists are patient and understanding about the formidable political and legal difficulties which they are asking governments to solve. We must not forget these difficulties. Most of them can eventually be solved under the umbrella of the Antarctic Treaty. But we must not go too fast. The Ambassador of one of the Antarctic Treaty governments recently put this to me most clearly; the Treaty is like crystal glass. It is very beautiful but it is also so very easy to shatter.

E. M. NICHOLSON

It is certainly encouraging to learn of these extremely important advances in the Antarctic compared with the slow progress, for example, in obtaining the approval of other international conventions. That covering the pollution of the sea by oil took forty years to get adopted. Much comfort has been given to all areas of conservation from the progress made in the Antarctic.

J. T. RUUD

The Meeting might be glad to know that Norway accepted all the recommendations of the Santiago conference on the 7th July.

SPECIALLY PROTECTED AREAS AND THE PROBLEM OF CONSERVATION OF PLANT LIFE AND INVERTEBRATES

W. J. L. SLADEN

I would like to endorse the point Dr Holdgate made about Specially Protected Areas, and to emphasize that in the future we should think bigger when defining these areas. One of the most stimulating things about the United States National Parks is the vast extent of some of them; for example, areas of two million square miles in Alaska. Some of the specially protected areas in Antarctica are tiny, such as Cape Hallett and Green Island, and even the area of Cape Crozier measures only four miles by two. We really should set up larger samples for the future.

What does Dr Holdgate think of the problems surrounding the issue of permits for small animals? Should permits be issued for collecting fish, mosses and mites as well as for birds and seals? More damage could be done by a botanist collecting mosses around McMurdo where they are extremely rare than by collecting fifty penguins at the large 300,000-bird colony near by.

M. W. HOLDGATE

I agree that the Specially Protected Areas should include some places of considerable extent. We have a whole continent to look after and there is no reason why large areas which have a high habitat diversity should not be given special protection. The Dry Valley region may provide an example, for the evidence presented at this symposium has demonstrated the vulnerability of its desert pavements and the danger of contaminating the biologically poor or near-sterile soils by the passage of vehicles and scientists. It may be wise to set aside a substantial reference area in this region for the future.

Turning to Dr Sladen's second point, no permit is needed for fishermen in McMurdo Sound because these waters form part of the high seas. Like all open sea resources, international agreement on their conservation presents formidable difficulties. On the other hand, collection of land plants or vegetation samples from which to extract micro-arthropods does require a permit in a Specially Protected Area. If there are small and vulnerable areas of vegetation near McMurdo meriting protection, it would be reasonable for these to be made Specially Protected Areas, and in that way all collecting would be regulated.

W. J. L. SLADEN

Much can be done by individual national programmes without creating new Specially Protected Areas.

M. W. HOLDGATE

Conservation in the Antarctic can certainly be advanced as much by the careful selection and briefing of personnel as by the multiplication of permits.

R. E. BENOIT

I entirely agree with the idea that a region of the Dry Valleys should be set aside. The problem in this area comes not from tourists but the passing scientists, perhaps particularly physical scientists, who are doing quite a considerable amount of damage in the region. There are several available areas and it would be desirable to safeguard more than one because of the gradation of conditions in this whole region.

F. C. UGOLINI

The Dry Valleys are extremely different. Victoria, Taylor and Wright Valleys all contain scientifically unique features, and it would be wrong to set only one of them apart. I also feel that it would be very helpful in all this area if people undertaking work would mark the sites at which they had operated and would also take care to fill in the excavations they have made, and possibly to re-establish the desert pavement stones over the surface of these areas.

G. A. LLANO

Like Dr Sladen, I am concerned about the issue of permits and about other categories presently not covered by permits including plants. The United States stations have many visitors who make collections of obvious things, particularly lichens and mosses. Consequently, we have some concern for the loss of the relatively limited vegetation of the vicinity. Entomologists, for example, use large samples of plants for processing in Berlese funnels which can make serious inroads on the available vegetation, but even botanists can depauperate an area when visited repeatedly. In the Dry Valleys it is important to anticipate the damage which comes when the desert pavement is disturbed, since it can have very bad side effects on the ecology of the area and on work in other disciplines. It is apparent that we have grave problems in implementing conservation policy in Antarctica, and it is obvious that the solution is not controls. The activities at large stations present other problems, not the least of these is the disposal of refuse. The United States Antarctic Research Program is aware of these problems and every effort is being made to resolve them.

ANTARCTIC TOURISM

G. A. KNOX

We have to face the fact that tourism in the Antarctic will expand. During the most recent visits the scientific community took an essentially negative attitude. For example, it was said that we could not have mixed parties ashore at certain bases because there were no ladies' lavatories. This really is just not good enough. We need a positive approach; we must have adequate information available for the tourists and not just rely on their party leaders. We want SCAR to tell people what their responsibilities are towards conservation and science in the Antarctic zone.

J. Hedgpeth

One of the most important things about Antarctic tourism is that it allows the scientists to show the non-scientists on whom they depend for money how valuable the work they are doing is. Only well-off and potentially influential people are likely at the present time to tour such far distant parts, and I think it is a good plan to give them well-prepared brochures and politeness, and show them rather more than the McMurdo dump.

CONSERVATION OF THE MARINE ECOSYSTEM

D. Ashton

Would it not be reasonable to extend the provision of the Agreed Measures to the limit of the Antarctic pack ice?

M. W. Holdgate

Under the Agreed Measures protection extends to the margin of the ice shelves, but the areas of floating ice including pack-ice are excluded and form part of the high seas. It would be extremely difficult to obtain agreement on comprehensive measures for conservation of these international waters. However, progress is being made in a more limited field. Profiting from the lessons of the whaling industry, the Antarctic Treaty Governments have requested SCAR to give advice on the way in which any sealing industry which might develop in the circum-Antarctic seas might be controlled. Interim Voluntary Guide Lines for the regulation of such an industry were drawn up by the representatives at their meeting in Santiago in 1966, and during the last few days, members of the Working Group in Biology and experts attending this symposium have drawn up an improved form of these voluntary Guide Lines. We hope that the governments will accept these modified measures and that a proper international agreement, which will be binding on all concerned, can be entered into to conserve the seal stocks of the zone south of 60°S latitude before any industry actually develops.

A. W. Erickson

What provision has been made for the full use of the biological specimens resulting from these harvests? Dr Øritsland was fortunately able to make use of many of the specimens gathered on the first Norwegian sealing trip, but it is quite clear that further large samples will be needed if the population structure of Antarctic seals is to be fully understood. I hope that some provision will be made in any international agreement to require exploiting agencies to provide adequate samples for scientific study.

M. W. Holdgate

There is no obstacle preventing governments from collecting large quantities of Antarctic seal material. The pack-ice zone lies outside the area of application of the Agreed Measures, and at the SCAR meeting in Santiago, governments were urged to devote more of their resources to the study of these seal populations and the eco-system of the pack-ice zone as a whole. None the less I agree with Dr Erickson that use should be made of information collected by any industry, and this may be our most effective means of obtaining large samples. The Working Group believes that this should be done by agreement between the scientists of the different participating nations, rather than made a mandatory part of any measures or convention, and I have every confidence that in practice this information will be collected.

I. EVERSON

I have been somewhat disturbed in listening to the papers and discussions on population dynamics of seals to note that no proposals have been made for the development or utilization of mathematical models for analysis of the data. These in my view are essential if sustained yield figures are to be evaluated and submitted as a basis for the formulation of regulations. They are also essential for the predic-tion of the effect on populations of exploitation.

CONSERVATION OF THE SUBANTARCTIC ISLANDS

N. M. WACE

I think we should be particularly concerned to secure the proper conservation of the islands around the Antarctic. The recent case of Aldabra has shown us some-thing of the way in which events may go in the Subantarctic. The proposed military base on Aldabra was abandoned not because of the conservationist's re-actions, but because of the finances of the British Government. The island was well known by biologists to be of great scientific importance, but when this point was stressed, the military authorities immediately asked why in view of this importance no research had recently been done there. It is essential that if we are to conserve the islands of the Subantarctic zone, we also establish a research presence among them. Those who get in first to use an area have an advantage and are in a position decisively to influence future policy. I believe that scientific research is the right use of many of these Subantarctic islands and that we must establish stations on them as soon as possible.

J. M. WINTERBOTTOM

This applies particularly to Prince Edward Island, which remains in an almost totally undamaged condition. It is not for want of trying that our scientists have not been able to establish a station there. Our biologists have kept up a continuing pressure on our Government, and I believe that this pressure must be maintained. It can then be clearly demonstrated that if the scientists are accused of failing to undertake the research on which they lay such stress, the cause is directly the failure of the Government to provide the necessary support.

B. STONEHOUSE

The Subantarctic islands are being subject to more and more changes as time goes on and the number of visits increases, and I should like to see research in these islands accelerated. We have seen the dramatic effect on Antarctica of the recent acceleration of research effort, and I think that parallels in the Subantarctic could be close. In my own view we could do in the first place with a two-year international expedition in which some people would stay for long periods on the lesser known Subantarctic islands, while others would tour in a ship to compare different areas. The fact is that no one in the world knows all these islands and it becomes more and more essential that we have a proper basis of comparison established between them before they are spoiled. I should like to see this plan developed over the next few years.

Author Index

The numbers in *italics* indicate the pages on which names are mentioned in the reference lists.

956

Beck, J. R., 509, *523*
Becquerel, P., 801, *810*
Beklemishev, K. W., 133, *134*, 166, *172*, 640, *649*
Belcher, J. H., 632, 635, *637*
Bell, R. A. I., 609, 611, 613, 620, *625*
Bellair, N., 37, *38*
Bellair, P., 36, *39*
Belyaev, G. M., 83, 85, 86, *93*, 178, *182*
Belyaeva, N. V., 154, *160*
Bendschneider, K., 120, *134*
Benedict, F. G., 480, *482*
Benes, N. S., 684, *690*
Benoit, R. E., 703, 707, *716*, 789, *798*
Benseman, R. F., 609, 611, *627*
Berg, T. E., 11, *14*, 613, *626*, 674, 678, 679, *690*
Bergersen, B., 207, *211*
Bertram, G. C. L., 209, *211*, 364, *364*, 377, *394*, 425, *428*, 763, *783*
Beschel, R. E., 741, *748*
Bigelow, H. B., *182*
Bigler, J. C., 344, *350*, *351*
Billings, W. D., 797, *799*, 858, *862*
Birse, E. M., 755, *783*
Birstein, J. A., 102, *103*
Bjork, N. A., 466, *470*
Black, R. F., 11, *14*, 678, 679, *690*
Blair, D., 154, *160*
Blakemore, L. C., 683, *690*
Blank, G. B., 703, 705, *716*
Blazka, P., 337, *343*
Bliss, L. C., 838, *850*, 859, 860, 861, *862*
Boalch, G. T., 637, *637*
Bodina, E. L., 673, *691*
Bogorov, B. G., 81, *93*
Bogorov, V. G., 214, *216*
Bohr, C., 480, *481*
Bold, H. C., 802, *810*, 814, *817*
Bondareff, W., 487, *488*
Bonner, W. N., 361, 362, *364*, 926, *944*
Boulton, P. S., 109, *111*
Bourne, W. R. P., 507, *523*
Boyd, J. C., 592, *595*, *596*
Boyd, J. W., 620, *625*, 655, *661*, 678, *690*, 712, *716*, 803, *810*, 815, *817*
Boyd, J. Morton, 572, *584*
Boyd, W. L., 620, *625*, 655, *661*, 674, 678, *690*, 712, *716*, 803, *810*, 815, *817*
Braun-Blanquet, J., 736, *748*

Bray, J. R., 860, 861, *862*
Brewer, M. C., 651, *661*
Briggs, J. C., 99, *103*
Brinton, E., 102, *103*
Brodie, H. J., 814, *817*
Brodie, J., 69, 71, 72, *93*
Broekhuysen, G. J., 565, *567*
Brown, D. A., 548, *549*
Brown, K. G., 364, *364*, 909, *918*
Brown, P. D., 731, *732*, *784*, 825, *837*
Brown, R. G. B., 565, *566*
Brown, R. H. J., 330, *336*
Brown, R. M., 802, *810*
Brown, R. M., Jr., 814, *817*
Brown, R. N. Rudmuse, 364, *364*, *366*, 377, *394*, 425, *428*, 775, *783*
Brown, S. G., 72, *95*, 196, 199, 207, *212*
Brundin, L., 4, *4*, 45, 48, 51, 52, *53*
Bryan, K., Jr., 651, *662*
Bryant, G. K., 483, *488*
Bryant, H. M., 617, *625*, 763, *783*
Buchner, A., 330, *336*
Bull, C., 678, 680, *690*, *692*, 705, *716*
Bullivant, J. S., 83, 84, *93*, 102, *103*, 245, 246, *258*, 261, 263, *266*
Bullock, T. H., 106, *111*
Bunt, J. S., 35, *38*, 71, 72, 73, 74, 75, 76, 77, 78, 81, *93*, 298, *303*, 620, 621, *625*, 634, *637*, 891, *894*
Burckle, L., 35, *39*
Burckholder, P. R., 74, 75, 77, 78, *93*, *95*, 119, 123, *134*
Burges, A., 768, *783*
Burton, R. W., 505, 517, *523*, 561, 563, 564, 566
Burukovskii, R. N., 220, *223*
Bushnell, V. C., 98, 101, *103*
Bussing, W. A., *182*

C

Calabrese, G. de, 279, *284*
Cameron, R. E., 703, 705, 707, *716*
Campbell, I. B., 684, 687, 688, 689, *690*, *691*
Cardot, J., 775, 776, *783*
Carrara, I. S., 397, *397*
Carrick, R., 4, *4*, 67, *67*, 361, *364*, 503, *503*, 505, 506, 510, 513, 514, *524*, 548, *549*, 551, *556*, 586, 592, *595*, 925, 933, *944*

Subject Index

Note: Further references to a group (e.g. Mosses) may be found under scientific names of species (e.g. *Bryum algens*).

SUBJECT INDEX

Cruciferae, 37
Crustacea, 84, 85, 88, 90, 173–6, 179,
  180, 183–5, 189, 217, 228, 229, 237,
  238, 248, 269–78, 279–84, 291, 295,
  300, 536, 558, 571, 578, 600, 607, 617,
  637, 639–50, 659
  feeding habits, 639–50
Cryptogams, 4, 61, 786, 794, 801, 842, 843,
  846, 876
Cryptopygus antarcticus, 869, 892, 902, 908–
  18, 919
  abundance, 909–13
  distribution, 909–13
  food, 916–17
  habitats, 909
  life cycles, 914–16
  taxonomy and morphology, 908–9
Cryptopygus cisantarcticus, 909
Cryopelagic fish, 297–304
Cryptomonas, 654
Cryptophyceae, 652
Cryptostigmata, 880
Crystalline continental shield, 7
C.S.I.R.O., 77, 856
Ctenophora, 89
Cuenotaster involutus, 263–6
Cumberland East Bay, 838, 842
Cumberland Sound, 430, 444
Cwm Idwal, 833
Cyanophyta, 615, 618, 654, 741
Cyclops scutifer, 659
Cyclotella, 618, 654
Cylindrocystis, 619
Cymatocyclis parva, 146
Cymbella, 619
Cypridopsis frigogena, 639, 666
Cyrtolaelaps racovitazai, 917
Cystophora cristata, 371, 429, 456
Cytherids, 56

D

Dactyliosolen antarctica, 140, 141
Dactylis glomerata, 857
Dailey Islands, 245, 289, 290
Danco Coast, 830, 832, 833
Daphnia, 617
Daption capensis, 509, 519, 542–6, 548, 549,
  562, 936
Darwin Glacier, 29, 687

David Valley, 702–3, 711, 714
Davis Sea, 85, 235–7, 299
Davis Strait, 430
Decapoda, 179, 181
Deception Island, 57, 77, 242–3, 289, 396,
  734, 738, 742, 743, 744, 757, 763, 765,
  774, 788, 791, 819
  colonization of new islet, 289
Delphinapterus, 455
Delphinapterus leucas, 299
Denmark, 657
Denticula, 619
Deschampsia, 864, 889, 890
Deschampsia antarctica, 674, 694, 737, 742,
  747, 759, 790, 792, 793, 809, 887, 935,
  937
Deschampsia klossii, 853
Desert conditions, 8, 14, 673, 685, 689, 705,
  733
Desiccation, 13
Desmarestia, 236, 240, 269, 287
Desmids, 616, 619
Detritus, 13, 83, 89, 90, 92, 107, 187, 256,
  257, 264, 265, 288, 299, 742, 743, 871,
  917
Devonian, Lower, 11
Diasmesinae, 45
Diatoma, 619
Diatom-radiolarian ooze, 20
Diatoms, 60, 76, 78, 81, 83, 88, 90, 107,
  117, 119, 133, 137, 139, 143–6, 148–53,
  186–8, 236, 237, 239, 240, 265, 287–9,
  295, 298–300, 302, 607, 616–17, 619,
  620, 628–31, 633, 654, 658, 663, 699,
  714, 741
Dicranoweisia, 760, 761, 770, 775
Dicranoweisia subinclinata, 757
Dicranum, 694, 739, 752, 763, 765, 773, 780,
  913
Dicranum aciphyllum, 717, 718, 757, 758,
  762, 763, 773, 775, 780, 781, 825, 831
Dicroidium-Otozamites, 9
Dictyocha speculum, 143
Dinobryon, 654
Dinoflagellates, 59, 76, 144–6, 186, 187,
  654, 656
Dinophysis, 144
Dinophysis ovum, 146
Dinosaur fossils, 54
Diomedeidea, 518, 522 (see also Albatross)

587–95, 596–603, 684, 743, 747, 934, 936, 937

Pygoscelis antarctica, 226, 500, 518, 526–8 534, 536, 562, 927, 930, 934, 936, 937

Pygoscelis papua, 518, 526–8, 531–6, 562, 934

Pyrrophyta, 137

Q

Quaternary, 3, 31–40

Quebec, 652, 657

Queen Mary Coast, 678, 685

Queen Maud Land, 607, 609, 610, 676–8, 736

R

Rabbits, 517, 928, 929, 940

Radiation, solar, 74, 89, 188, 236, 448, 453, 464–70, 529, 534, 598, 620, 633, 637, 651, 654, 664, 674, 701–3, 713, 734, 752, 789, 790, 791, 803, 841, 848, 850, 852, 861, 899

Radio-carbon dating, 17, 18, 23, 25, 33, 739

Radio-isotope techniques, 3, 119–21, 680–1, 682, 687, 724, 917

Radiolaria, 289

Radiometric dating, 32

Radish, 840, 843, 845, 847

Raja georgiana, 180

Rajidae, 177

Ramalina, 740, 864

Ramalina terebrata, 757, 761, 762, 771, 773

Ramalinetum terebratae, 737, 754

Ranunculus basilobatus, 853

Ranunculus repens, 788

Raphanus sativus, 840

Rats, 483, 487, 517, 927–9, 940

Red beds, 8, 13, 54

Reindeer, 928, 941

Reproductive cycles, 86–7, 284

Resolute Bay, 661

Resources development, 217–23

Resources, Management of, 221–3, 923, 924, 932, 935–9, 943

Resources, utilization, 227–30, 925, 942

Resources, conservation, 924

Rhabdammina, 84

Rhacomitrium, 760

Rhacomitrium crispulum, 757, 852

Rhagidiidae, 871, 880

Rheophil insects, 47

Rhigophila dearborni, 322–5

Rhincalanus, 164

Rhincalanus gigas, 80, 82, 162–72

Rhizocarpon, 747, 761, 779

Rhizocarpon geographicum, 808

Rhizopoda, 876

Rhizosolenia, 137

Rhizosolenia alata, 137, 139

Rhizosolenia antarctica, 140

Rhizosolenia chunii, 139–41

Rhizosolenia curvata, 137

Rhizosolenia hebetata f. *semispina*, 138, 140, 141

Rhizosolenia rhombus, 133

Rhizosolenia simplex, 133

Rhodesia, 740

Rhodomonas minuta, 654

Rhodotorula, 814, 815

Rhodotorula minuta, 815

Rhodotorula texensis, 815

Rhopalodia, 619

Riccardia, 739

Right whales, 218

Ringed seal, see *Pusa hispida*

Rinodina, 744, 747, 761

Rinodina frigida, 807

Rinodina petermannii, 744

Rissa tridactyla, 298

Rivulogammarus buebeni, 270

Rivulogammarus lacustris, 271

Rivulogammarus pulex, 269, 271

Robert Island, 396, 758, 763–6, 783, 869, 898

Roberts Massif, 687, 688, 689

Robertson Bay, 86, 407

Rockhopper penguin, see *Eudyptes crestatus*

Rookery Islands, 936

Rose Island, 929

Ross Dependency area, 29

Ross Ice Barrier, 27

Ross Ice Shelf, 25, 29, 30, 59, 399, 595, 676, 677, 723, 738

Ross Island, 305, 313, 345, 399, 568, 571, 585, 589, 609, 616, 617, 620, 623, 629, 630, 634, 678, 683–4, 700, 724, 736, 737, 880, 881, 936